ATOMIC WEIGHTS AND PHYSICAL PROPERTIES, 1957

Element	Symbol	Accurate Atomic Weight	Approximate Atomic Weight (for calculations)	Atomic Number	Melting Point °C	Density (gm./c.c.)
Lithium	Li	6·940	—	3	186	0·5
Magnesium	Mg	24·32	24	12	651	1·7
Manganese	Mn	54·93	55	25	1260	7·4
Mendelevium	Mv	—	—	101	—	—
Mercury	Hg	200·61	—	80	−39	13·6
Molybdenum	Mo	95·95	—	42	2620	10·2
Neon	Ne	20·183	—	10	−249	—
Neptunium	Np	237	—	93	—	17·6
Nickel	Ni	58·69	—	28	1455	8·9
Nitrogen	N	14·008	14	7	−210₅	—
Oxygen	O	16·0000	16	8	−218	—
Phosphorus	P	30·98	31	15	44	1·8
Platinum	Pt	195·23	—	78	1773	21·4
Plutonium	Pu	239	—	94	—	16·0
Potassium	K	39·096	39	19	62	0·8
Radium	Ra	226·05	—	88	960	5·0
Rhodium	Rh	102·91	—	45	1985	12·4
Silicon	Si	28·06	28	14	1420	2·4
Silver	Ag	107·880	108	47	960	10·5
Sodium	Na	22·997	23	11	97	0·9
Strontium	Sr	87·63	—	38	800	2·5
Sulphur	S	32·066	32	16	119	2·1
Thorium	Th	232·12	—	90	1845	11·5
Tin	Sn	118·70	—	50	232	7·3
Titanium	Ti	47·90	—	22	1800	4·5
Uranium	U	238·07	—	92	1850	18·7
Vanadium	V	50·95	—	23	1710	5·9
Wolfram	W	183·92	—	74	3370	19·0
Xenon	Xe	131·3	—	54	−112	—
Zinc	Zn	65·38	65	30	419	7·1

King Edward VI School

This book is the personal responsibility of the boy last named below, who must see that it is maintained in good condition and pay for its replacement if lost.

NAME	FORM	DATE OF ISSUE
R. BALL	III A	15.9.59.
A. Ravenscroft	III A	14/9/60.
M. L. WHITEHEAD	III B	21st SEPT 1961.
~~C. Reynolds.~~		
C. Reynolds.	3B	7-9-62
J. Howard.	II B	

A SCHOOL CHEMISTRY
FOR TODAY

[Photo by courtesy of I.C.I. Ltd.

THE LARGEST CHEMICAL FACTORY IN THE BRITISH COMMONWEALTH

The factory of Imperial Chemical Industries Ltd. at Billingham-on-Tees, Co. Durham, extending for over a square mile. It makes fertilizers from the air, petrol from coal. Pipe-bridge in the foreground carries gases, acids, water-supplies, to the different buildings.

A SCHOOL CHEMISTRY FOR TODAY

By
F. W. GODDARD, M.A., F.C.S.
FORMERLY SCIENCE MASTER, THE COLLEGE, WINCHESTER
and
KENNETH HUTTON, M.A., D.Phil.
HEADMASTER, HATFIELD SCHOOL, HATFIELD, HERTS

With many illustrations

LONGMANS, GREEN AND CO
LONDON • NEW YORK • TORONTO

LONGMANS, GREEN AND CO LTD
6 & 7 CLIFFORD STREET, LONDON W1
THIBAULT HOUSE, THIBAULT SQUARE, CAPE TOWN
605–611 LONSDALE STREET, MELBOURNE C1
443 LOCKHART ROAD, HONG KONG
ACCRA, AUCKLAND, IBADAN
KINGSTON (JAMAICA), KUALA LUMPUR
LAHORE, NAIROBI, SALISBURY (RHODESIA)

LONGMANS, GREEN AND CO INC
119 WEST 40TH STREET, NEW YORK 18

LONGMANS, GREEN AND CO
20 CRANFIELD ROAD, TORONTO 16

ORIENT LONGMANS PRIVATE LTD
CALCUTTA, BOMBAY, MADRAS
DELHI, HYDERABAD, DACCA

First published	*1950*
Second impression, with minor corrections	*1951*
Third impression, with minor corrections	*1952*
Fourth impression, with minor corrections	*1953*
Fifth impression	*1954*
Sixth impression, with corrections . .	*1955*
Seventh impression, with corrections .	*1957*
Eighth impression, with minor corrections	*1958*
Ninth impression, with minor corrections	*1959*

Made and printed in Great Britain by
William Clowes and Sons, Limited, London and Beccles

WHAT THIS BOOK IS MADE OF

Chemistry is the study of what things are made of : it therefore seemed appropriate to give a chemical description of the materials and processes used in making this book.

This book is made of *Coated* PAPER : the paper is 96% **cellulose** C_{6000} $H_{10,000}$ O_{5000} (see overleaf p. vi) obtained from *wood pulp* (spruce and pine from Scandinavia), *bleached* by **chlorine** ; the remaining 4% is mostly **moisture, rosin** (left when the turpentine of pine trees is distilled), and **alum**. The COATING is **china-clay** $H_4Al_2Si_2O_9$ (mined in Cornwall), fixed with **casein** (from milk) as the adhesive.

The writing, drawings and photographs are in PRINTER'S INK : **amorphous carbon** (specially prepared soot), suspended in boiled **linseed oil** and volatile hydrocarbons which ' dry-up ' by being oxidized in the air, by being absorbed into the paper, and by evaporating.

The *photographs* are printed by HALF-TONE BLOCKS of pure **copper** ; each was covered with a photo-sensitive coating and the photograph 'printed' on it through a *half-tone-screen* ; the latter converts the picture into a series of dots, as can be seen by looking at PLATE 1B (p. 7) through a magnifying-glass. The exposed block is processed and then *etched* by **ferric chloride** solution ; the unattacked ' high spots ' will take ink and therefore print black, while the others print white.

The *line-diagrams* (e.g. fig. 1, p. 10) are printed by LINE BLOCKS of pure **zinc** : photographs of the original drawings (in Indian ink, i.e. amorphous carbon) were 'printed' on them, and the blocks etched as above to a depth of $\frac{1}{2}$ mm., but using dilute **nitric acid**.

All the rest of the book is printed by TYPE METAL (approx. 70% Pb, 20% Sb, 10% Sn) ; **lead** melts easily and can therefore be cast cheaply, the addition of **antimony** makes it much harder, and the **tin** makes the alloy flow more freely into the mould.

The BINDING uses *cotton thread* (100% **cellulose**), *glue* (**gelatin**), and *paste* (60% **water**, 40% wheat flour, i.e. **starch** and **gluten**).

The COVER of the book is *cotton cloth* (strong **cellulose**), and is *dyed* with a solution of *dyestuff*, e.g. **" Direct Fast Scarlet 4BS"** (see overleaf).

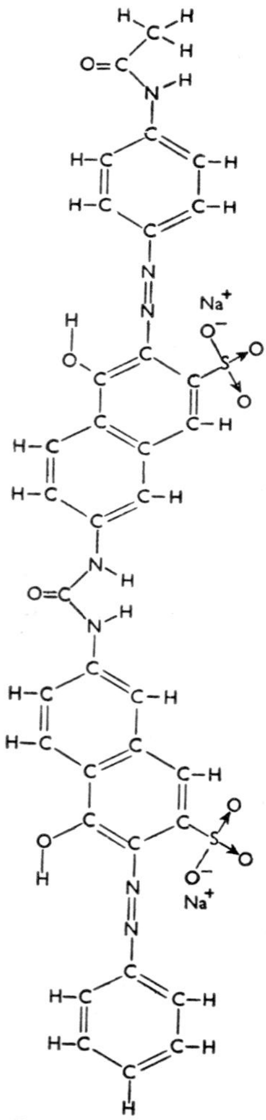

Direct Fast Scarlet 4 BS

The dyestuff has the formula shown on the left. Because it has a long thin molecule, similar in shape to that of the cellulose (shown on the right), it is able to dye the fabric directly; other classes of dyestuffs have to be prepared in the fabric itself by first attaching one reagent and then treating it with another reagent.

Direct Fast Scarlet 4BS is manufactured from **naphthalene** (obtained from **coal tar**), by reactions involving the use of concentrated **sulphuric acid,** concentrated **nitric acid, sodium nitrite, carbonyl chloride** ($COCl_2$), **sodium hydroxide,** and other reagents.

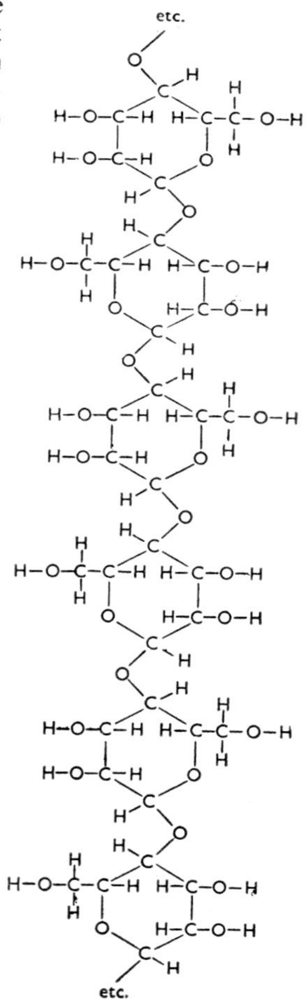

Cellulose

INTRODUCTION

This book is an attempt to reconcile examination requirements with the more important claims of education as a whole.

First, the practical applications of chemical substances—
such as sulphuric acid—are shown to be closely dependent on
their chemical behaviour; in this way it is hoped to bridge the
wide gulf which usually exists between "properties" and "uses."

Secondly, the working of the scientific method is stressed,
with its dependence on observation and experiment, and
suggestions for practical work are given at the end of each
chapter. There is a great need for the scientific method as
learnt in the laboratory to be consciously used in everyday life.

Thirdly, an attempt has been made to relate the knowledge
gained in any one place to all other places where it is relevant,
and over one thousand cross-references are given. Thus the
reaction $CaCO_3 \rightleftharpoons CaO + CO_2$ is not only a reaction of carbonates, a use of limestone, and a method of preparing a base
or quicklime or carbon dioxide; but also a reversible reaction
illustrating the effects of temperature and pressure, which is
related to the use of mortar, the preparation of salts, and the
lime-water test for carbon dioxide. Much of the sheer
drudgery of remembering isolated facts can be eliminated by
thinking of a few of the most important reactions in this way.

Fourthly, the relationship of chemistry to other studies and
other problems is pointed out wherever possible. Thus the
above preparation of quicklime is relevant to history (bleaching-
powder and the Industrial Revolution), public health (increased
food production depends on adequate liming of the soil, for
reasons which are biological), economics (the use of hard steels
for grinding limestone has made the reaction obsolete and
wasteful as a source of agricultural lime), and politics (the
dangers of quarrying to town and country planning).
Similarly the opening up of tropical territories has been made
possible by new drugs such as Paludrine and Antrycide.

All the various "Certificate" (ordinary level) requirements have been adequately covered and the book may be used either in the final two years, or as a course which is complete in itself. It is hoped that the way in which the subject is approached may help to produce practical-minded citizens with a wide understanding of the implications of chemistry, as well as thoroughly trained specialists possessing a secure knowledge of the elementary groundwork.

Sections in small type are demanded by only a few examining bodies or by none; many of them are concerned with recent advances and are included for the sake of general interest.

The reactions of the most important industrial substances are summarized in large diagrams: these are given for Hydrogen, Coal, Limestone, Nitrogen compounds, Sulphur compounds, and Salt.

Finally, an attempt has been made to provide an unusually complete and useful index.

We wish to express our thanks to our colleagues, Messrs. Lucas Humby and Crompton for helpful comments; to Dr. Walter P. Joshua for assistance in obtaining photographs; to Mr. G. E. Howling of the Imperial Institute; to Mr. N. Garrod Thomas of the National Sulphuric Acid Association; to Miss M. Hannan, Mr. E. D. Catton and Mr. Gordon Long of I.C.I., and to Mr. David Bolton for supplying much helpful information; to the staff of Winchester Public Library for obtaining references; to the Isotype Institute for preparing fig. 131; to those firms and individuals who have supplied photographs; to the authors of the books mentioned on p. 530; to Mr. Peter Parker for proof reading; and to Mrs. Barbara Hutton for help in preparing the index; and especially to all pupils and correspondents who have suggested improvements.

We also thank the various Certificate, etc., examination boards for permission to reproduce some of their recent questions: A=Army and Navy; B=Bristol; C=Cambridge Local; D=Durham; L=London; N=Northern Universities; O=Oxford Local; O and C=Oxford and Cambridge; S=Scottish Education Dept.; W=Welsh Joint Education Committee.

THE SCIENCE SCHOOL.   F. W. G.
    THE COLLEGE,   K. B. H.
        WINCHESTER.

CONTENTS

PART 3. NON-METALS

PART 4. THE METALS, ANALYSIS AND REVISION

PHOTOGRAPHS IN THE TEXT

CHARTS AND TABLES

PART 1

FIRST PRINCIPLES

CHAPTER I

THE HISTORY AND IMPORTANCE OF CHEMISTRY

The Properties of Substances
Chemical and Physical Changes

What Chemistry is About

Chemistry is the study of *what things are made of.* When we know the nature of air and water, of rocks and metals, and of trees and human beings, we are then in a position to make other things which were not known before, such as plastics and penicillin. Chemistry is therefore a live and fascinating subject.

Chemistry is one of the branches of science. Science is different from other subjects in the way in which its knowledge is obtained: that is, through *observation* and *experiment.* Instead of believing that everything is made of fire or of water as men did in the Middle Ages, merely because some famous man had said so, scientists try out their ideas to see if they pass the tests of practical experience. We now believe that every thing is made up of atoms, and that atoms contain smaller particles called electrons; the reason why we believe this is because if we *predict* the consequences of these beliefs, we discover new things like radio and atomic energy which could not possibly have been guessed at otherwise. All the way through this book you will find statements which you yourself can test in the laboratory; and although, naturally, many of the more advanced ideas can only be checked by highly trained scientists, these ideas too are accepted or rejected because they do or do not *work in practice*, rather than because Einstein or some other eminent person said that they must be right or wrong.

Another feature of chemistry, as of any other scientific subject, is that the knowledge is *organized.* It does not consist of isolated scraps of unrelated information which merely have to be remembered as such, but it collects these together and gives fundamental reasons which explain them all. For example, one and the same reason explains why steel is made in Sheffield but aluminium in the Highlands of Scotland; why iron weapons were used as far back as 2000 B.C., but aluminium was not discovered till A.D. 1827, and why iron costs about £20 per ton, whilst aluminium costs about £200.

The History of Chemistry

As man is endowed with boundless curiosity and an urge to make life more pleasant, it was natural even in very early times that he should try to find out what the shiny red lumps were in the ashes of his fire, and to try to use them for tools instead of the more cumbersome pieces of stone. The early history of chemistry is therefore largely the story of how metals were worked. Gold, silver, mercury, copper, lead, tin, and iron were all well known and used by the Greeks and Romans before the birth of Christ.

From this period until less than 200 years ago there was little real progress in chemistry, and it is interesting to seek the reasons for this. Probably the most important reason was the divorce between theory and practice. The everyday work of the Ancient World was mostly done by slaves, whilst those who thought about the nature of things had a more leisured existence and usually despised practical matters as being beneath them. The other reason was partly a result of this: the ideas which were developed had no basis in experimental facts, and attempts were made to find "facts" which fitted the ideas. Both these attitudes were extremely dangerous, and had disastrous consequences. As the state of mind which gave rise to them was completely unscientific, we must study what happened in rather more detail.

The idea which caused so much harm was put forward by Aristotle in about 350 B.C. This was that everything is made up of earth, air, fire, and water. Although it was not based on fact it survived for over two thousand years, and even as late as 1624 the Parliament of Paris passed a law compelling all chemists to teach Aristotle's idea, on pain of death and confiscation of goods.

Now if this idea is true that everything is made up of these four so-called "elements," it follows that any one substance can be turned into any other; why not, in fact, turn lead into gold and so get rich quickly? The vain attempt to "transmute

[*Reproduced by courtesy of Prof. J. Read, F.R.S., from his book* "*The Alchemist in Life, Literature and Art.*"

PLATE 1A. "HOCUS POCUS"

Picture by T. Rowlandson (1800) of attempts by alchemists to produce fake gold.

the elements" occupied almost all the attention of the early chemists, or *alchemists*, as they were called. When in fact no gold could be obtained, the alchemists cheated by making substances which looked like gold, but which really had only a surface coating of it. (PLATE 1A.) Such fraud and trickery caused the alchemists to be despised by honest men.

Another result of this idea was that anything which we now call a gas was thought to be merely another kind of air. Although the true natures of the air and of burning were almost discovered by the founders of the Royal Society in the 1660s, a false theory prevented progress for another hundred years (see p. 522).

Modern Chemistry

Chemistry as we know it dates from the time when these ideas were finally overthrown. It is no accident that the American Revolution and the French Revolution occurred at about the same period; men no longer believed in things just because they were customary. In the same way, the new attitude to chemistry resulted in the discovery of a new gas, chlorine, which had the power of bleaching cotton; this use was put to good effect in the development of the Lancashire cotton industry which was so important a feature of the English Industrial Revolution.

After that, new discoveries came thick and fast. Very often an advance in one field of science would make possible further advances in another. For example, the discovery of electricity led to the preparation of the new metals magnesium and aluminium, which will soon be serious competitors of steel. The increasing use of coal gas and the investigation of coal tar led to a branch of chemistry, "organic chemistry," which deals with drugs and dyes, plastics and explosives; most of these substances are not known in nature and were made artificially ("synthesized") by man. These man-made substances are in many cases *better* than any natural product. For example, "Paludrine," prepared in 1944, is more effective than quinine in treating malaria; and the quinine itself which was synthesized in that same year is exactly the same as the drug prepared from the bark of the cinchona tree. The unfortunate and incorrect idea that man-made products are inferior substitutes began when rayon was first prepared; it should never have been called "artificial silk" because it has entirely different properties from silk.

A **synthetic** product is also nearly always far **cheaper** than

the same substance obtained from plants or animals.   The new
" Compound E " (Cortisone) will only be a possible cure for
rheumatism if it can be prepared synthetically, because otherwise it will be far too expensive.

[Photo by courtesy of Glaxo Laboratories.

PLATE 1B.   CRYSTALS OF PURE PENICILLIN
(Magnification 120 diameters)
A real triumph of modern chemistry (p. 8).

Finally, organic chemistry helps in the understanding of
biology, which deals with the complex processes going on in
the human body and the living plant.   The manufacture of
artificial fertilizers for increasing the supply of food, and the

synthesis of vitamins and penicillin (PLATE 1B) to keep us healthy are the results of attempts to answer the great question "What are things made of?" And still the search goes on.

NOTE: Some dates of discoveries, etc., mentioned in this book are given in the Appendix on pp. 521–526.

The Importance of Chemistry

From all this it is easy to see a number of good reasons why we should study chemistry, even though probably only a few readers of this book will be doing chemical experiments in their future careers.

First, chemistry satisfies our natural healthy curiosity about the world we live in. When anyone stops thinking about the nature of things, they might just as well be dead, because they can find little interest in life. Also practical work gives us the satisfaction of doing something with our hands. The pride of growing a beautiful crystal and the excitement of analysing an unknown substance are active pleasures which are more real than those of being a mere spectator.

Secondly, the world has been so changed by science, including chemistry, that it is impossible to understand it properly without some knowledge of elementary scientific facts. All scientific discoveries can be used either for good or for evil, e.g. the same chemical substance may be used either as a fertilizer or as an explosive. At the moment, even in peacetime, far more money is spent on war research than on developing peaceful uses; this will not be changed until everyone realizes fully how many problems science could solve if properly applied.

Thirdly, we can gain some experience of the scientific method which will help us both in our everyday lives and in our studies of other subjects. We will not necessarily believe the claims of the makers of patent medicines or of new soap powders; instead, we can carry out some simple experiments to test whether they are true or not. Also the scientific attitude of mind, which requires hard facts before accepting any generalization (possibly a wild one), and which tests such generalizations by experiment, is of value in all walks of life.

The Properties of Substances

In order to find out what things are made of, we must know how things behave. The behaviour of a substance is considered by the chemist under two headings, namely physical properties and chemical properties.

Physical Properties

The most obvious properties are those which affect our five senses, i.e. sight, touch, smell, taste, and hearing. Thus sulphuric acid, when pure, is a colourless liquid, heavier than water, with no smell, a burning taste, and which gives no sound. We shall find the colours and smells of substances very useful for recognizing them; normally no substance should be tasted, as some are poisonous or extremely dangerous; and noises are made only by gases escaping or exploding.

We soon find, however, that physical properties which can be *measured* (fig. 1, p. 10) are much more useful.

If we find a colourless liquid which has a freezing-point of 0° C., a boiling-point of 100° C., a density of 1·0 gm./c.c. (i.e. a specific gravity of 1·0) and a specific heat of 1·0, (as well as having no taste or smell), we may be fairly certain that it is water. Similarly, the simplest test for seeing if a person is healthy enough to give a blood transfusion is to measure the density of the blood; if enough red cells are present, a drop of blood will sink in a copper sulphate solution of density 1·052 gm./c.c.

There are two other important uses of physical properties besides helping us to identify substances. One is for obtaining substances in a state of purity. Most minerals when they are dug up from the earth have a large amount of unwanted stones and rocks mixed up with them. For example, the "ore" of tin contains only about 2% of the tin oxide, "tinstone"; whilst if 1 part of gold was found in as much as a hundred thousand parts of other stuff, it would still be worth recovering. In order to separate the substances we make use of the difference in their densities and wash away the impurities with powerful jets of water, leaving the heavier tinstone or gold behind. Similarly, if more of our coal was "washed"

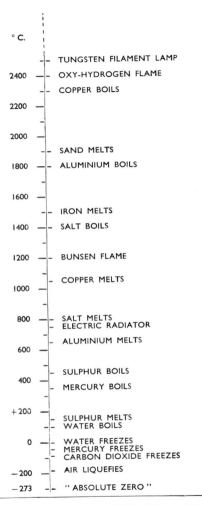

FIG. 1. TEMPERATURE CHART

to remove iron pyrites, there would be less pollution of our air by harmful sulphurous fumes.

The other way in which physical properties are helpful is in deciding how substances can be used.   Aluminium, with a low specific gravity (2·7), can be used for aeroplanes, whilst iron (7·8) cannot.   Diamonds, which are harder than any other known substance, are more used in tools for cutting than they are as jewels.

Chemical Properties

Now we come to consider the very different behaviour of substances when they are acted on by air or water or acids or alkalis or even by heat alone   Often they are changed into new substances which have completely different physical (and chemical) properties from the substance we started with. These chemical properties are the main subject of this book, and they are so important that we must find out which changes in a substance are chemical ones and which are merely physical. This we shall do by examining in detail a number of apparently similar experiments, one of which produces a chemical change and the other a physical change.

Chemical Changes and Physical Changes

CHEMICAL CHANGES	PHYSICAL CHANGES
1. When a lighted match is put to the wick of a candle, the wax melts and then burns. The candle will go on burning for a long time and giving out heat until all the candle has burned away. If a piece of paper is held above the candle, it will be seen that black soot has been formed from the wax.	1. When a lighted match is put to the bottom of a candle, the wax melts and drips off. If a piece of paper is held below the candle, the molten wax will set again to a solid and seems to be the same stuff as before. When the match has burned out, no more wax will melt and no heat is given out.
2. When small crystals of washing soda are added to vinegar or to dilute sulphuric acid, they dissolve and fizz and become warmer. If the solution is then heated to drive off some of the water, crystals will be obtained which do *not* fizz when added to acid.	2. When small crystals of washing soda are added to water, they also dissolve, but do *not* fizz and do not become warmer. If the solution is then heated to drive off some of the water, crystals will be obtained which *do* fizz when added to acid, and which can be shown to be the original washing soda.

CHEMICAL CHANGES	PHYSICAL CHANGES
3. When iron filings are mixed with powdered sulphur *and heated* in a test-tube, more heat is given out and the whole mass becomes red hot The hard substance remaining (iron sulphide) can no longer be separated by a magnet; and it behaves quite differently from the original iron when treated with acids.	3. When iron filings are mixed with powdered sulphur without being heated, no heat is given out. The iron can be separated by using a magnet; and the mixture behaves in the same way as iron when treated with acids.

From these examples we can see the essential differences between the two types of changes. These will be put in the form of a table, in order of importance.

CHEMICAL CHANGES (*Changes of Substance*)	PHYSICAL CHANGES (*Changes of State*)
1 A *new substance* is always formed, e.g. soot or iron sulphide, with a very different chemical composition.	1. *No* new substance is ever formed. It may have different physical properties, but the chemical composition will be the same.
2. *Much heat* is often given out (or, sometimes, taken in).	2. *Very little* heat is usually given out or taken in.
3. It is usually *difficult to reverse* the change and obtain the original substance.	3. It is usually *easy* to reverse the change, simply by reversing the conditions, e.g. temperature.
4. Often there seems to be a *change in weight*.	4. There is *no* change in weight.

Further examples of physical changes are: (*a*) ice $\rightleftharpoons$ water $\rightleftharpoons$ steam; (*b*) iron $\rightleftharpoons$ magnetized iron; (*c*) the change in the tungsten filament of an electric lamp when switched on or off.

Many of the chemical changes which we meet from now on will be described not only in words but also in symbols; these formulae and equations are especially useful as a convenient kind of shorthand. The method by which such equations can be compiled is explained in Section 2 of this book, and we shall see how they give us a great deal of useful information about the *quantities* in which substances react.   The weighing and measuring of these leads to the atomic theory, on which all our modern chemistry is based

Suggestions for Practical Work

The three chemical and three physical changes described on pp. 11-12.

NOTE: An account of the history of theoretical chemistry is given in Philbrick and Holmyard's " Text Book of Theoretical and Inorganic Chemistry " pp. 3-56 (Dent).

QUESTIONS ON CHAPTER 1

1. Discuss the differences between physical and chemical change. Illustrate your answer by referring to *three* examples of each.

2. Why is a knowledge of the physical properties of substances useful?   Give examples as far as possible from your own experience and from your knowledge of other subjects.

3. 'A complete educational course should include some knowledge of chemistry."   What arguments can you give in support of this statement?

4. Write a short essay on the contribution of the science of chemistry to the comfort and happiness of mankind.

CHAPTER II

THE SCIENTIFIC METHOD AND THE PROBLEM OF BURNING BREATHING AND RUSTING

We shall now consider three of the most important of all the chemical changes which affect our daily lives. The first one, burning, will be treated so as to show the working of the scientific method in a series of practical experiments; it will be noticed that the *weights* of the substances taking part are specially important.

BURNING

The importance of burning has been obvious from the earliest times, because it is used to keep one warm, especially in cold climates like our own. Fire was also used for cooking and for the extraction of metals from their naturally occurring ores.

Men were naturally curious about the nature of such a change, and put forward various ideas to account for it; but the truth was not known until near the end of the eighteenth century, because up till then attempts were made to fit the facts to the theories rather than the other way round

The first step in the scientific method is to get the facts

Experiment no. 1. Burn a weighed candle in the open air. Weigh again after a few minutes. As expected, the candle will be found to be lighter in weight. This raises the question: "Where does the weight go to?" Presumably it can only go off into the air, unless we are to assume that it vanishes completely.

Experiment no. 2. Burn some coal on a piece of broken porcelain or in a crucible (weighed before starting). In this case not only does the weight decrease as before, but the smoke which is given off suggests strongly that this is where some of the weight which is lost goes to.

14

Similar results are obtained with wood or paper or sulphur, and suggest that this is how *all* substances behave.   But it is necessary to be cautious and ask:

Have all the important facts been collected?

Experiment no. 3.   A different kind of substance is burned, e.g. a metal such as magnesium (or iron).   The magnesium ribbon (weighed) is put into a weighed crucible, with a lid partly on, and heated with a bunsen-burner.   The metal burns brightly, especially if the lid is slightly lifted.   The latter agrees with our everyday experience that a fire burns better if there is a good draught, and suggests that air is necessary for burning.   When the crucible with the ash from the burnt magnesium is weighed, the surprising fact is discovered that there has been an *increase* in weight!   (The same is found with iron filings.)   This cannot have come from the flame of the burner, because the weight of the crucible is found to be unchanged if it is heated alone.

The second step in the scientific method is to put forward a hypothesis

A "hypothesis" is simply one possible explanation which may account for the facts.   The only reasonable hypothesis at this stage is that (*a*) Any decrease in weight results from smoke, etc., going off into the air, and (*b*) Any increase in weight comes from the air (we know that air has weight, from our knowledge of barometers).

The third step is to check the hypothesis by further experiments

Although it is often fairly easy to put forward some hypothesis which may explain everything yet known, the truth of a hypothesis can only be judged by its success or failure in **predicting** the results of experiments which have not yet been tried.

If our hypothesis (*a*) is true, then if we collect the smoke, etc., and prevent it from escaping into the air, there should be an increase in weight in all cases, even with a substance like a candle.

Experiment no. 4.   If a candle is burned for a few minutes in the apparatus shown in fig. 2, with air being sucked through, and with chemicals in the U-tube to absorb the products of burning, it will be found that there is a slight increase in weight, as expected.

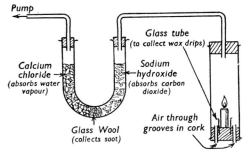

Fig. 2.   Burning a candle and collecting the smoke.

At this stage we must beware of being so in love with our hypothesis that we rejoice too soon, and ask:

Is there any alternative explanation?

Possibly there is enough dust and dampness in the air which is sucked through to account for the 0·1 gm. or so by which the weight has increased.   To check this we must do a "control experiment" or "blank determination."

Experiment no. 5.   In this control experiment, we do everything exactly the same as in no. 4, except that we do *not* burn the candle. The air is sucked through at the *same* rate for the *same* length of time.   This time we find that although there is still a small increase in weight, it is only about one-third of the increase in experiment no. 4.   We have therefore confirmed (*a*) that the apparent loss in weight, when a candle is burnt normally, is due to the smoke, etc. not being collected.

We must now test the truth of hypothesis (*b*).   If the increase in weight comes from the air, then there should be *no* increase if we make something burn in a confined space.

Experiment no. 6.   Not many substances will burn in a very limited amount of air, so we use phosphorus, which is the basis of matches.   Sand is placed in the bottom of the flask shown in fig. 3 to prevent it being cracked by the high temperature. The screw clip is firmly done up to prevent anything getting in or out, the flask+phosphorus weighed, and the flask warmed very gently until the phosphorus bursts into flame. Clouds of white smoke are formed, which settle into a powdery ash very different from the original phosphorus.   After the reaction is over, the flask is allowed to cool thoroughly for about 5 minutes and then re-weighed.   The weight is then found to be exactly *the same*, thus confirming the truth of our hypothesis.

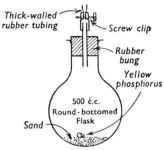

FIG. 3.   Burning phosphorus in a sealed flask.

(If the flask is weighed too soon after the reaction is over, there seems to be a very slight decrease in weight; this is due to the heat of the reaction driving off the film of moisture which normally exists on the surface of the flask.)

If the screw clip is now opened and a finger placed over the end of the tube, air will be felt to rush in.   When the flask is weighed again, the usual increase in weight will be found.   Presumably the air which rushes in is replacing some air which has been used up.

During the reaction:

Phosphorus + Air (in the flask) $\longrightarrow$ (Phosphorus+Air) i.e. Ash   Same weight

When the clip is opened:

(Phosphorus+Air) i.e. Ash $\xrightarrow{\text{+Air coming in}}$ (Phosphorus+Air) i.e. Ash + Air (in the flask)   Increase in weight

Our hypothesis may now be made somewhat more complete : " When a substance burns it uses up air *and combines with* it thus increasing in weight."

The fourth step is to alter or abandon the hypothesis if even one fact contradicts it

Experiment no. 7.   By putting into words the further idea that the air is used up, we do in fact ask ourselves another question:

"Are we sure that *all* the air is used up?" Experiment no. 6 certainly appeared to give a reaction vigorous enough to use it all up, but even when we are fairly confident and the answer seems "obvious," there is no harm in trying to make sure. If we repeat experiment no. 6, but open the clip whilst holding the tube under water, water will rush in to fill the space left by the air which was used up. Only about one-fifth of the 500 c.c. flask is in fact filled by the water (the volume of water is measured in a measuring cylinder and found to be 100 c.c.), and so *only about one-fifth of the air is used up* by the burning.

Experiment no. 8. This conclusion is so important that a further experiment should be done to make sure that the active portion of the air is only about one-fifth of the whole, and to measure the proportion of it as accurately as possible. *Yellow* phosphorus will burn slowly in air, even without being heated, and is therefore always kept under water. A small piece of it is put on the end of a stiff wire in air confined in a long, narrow measuring-tube over water. It will smoulder slowly until, after a few days, all the active portion of the air has been used up, and the level of the water has stopped rising when one-fifth of the way up (fig. 4). It can be shown that it is not the phosphorus which is used up, because it will burn again when brought into the open air.

If the water-levels are made equal inside and outside both before and after the experiment and if the temperature and pressure have not altered, it will be found that 21% of the air has been used up. The way to measure volumes of gases accurately is explained in Chapter IX (p. 130).

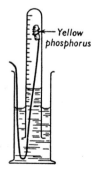

Fig. 4.   One-fifth of the air is used up.

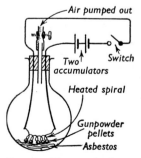

Fig. 5.   Gunpowder burns in a vacuum.

The fifth step is to continue experimenting until an effective theory is built up which explains all the facts

Experiment no. 9. Gunpowder burns without air. This can be shown by using the apparatus of fig. 5, which is put behind the thick glass window of a fume cupboard in case the explosion is violent. All the air has been pumped out of the flask, and the few small pellets of gunpowder are set on fire by the heat of the electric current passing through the wire which is coiled round them. It will be seen that the gunpowder *first* bursts into flame without any air being present; *then* the rubber bung is blown out.

This can only be explained if the gunpowder contains either air or the active portion of it (which is called "oxygen").

Experiment no. 10. Gunpowder contains combined oxygen, though not as a gas. Gunpowder is a mixture of sulphur (which

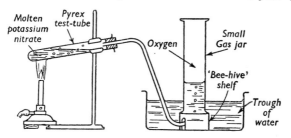

FIG. 6. Potassium nitrate contains combined oxygen.

can be shown to contain no air or oxygen), charcoal (which contains only a small amount of air: see p. 244), and potassium nitrate (known as "saltpetre" or "nitre").

When potassium nitrate is heated strongly in a hard-glass test-tube with two bunsen-burners, it melts and then slowly gives off a gas which may be collected in a small gas jar over water, after the air in the tube has been allowed to escape (fig. 6). This gas makes a glowing splinter of wood burst into flame, showing that it is not ordinary air, but must be oxygen, the active part of it. Other substances, such as a candle, will also burn far more brightly in oxygen than in ordinary air.

The final experiment to be described is of great historical importance because it led directly to the establishment of the mcdern theory of burning. Scheele, a Swede, discovered in 1769 that the red solid obtained by heating mercury in air (which we now call mercuric oxide) gave off oxygen when it was heated. The same discovery was made by Priestley, an Englishman, quite independently in 1774. When Priestley told this to the Frenchman Lavoisier, the latter repeated the whole experiment and was able to overthrow the older ideas on burning and to put forward the theory which we now hold today.

Experiment no. 11. Lavoisier (1743–1794) heated 4 oz. of mercury in a retort, connected with air in a bell-jar over mercury (fig. 7);

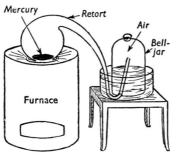

the total volume of the air in the apparatus was 50 cubic inches. Red specks of mercuric oxide were formed in the retort, until after 12 days no more appeared; the volume of air was found to have decreased to 42 cubic inches.

Then the mercuric oxide was removed and heated by itself; it gave off 8 cubic inches of a gas which was found to be oxygen.

FIG. 7. Lavoisier's experiment.

This shows clearly that the *same amount* of oxygen is given off on decomposing mercuric oxide as was taken from the air by the mercury when it burned.

Law of Conservation of Mass

This experiment, and the one when phosphorus was burnt in a sealed flask (p. 17), illustrate the *experimental law* that **In a chemical change, matter is neither created nor destroyed.** This was first clearly stated by Lavoisier in 1774.

Complete Explanation of Burning

We are now in a position to state our theory of burning. A *theory* is an idea (hypothesis) which has stood the test of repeated experiment and is generally accepted, as is the case with the modern theory of burning.

*Burning is a chemical change in which a substance combines
with oxygen to form an oxide*

The oxygen may be got from the air (of which it forms
about one-fifth) or from substances which contain it in a combined form (e.g. potassium nitrate).   The *oxide* formed by
burning weighs more than the original substance, because it
contains the original substance plus oxygen.   If any such oxide
is a gas, there will seem to be a loss in weight unless this gas
is collected.

*Finally we must remember that our theory is only an
approximation to truth*

It may be possible to get still closer to the truth (see p. 296),
and many theories which have been held for a hundred years or
so have had to be modified to make them fit still more experimental facts.   Dalton's Atomic Theory and Newton's Theory
of Gravitation are examples of this; they are still very good
explanations of the elementary facts, but they have been
improved upon in the constant search to learn more of the
truth.

SCIENTIFIC METHOD

Summary of Scientific Method

1. Get the facts.
2. Explain the facts.
3. *Predict other facts and test the predictions.*
4. Modify the explanation.
5. Continue experimenting.

Scientific Method in Everyday Life

It must not be thought that the scientific method can only
be applied to problems in the laboratory.   We can apply
it equally well in everyday life, and indeed the world problems
of today urgently call out for such application.

Very many questions are argued about, often with great
heat, when they could be settled definitely by a simple experiment ("Try it and see!")   In other cases, enough facts are

already known for the problem to be solved, but the people concerned remain obstinately unaware of them, and prefer to let the matter be decided by unreasoning prejudice and emotion.

The tremendous discoveries of the past 180 years have been due to the application of the scientific method to scientific matters.   Surely it is likely that equally startling and valuable results will follow its use in other fields as well.

NOTE: In the late war, scientific method was applied with spectacular results under the name of " Operational Research " : an interesting account of this is given in " Science at War " (H.M. Stationery Office).

BREATHING

Breathing is a process which is essentially similar to burning. At first sight this seems surprising, because we think that burning means flames and smoke, and because we do not realize the true purpose of breathing.

Breathing ("respiration") is necessary to all living things in order to supply *energy*; this is equally true of man himself and of every one of the thousand million million tiny living cells of which man is made up.   In man and other animals which need a great deal of energy for moving about to find their food, the energy is produced by carbon compounds (food) being *combined with oxygen* (from the air).   Combination with oxygen is the essential feature of burning, and, as you will remember, this reaction gives out energy in the form of heat.   Burning and breathing therefore produce a similar chemical change, as was shown by Lavoisier in 1785 (p. 522).

Carbon compounds, whether as fuels or as foods, combine with oxygen to form the *oxide* of carbon, carbon dioxide. This can be shown in the following two experiments.

Experiment no. 12.   A small amount of sugar is put in the bowl of a "deflagrating spoon" (fig. 8), heated until it begins to burn, and the spoon then placed in a gas-jar of oxygen (or air) so that the lid covers the top of the jar.   The burning of the sugar, which is a compound of carbon, produces the gas carbon dioxide.   This can easily be tested for by lifting the lid, pouring in a little of a clear solution *lime-water*, and shaking up; a white cloudiness in the liquid proves that carbon dioxide has been formed, as this is the only gas which gives the test (see p. 250).

Experiment no. 13. Air is breathed in through a solution of calcium hydroxide (lime-water), and breathed out through another flask of lime-water (fig. 9). After about 10 seconds the lime-water in the flask on the right begins to turn cloudy ("milky") whilst the one on the left remains clear; this shows that the air which we breathe out contains more carbon dioxide than the air we breathe in. This is because the foods which we eat, including sugar, are all burned up to give out energy and to form carbon dioxide (see p. 304):

$$C_6H_{12}O_6 \quad + \quad 6O_2 \quad = \quad 6CO_2 \quad + \quad 6H_2O \quad (+ \text{ energy})$$
Glucose (a sugar)   Oxygen   Carbon Dioxide   Water

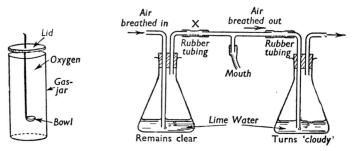

FIG. 8. Deflagrat-
ing spoon.

FIG. 9. Air is different after being breathed out.

We should expect the air which we breathe *in* to contain *some* carbon dioxide, because it is constantly receiving the carbon dioxide which we breathe out.

We can show that this is so, by continuing to breathe in through the apparatus for a long time; as this is tiring, it is better to disconnect the apparatus at X and to attach this to a pump which will suck the air through. After about 10 minutes the lime-water begins to go cloudy, showing that there is some carbon dioxide (though very little) in ordinary air. This very small amount is, however, extremely important, because it serves as food for all green plants (see p. 36), and if there were no plant life there could be no animal life, because animals depend on plants for their food.

It is interesting to consider this process of breathing in

rather more detail.   The air which we breathe into our lungs
contains about 21% of oxygen (by volume) and about 0·03%
of carbon dioxide.   In the lungs it combines with the red
pigment of the blood, a complicated compound of iron named
"haemoglobin."   The blood transports the oxygen and also
food substances (mostly broken down to sugars) throughout
the body to every living cell; here the reaction—

Sugars + Oxygen = Carbon Dioxide + Water (+ Energy)

takes place; the energy set free is partly used in the muscles
and partly for keeping the temperature of the body at 98·4° F.
(about 37° C.), which is much above that of the surrounding
air (say 60° F. or about 15° C.).   The carbon dioxide is then
carried back, combined in the blood, to the lungs, where it is
exchanged for oxygen.   The air which is breathed out contains
about 18% of oxygen and 3% of carbon dioxide, the remainder
of the air (mostly nitrogen) being quite unchanged.

The supreme necessity of oxygen for breathing is shown by
the fact that whilst we can survive for a few weeks without
food or for a few days even without water, to go without
breathing for more than a few minutes results in death.

RUSTING

The third chemical change which we consider in this chapter
is also related to burning, as we shall see, and is of vital

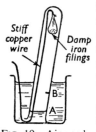

importance in our modern industrial civilization.   More than ten times as much iron is
used today as all the other metals put
together, and the cost all over the world
of preventing rust is about £500 million
per year.

Experiment no. 14.   If some iron filings are
put on a watch-glass, weighed, and left uncovered in the laboratory, they will become
rusty after a few days and show an increase in
weight.

FIG. 10. Air used
up by rusting.

Experiment no. 15.   Some slightly damped iron filings are tied
up in a piece of muslin (fig. 10) and suspended on a piece of stiff

wire in a volume of air confined in a boiling-tube over water in a beaker. After a few days, when the iron has become rusty, the water-level has risen about one-fifth of the way up the tube from the original level A (marked with a rubber band) to B. These two experiments suggest that the iron combines with the oxygen of the air.

Experiments nos. 16 and 17. We can show, however, that a piece of polished iron wire will remain bright in the dry air of a desiccator, although it will rust rapidly in the moist air outside: (fig. 11 (*a*)).

Also, iron wire will not rust when placed in boiled water (free from air) which is covered with a layer of oil, although it does so in ordinary tap-water, which contains dissolved air: (fig. 11 (*b*) and (*c*)).

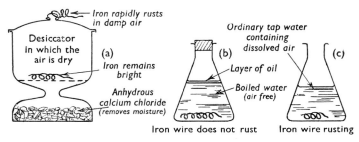

FIG. 11.   The rusting of iron.

Our conclusion, therefore, is that the rusting of iron (unlike burning) needs both air (oxygen) and water; to prevent rust, the air and water must be kept away from the iron by a coating of some other substance, such as oil (for tools); paint or tar (for bridges, etc.: PLATE 2, p. 26) ; zinc ("galvanizing"); tin (in tinplate); or plastics for food containers; alternatively stainless steel (p. 469) may be used, but this is very expensive.

Even this is not quite the whole story, because the carbon dioxide in the air plays some part in rusting; and more strongly acid gases, such as the sulphur dioxide (p. 263) resulting from smoke pollution, cause iron to rust three times more rapidly in Sheffield than it does in country towns.

Suggestions for Practical Work

Experiments nos. 1, 2, 3. Instead of a crucible and lid, a piece of broken porcelain may be used and covered with another similar piece.

Experiments nos. 14 and 15 should be set going and left for a few days.

[Fox Photos Ltd.

PLATE 2.   OXYGEN IS NECESSARY FOR RUSTING

The Forth Bridge being painted to prevent it from rusting (p. 25) Twenty-four painters are continuously employed, and 50 tons of paint are used in the three years before the task is begun again.

QUESTIONS ON CHAPTER II

1. State the Law of Conservation of Mass.

2·16 gm. of mercury oxide are heated and give 114 c.c. of oxygen. The density of oxygen under the conditions of this experiment is 1·40 gm./litre. Calculate the weight of mercury left if all the oxygen is driven off.

2. Describe three experiments you would carry out to determine the conditions under which iron rusts, and state clearly the conclusion to be reached from each experiment. Mention three different methods which are used to protect iron from rusting. (C.)

3. Why do we breathe? Design experiments to show as completely as possible how the air has been changed by being breathed.

4. Give a summary of the modern theory of burning. State very briefly the experimental evidence for *each* point you make.

5. Look up in some other book (e.g. Partington's "Everyday Chemistry") the ideas on burning which were held before Lavoisier's time. Summarize them briefly and show how they are disproved by the evidence given in this book.

6. "Rain before seven, fine before eleven (o'clock)" is an old saying. Explain how you would use the scientific method to find out if this is true.

CHAPTER III

THE ATMOSPHERE AND ITS CONSTITUENTS

*Oxygen, Nitrogen, Argon, Carbon Dioxide, Water Vapour, Dust,
Impurities, and Bacteria*

THE ATMOSPHERE

We are now in a position to consider the nature of that ocean of gas which surrounds the earth, and which is so essential to life as we know it. The part of it which is active in burning, breathing, and rusting is *oxygen*; the inactive part is nearly all *nitrogen*; but there are small amounts of completely inert gases, the chief of which is *argon*. In addition, water vapour—as we know from rusting—is present in very variable amounts, usually about 1%, depending on the weather; the amount of carbon dioxide is also variable, though never less than 0·03%, and there are also fine particles of dust, soot, impurities (especially sulphur dioxide), and bacteria. These will be dealt with in turn.

AVERAGE COMPOSITION OF AIR BY VOLUME

	%		
Nitrogen	78·1		Water vapour almost *nil* — 4%
Oxygen	20·9	also	Carbon dioxide 0·03 — 0·3%
Argon	1·0		Pollution, bacteria, etc.
	100·0		

1. OXYGEN

Laboratory Preparation. Two methods of preparing oxygen from substances which contain it have already been described (expts. 10, 11, pp. 19, 20):

(1) Potassium Nitrate=Potassium Nitrite+Oxygen
$$2KNO_3 \qquad\qquad 2KNO_2 \qquad\qquad O_2$$

(2)   Mercuric Oxide=Mercury+Oxygen
$$2HgO \qquad\qquad 2Hg \qquad\qquad O_2$$

Method (1) is slow, and gives only a small amount of gas, and needs a high temperature; method (2) is far too expensive for general use.

(3) **Expt. 18.** A much better method is to heat another substance which contains oxygen, called potassium chlorate, mixed with manganese dioxide which acts as a *catalyst*.

A catalyst is defined as a substance which increases the speed of a reaction, but does not itself undergo any permanent chemical change.

$$\text{Potassium Chlorate} = \text{Potassium Chloride} + \text{Oxygen}$$
$$2KClO_3 \qquad 2KCl \qquad 3O_2$$

The same apparatus may be used as for the heating of potassium nitrate (expt. 10, p. 19), except that an ordinary test-tube may be used and only one bunsen-burner, because a much lower temperature is needed.

Proof that manganese dioxide acts as a catalyst may be obtained as follows:

Expt. 19. (a) Heat some potassium chlorate alone gently in a test-tube until it melts; no bubbles of gas are seen. If a small amount of manganese dioxide is now added, oxygen is rapidly given off (glowing splint test, see expt. 10, p. 19), showing that it increases the speed of the reaction.

(b) Heat some potassium chlorate, mixed with a weighed amount of manganese dioxide in a test-tube or crucible until no more oxygen is given off. When cool, add water to dissolve the potassium chloride which remains, and filter off the manganese dioxide. This when dry will be found to have almost exactly its original weight (and the same chemical properties), showing that it has not undergone any chemical change.

Catalysts, as would be expected, are very important in many industrial processes, which would often not be possible without them (see pp. 234–236).

(4) Supplies of oxygen are most conveniently obtained from steel cylinders containing the gas, prepared commercially, and compressed (but not made liquid) under 120 times atmospheric pressure.

If required pure and dry, it should be dried by concentrated sulphuric acid and collected over mercury (see fig. 28, p. 92).

2⁴

Commercial Preparation of Oxygen

Oxygen is produced from the cheapest possible raw material, i.e. air, by taking advantage of the different boiling-points of the oxygen and nitrogen; when air is liquefied and allowed to warm up slightly, the nitrogen (b.p. $-196°$ C.) will boil off before the oxygen (b.p. $-183°$ C.).

The liquefaction of air takes place in four main stages: (a) water vapour and carbon dioxide are removed (see pp. 40, 252), because these would freeze first and block up the apparatus, (b) the purified air is compressed, thus becoming *hotter*, but is cooled once more to room temperature by means of cold water; (c) this compressed air is then allowed to expand and so becomes very cold; (d) this cold air is used to cool some more air which has finished stage (b); the latter then liquefies on being expanded in stage (c).

The process for separating the two liquids is known as "fractional distillation," and the apparatus is complex.

Oxygen so obtained is $99·5\%$ pure, costing less than a penny per cubic foot; the main impurity being nitrogen.

Oxygen is also produced, in countries where electric power is cheap, by the electrolysis of water (p. 84).

Physical Properties

Oxygen is a colourless gas without taste or smell. It is very slightly heavier than air, its density relative to hydrogen being 16 (air$=14·4$: see p. 196). It dissolves to a small extent in water, 4 volumes in 100 volumes of water at $8°$ C.; this is enough for the breathing of fishes.

Chemical Properties

Oxygen is a very reactive gas and combines directly with nearly all the other elements (see p. 47) except gold and platinum, the halogens (the chlorine family), and the inert gases (the argon family).

The behaviour of the oxides which result from these reactions is discussed later (p. 47), and a complete classification is given on p. 390.

As has been found already, all substances which burn in air do so more brightly in oxygen.

Tests for Oxygen

The best test for fairly pure oxygen (i.e. over 40% oxygen) is that a glowing splint bursts into flame when put in the gas.

To test for oxygen when other gases are also present (as in air), add the colourless gas nitric oxide, which immediately combines with oxygen to form the brown gas nitrogen dioxide.

$$\text{Nitric Oxide} + \text{Oxygen} = \text{Nitrogen Dioxide}$$
$$2NO \qquad O_2 \qquad 2NO_2$$

Oxygen does not affect litmus-paper or lime-water

Oxygen is completely absorbed by alkaline pyrogallol, a fact which is used in finding the percentage of it in air (e.g. in mines).

Uses of Oxygen

These depend upon the three main properties of oxygen, i.e. its action in burning, breathing, and rusting.

(1) The use of oxygen instead of air for burning results in much higher temperatures being reached. Thus a mixture of oxygen with coal gas or hydrogen or especially acetylene burns with an extremely hot flame ($3000°$ C. with the latter), in which pieces of iron easily melt (m.p. $1500°$ C.) and weld together. Oxy-acetylene welding accounts for about 25% of the oxygen used commercially.

(2) Although the total amount used for helping breathing is small ($1–2\%$), the importance is very great. In pneumonia and other lung diseases, the patient may be given oxygen to breathe so that he does not have to cope with the 80% of nitrogen in air which he does not use in breathing. Also oxygen is used for breathing in all cases where there is either no oxygen (in diving under the sea, or underground in coal-mines after explosions; p. 255), or too little oxygen (in mountain-eering and in high-altitude flying).

(3) Over half the oxygen produced is used for cutting metals, both as scrap and in construction. When the metal, usually iron, has been heated to a high temperature in an oxy-acetylene flame, extra oxygen is turned on, the metal combines with the oxygen and the oxide falls away, leaving

a clean cut. This is not, of course, "rusting," but is similar in that it is the action of oxygen on iron.

2. NITROGEN

Importance of Nitrogen

The importance of nitrogen lies in the fact that it forms compounds, known as proteins, which are essential to life. Plants can only make proteins from *compounds* of nitrogen, very few of which occur naturally as minerals Such compounds when applied as fertilizers must therefore be obtained mostly from atmospheric nitrogen.

Laboratory Preparation of Nitrogen

Nitrogen has already been prepared by removing oxygen from the air by means of phosphorus (expt. 8, p. 18), or iron (expt. 15, p. 25).

The two normal methods are:

1. *From the Air*

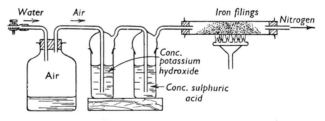

FIG. 12. Laboratory preparation of nitrogen.

Expt. 20 (fig. 12). A slow stream of air is passed through wash-bottles containing potassium hydroxide solution (to remove carbon dioxide) and concentrated sulphuric acid (to remove water vapour); and then through a strongly heated iron tube packed with iron filings (to remove the oxygen). The nitrogen ($+$argon) is collected over water (see expt. '0, p. 19), and is called "atmospheric nitrogen."

$$\text{Nitrogen} + \text{Oxygen} + \text{Iron} = \text{Nitrogen} + \text{Iron Oxide}$$
$$8N_2 \qquad 2O_2 \qquad 3Fe \qquad 8N_2 \qquad Fe_3O_4$$

2. *From Compounds of Nitrogen*

Expt. 21. Ammonium nitrite (or, more safely, mixed solutions of another ammonium salt and a nitrite) gives off nitrogen when heated:

Ammonium Chloride + Sodium Nitrite
     NH_4Cl $NaNO_2$
                     = Ammonium Nitrite + Sodium Chloride
                         NH_4NO_2 NaCl
     Ammonium Nitrite = Nitrogen + Water
       NH_4NO_2 N_2 $2H_2O$

This gas does *not*, of course, contain argon.

Commercial Preparation

Nitrogen can be made from liquid air (p. 30), but by far the largest amount is made by burning coke in air and removing the carbon dioxide by dissolving it in water under pressure:

Coke + Oxygen + Nitrogen = Carbon Dioxide + Nitrogen
   C O_2 $4N_2$ CO_2 $4N_2$

Physical Properties

When pure, nitrogen is a colourless, odourless gas. (As prepared in method 1 it is more often cloudy and smells of burnt grease—from the iron filings.) From its method of collection it can be deduced that it is only slightly soluble in water (2 volumes per 100 volumes of water at 8° C., i.e. half that of oxygen). It is very slightly lighter than air, its density relative to hydrogen being 14 (air = 14·4).

Chemical Properties

Nitrogen shows few positive reactions on the laboratory scale. Metals such as calcium and magnesium, if set on fire, will often continue to burn in the gas to form the nitrides. These compounds are decomposed by hot water to form ammonia with its well-known smell.

Magnesium + Nitrogen = Magnesium Nitride
       3Mg N_2 Mg_3N_2
Magnesium Nitride + Water = Magnesium Oxide + Ammonia
     Mg_3N_2 $3H_2O$ 3MgO $2NH_3$

At high temperatures nitrogen will combine with oxygen (see nitric oxide, p. 336), and at high pressures with hydrogen (see ammonia, p. 313).

Test for Nitrogen

Apart from the reaction with burning magnesium (above), the best test for nitrogen is that it is the only common gas which does not burn or assist burning and is without colour or smell or action on litmus-paper or on lime-water.

Uses of Nitrogen

Nitrogen is used on a very large scale for the manufacture of ammonia (p. 313), which is made into fertilizers or into nitric acid.

3. THE INERT GASES

Discovery

The story of the discovery of argon and the other inert gases is a thrilling one which can only be told here in bare outline. (A very good account is given in Nechaev's "Chemical Elements.") For over a hundred years after the time of Lavoisier, chemists had thought that they knew all about the air. Then in 1890 Lord Rayleigh, who was trying to prepare very pure nitrogen, found that specimens obtained from the air (method 1 above) had a density slightly greater than those obtained from nitrogen compounds (method 2 above). The difference was only 1/1000 of a gram per litre (1·2572 gm. per litre and 1·2560), but even though he could not explain these figures Rayleigh was far too good an experimenter to pretend that they agreed, because the difference was more than 10 times his experimental error.

Preparation of the Inert Gases

Eventually, in 1894, with the aid of Ramsay, Rayleigh discovered that there was another gas, heavier than air, present in atmospheric "nitrogen"; this they succeeded in isolating by removing the actual nitrogen with red-hot magnesium, which forms the nitride. Later, this gas was found to contain about 99·8% of argon, the remainder being other similar gases called neon, helium, krypton, and xenon. On the commercial scale, argon (b.p. $-186°$ C.) and neon (b.p. $-246°$) are obtained from the liquefaction of air.

Properties and Uses

The astonishing property of all these gases, which explains why they remained undiscovered for so long, is that they form no chemical compounds whatever.

This inertness is made use of by filling electric light bulbs with argon—the commonest of them—which cannot undergo any reaction; it makes the lamps much more efficient than the older vacuum ones, because they can be used at a higher temperature without the filament turning to vapour and so blackening the bulb. Similarly helium, which is very light, can be used to fill balloons because, unlike hydrogen, it cannot catch fire. Neon is used in advertisement signs because it gives a bright light when an electric current is passed through it at low pressures (see PLATE 10, p. 136).

4. CARBON DIOXIDE

Formation and Removal

Carbon dioxide is continuously being formed by the burning of fuels and by the respiration of all animals and plants (pp. 22–24). In a crowded room the percentage of carbon dioxide may rise to as much as $0·3\%$, i.e. 10 times the normal figure. The amount of it which is present in the atmosphere does not, however, increase, because equally large quantities of it are being removed all the time, mostly by the feeding of plants. Some is also dissolved by the rain; most of this finds its way to the sea, where marine plants (which fish eat) feed on it, but a certain amount is responsible for the weathering of rocks (p. 434) and the hardness of water (p. 272).

The Feeding of Green Plants

Plants, unlike animals, feed by absorbing carbon dioxide from the air through their leaves; this carbon dioxide, together with water, is built up with the aid of the energy of sunlight into sugars, and thence into the other carbon compounds of which the plant is made.*

Carbon Dioxide + Water $\quad\quad$ = $\quad$ Sugar + Oxygen
$\quad$ $6CO_2$ $\quad\quad$ $6H_2O$ (+energy of $\quad$ $C_6H_{12}O_6$ $\quad$ $6O_2$
$\quad\quad\quad\quad\quad\quad\quad\quad$ sunlight)

This process, known as **photo-synthesis** (light-building-up), can only take place in the presence of a catalyst, **chlorophyll**, which is the green pigment of the leaves.

It will be noticed that this reaction is exactly the reverse of the change which occurs in breathing (p. 23). As breathing produces energy, so this building-up process cannot take place

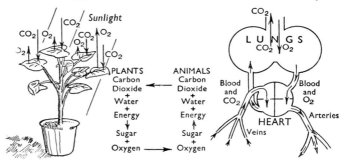

FIG. 13A. The carbon dioxide and oxygen cycle.

unless energy is supplied (fig. 13A). This means that plants—other than bulbs, which have a store of food—cannot grow in darkness; and that in industrial areas the growth will be slower because as much as half the daylight may be cut off by smoke pollution. (Only 1% of the energy is actually absorbed.)

The plant, of course, builds up far more sugars in the daytime than it uses in its respiration, which continues day and night. The sugars are built up into starch and cellulose (see p. 301), and the energy of the sunlight which is stored up in them is set free once more as a result of the digestion of food Similarly, the buried remains of plants which lived 250 million

* The essential substances absorbed by the roots include compounds of nitrogen, phosphorus, and potassium, but *no* carbon compounds.

years ago formed coal (p. 264); and when this is burnt, the energy we obtain is also derived from the sunshine which was used to build up the plants.

The real revolution caused by the atomic bomb is that up till now all mechanical or animal energy has come from carbon or its compounds (coal, sugars, petrol, etc.), which were formed by the reaction of photosynthesis; from 1954, civilization has used the energy of atomic nuclei and so can continue instead of probably coming to a full stop in about 500 years time, when all the coal and oil is used up.

Physical and Chemical Properties, etc., of Carbon Dioxide

These are dealt with later, in Chapter XVI (p. 247).

5. WATER VAPOUR

At any given temperature there is a limit to the amount of water vapour which the air can hold; if we try to exceed this amount, the excess of vapour will condense, often in the form of rain. At $18°$ C. ($65°$ F.), there can be up to 4% of water vapour by volume; at $0°$ C. ($32°$ F.), not more than 1%.

As water vapour is only half as heavy as air (see p. 196), the arrival of warm, wet air—usually from the south-west—results in a fall of the barometric pressure.

Expt. 22. To measure the volume of water vapour in a given volume of air. Add pieces of ice to water contained in a beaker, the outside of which is dry and polished. Stir gently, and measure the temperature at which a film of moisture collects on the outside of the beaker. At this temperature, the *dew-point*, the air is saturated with water vapour. From a graph of the pressure of water vapour at different temperatures (p. 128), we can then calculate the "relative humidity"; this is the amount of water present compared with the maximum possible. Thus if air at $12°$ C. (maximum water-vapour pressure, $10\cdot5$ mm.) has a dew-point of $7°$ C. ($7\cdot5$ mm.), then the relative humidity is $\frac{7\cdot5}{10\cdot5}$, i.e. $71\cdot5\%$.

Water Vapour and Living Things

The relative humidity of the air affects our personal comfort because we regulate our body temperature by evaporating sweat from our skins; if the atmosphere is nearly saturated, this becomes very difficult and so we get the "muggy" feeling of damp days, especially when warm.

Plants also lose water from the surface of their leaves; those which live in exceedingly dry conditions, such as cacti, therefore become cylindrical or spherical so as to store a lot of water, and have no leaves which expose a large surface from which water can be lost.

Water Vapour and Chemical Substances

Many compounds tend to absorb moisture from the atmosphere if they are left exposed to it. Common salt has an impurity in it (magnesium chloride) which does this, and so the salt in a salt-cellar tends to go into lumps, and our hair remains sticky when we try to dry it after sea-bathing. Such substances, which are called *hygroscopic*, can be used as drying agents for the air and for other gases which they do not react with. We have already seen two examples of this use: calcium chloride in expt. 4 (the burning of a candle, p. 16), and concentrated sulphuric acid in expt. 20 (the preparation of nitrogen, p. 32).

This phenomenon is discussed further in Chapter VI (p. 87).

TABLE OF COMMON DRYING AGENTS FOR GASES

Concentrated sulphuric acid	For all gases except ammonia, hydrogen sulphide, nitrogen dioxide
Calcium chloride	For all gases except ammonia, hydrogen sulphide
Phosphorus pentoxide	For all gases except ammonia
Silica gel	For all gases
Quicklime	For ammonia

Calcium chloride takes in large quantities of moisture and is therefore used in desiccators (fig. 11 (*a*), p. 25); phosphorus pentoxide, which takes up relatively little, is useful for removing the final traces of moisture from gases (fig. 24, p. 85).

6. DUST, SOOT, AND OTHER SOLIDS

Dust

The wind blows fine particles of solids from the ground into the atmosphere. This is normally removed from the air we breathe by the hairs and mucus in our nostrils to prevent it damaging the lungs; but in mining and other dangerous industries where there are very dusty atmospheres, lung diseases such as silicosis (p. 437) are only too common.

Soot and Ash

Solid particles of unburnt carbon, tarry matter, and fine ash carried up our chimneys, are suspended in the air as smoke. The atmosphere of London and other large towns contains about $\frac{1}{2}$ milligram of solids per cubic metre of air, which may seem small until it is realized that this results in a deposit of 20 tons per square mile per month. Domestic fires are responsible for about half this total.

Such pollution (a) damages crops so that they give only half the possible yield of food; (b) cuts off sunlight, causes twice as much artificial light to be used, and makes fogs much worse; (c) cuts off ultra-violet light, thus causing diseases such as rickets; (d) results in waste of labour and money in cleaning and laundry, apart from the fuel which is wasted (see PLATES 16B and 16C, pp. 261–262).

This can very largely be prevented by the increased use of smokeless fuels, such as anthracite, and of gas and electricity; or even by the more efficient burning of ordinary coal (p. 232).

7. GASEOUS IMPURITIES

Sulphur dioxide is present in the air of industrial areas to the extent of about 2 parts per million; it is formed by the burning of sulphur compounds present in coal. Such concentrations have bad effects on plants, attack the stonework of buildings and paint and fabrics, cause increased rusting of iron, and probably cause increased ill-health. Such pollution is prevented by gas-washing plants at modern electric power stations like Battersea and Fulham, and by the purification of coal gas at gasworks (p. 259); and it can be lessened by the "washing" of coal for domestic use (p. 9).

Hydrogen sulphide (p 353) and *carbon monoxide* (p. 255) may also occur in air.

8. BACTERIA

These are extremely minute living organisms, of which there are normally about 100 in every cubic metre of air, and enormous numbers in the soil.   Most of them are harmless, some are very useful (see Nitrogen Cycle, p. 311), and some are actively dangerous.   Harmful organisms occurring in the atmosphere under suitable conditions include the bacteria which cause pneumonia (PLATE 3), whooping-cough, diphtheria, tuberculosis and the virus of the common cold.   The main reason for proper ventilation is to reduce the concentration of harmful bacteria—most of which can be killed off by fresh air and sunshine—rather than to provide enough oxygen for breathing, because there is very rarely any shortage of that.

The Composition of Air by Weight

If it is required to find the percentage of carbon dioxide and of water vapour in the air of an elementary laboratory, the apparatus of fig 13B is suitable.

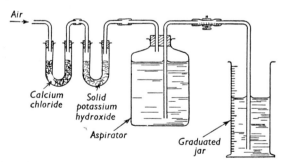

FIG. 13B.   Finding the percentage by weight of water vapour and carbon dioxide in air.

A measured volume of air is sucked through the U-tubes by allowing water from the aspirator to run into the measuring cylinder.   The increase in weight of the calcium chloride U-tube gives the weight of water vapour in this volume of air; and the increase in weight of the potassium hydroxide U-tube gives the weight of carbon dioxide.   The weight of the known volume of air may then be calculated (see Chapter IX) if room temperature and atmospheric pressure are observed, and the results may then be given as a percentage.

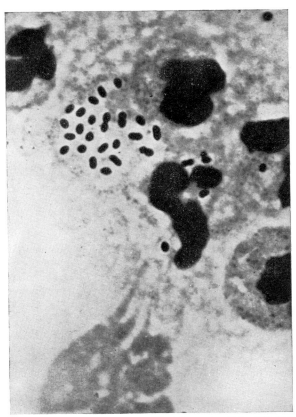

[*Photo by courtesy of* **Dr.** *John* *Drew*

PLATE 3. BACTERIA IN THE AIR

The two dozen small objects are pneumococci, sneezed out
during a bad cold; magnified about 2,000 diameters.

Suggestions for Practical Work

Preparation and properties of oxygen (Expt. 18, and Expt. 23, p. 47). Expts. 19, 21.

QUESTIONS ON CHAPTER III

1. Name three substances which on heating evolve oxygen (give equations for the reactions which occur), and describe the residues left in each case.

Indicate, without giving manufacturing details, how oxygen is nowadays produced on a large scale and stored.

Name *two* common uses for oxygen. (N.)

2. Explain how, except for small local variations, the percentages of oxygen and carbon dioxide in the atmosphere are maintained constant over long periods.

Describe with full practical details how you would determine the amount of carbon dioxide in a sample of air. (Civil Service Commission.)

3. Name four gases present in the atmosphere. Describe how you would prepare and collect samples of any two of these gases from the air. (C.)

4. Describe, with the aid of a diagram, how you would obtain several gas-jars of nitrogen from the air. What impurities would you still expect to be present? What other method and materials would you use to obtain pure nitrogen? (O.)

5. Air contains oxygen, nitrogen, carbon dioxide, water vapour, and other gases. Give the name of one of these other gases and state any use to which it is put. What is the source of the carbon dioxide in the air and what important part does it take in supporting life? (C. Gen. Sc.)

6. How would you show that ordinary air contains traces of water vapour and carbon dioxide? Sketch the apparatus that you would use to determine quantitatively the amounts of these substances present in air. (N.)

7. Describe experiments by means of which you could demonstrate the presence in air of oxygen, nitrogen, carbon dioxide, water vapour, and argon. (D.)

CHAPTER IV

ELEMENTS, MIXTURES AND COMPOUNDS

Metals and Non-Metals *The Separation of Mixtures*
Classification of the Elements *Air is a Mixture*
Relative Abundance of the Elements

Elements, Mixtures and Compounds

All chemical substances belong to one of the three classes: elements, mixtures, or compounds.

An element can *not* be split up by a chemical or physical change into any simpler chemical substance, i.e. a smaller weight of a different substance. (E.g., oxygen, carbon.)

A mixture can be split up into two or more simpler substances by means of a physical change. (Examples: sugar + sand crushed up together, potassium chlorate + manganese dioxide.)

A compound can *only* be split up into two or more simpler substances by a chemical change. (Examples: carbon dioxide, potassium chlorate.)

ELEMENTS

We now know of the existence of 96 elements, including those most recently discovered such as neptunium, plutonium, americium, and curium; it is possible that there may be more.* All the million or more chemical compounds so far prepared are made up of some of these 96 elements.

Although the atoms of which elements are composed (see p. 157) are all made of the same three fundamental particles (the proton, the electron, and the neutron), these are not really "chemical substances"; and although the element uranium, and many others, can be split up or changed into other elements, the amounts of energy set free or absorbed are many millions of times greater than those involved in chemical changes. Our definition of an element is therefore still correct.

Only about half the elements will be mentioned in this book and only about twenty in any detail. The most important

* By 1957 six more elements had been discovered: berkelium, californium, einsteinium, fermium, mendalevium, nobelium.

classification of the elements divides them into two groups, the metals and the non-metals, on the basis of certain physical properties.

Metals and Non-Metals

A metal is an element which has a characteristic lustre, is a good conductor of heat and of electricity, and can be worked into shape by hammering (i.e. is "malleable") or by pulling into wire (i.e. is "ductile"). (Example: iron.)

A non-metal is an element which has no metallic lustre, is a bad conductor of heat and of electricity, and is not malleable or ductile. (Example: sulphur.)

As in nearly all classifications, there are certain border-line cases, such as arsenic; but if we draw up a fairly complete list of properties of metals and non-metals, divided on the basis of the above definitions, we shall find that the distinguishing line becomes clearer. Chemical properties, especially the properties of the oxides, are then found to be most useful in deciding to which class an element belongs.

METALS	NON-METALS
(E.g. platinum, gold, silver, mercury, copper, lead, tin, iron, zinc, aluminium, magnesium, calcium, sodium, potassium)	(E.g. hydrogen, oxygen, nitrogen, helium, neon, argon, fluorine, chlorine, bromine, iodine sulphur, phosphorus, carbon, silicon, boron)

PHYSICAL PROPERTIES

METALS	NON-METALS
1. Characteristic appearance, usually described as a metallic lustre, e.g. mercury, tin. (But often the surface must be freshly cleaned to remove an oxide, etc., e.g. iron, potassium.)	1. No "metallic lustre," e.g. sulphur, phosphorus. (But iodine crystals and carbon as graphite have a "sheen" resembling that of a metallic surface.
2. Good conductors of heat, e.g. aluminium for saucepans	2. Bad conductors of heat, e.g. sulphur melts slowly.
3. Good conductors of electricity, e.g. copper or aluminium wire for transmission; sodium	3. Bad conductors of electricity, e.g. sulphur used as an insulator (but carbon as graphite conducts moderately).

METALS	NON-METALS

PHYSICAL PROPERTIES—*contd.*

4. Malleable (PLATE 4), e.g. gold leaf, iron by a blacksmith, and ductile (see above, 3).	4. Brittle and not easily worked, e.g. carbon as diamond.
5. Tensile strength, e.g. magnesium, iron.	5. Will not stand stress or strain, e.g. sulphur.
6. High melting-points, e.g. iron, 1500° C. (but many exceptions, mercury −39°; sodium and potassium less than 100°; tin, 232°).	6. Low melting-points, e.g. sulphur, 119° C., and all the gases (but carbon, 3500°; boron, 2300°; silicon, 1400°).
7. None are gases at room temperature and pressure.	7. Half are gases at room temperature—the first eight listed above.
8. High densities, e.g. zinc, 7·1 gm./c.c. (but the five last-named are much lower, e.g. aluminium, 2·7; sodium, 0·97).	8. Low densities, e.g. carbon (diamond) 3·5 gm./c.c. (but iodine, 4·9).
9. Give out a note when struck, e.g. the blacksmith hammering iron.	9. Do not give out a note when struck, e.g. phosphorus.

CHEMICAL PROPERTIES

1 At least one oxide is basic (see p. 47), e.g. iron oxide, calcium oxide.	1. Oxides are usually acidic (see p. 47), e.g. sulphur dioxide, and are never basic.
2. React with dilute hydrochloric or sulphuric acids to give hydrogen, e.g. iron (except the six first-named).	2. Do not react with dilute acids, e.g. nitrogen, carbon.
3. Their chlorides are high-melting solids, and do not usually react with water, e.g. sodium chloride (but aluminium chloride and some others react partly).	3. Their chlorides are usually volatile liquids which are decomposed by water, e.g. phosphorus chloride (but carbon tetrachloride is not decomposed).
4. Their hydrides, even when they exist, are usually unimportant, unstable solids, e.g. calcium hydride.	4. Their hydrides are important stable gases, e.g. hydrogen chloride (but those of oxygen are liquids).
5. Are electropositive (see p. 212), e.g. Na^+, Cu^{++}, Al^{+++}.	5. Are electronegative (see p. 212) usually forming part of a radical, e.g. Cl^-, NO_3^-, SO_4^{--}.

PLATE 4.   METALS ARE MALLEABLE (p. 44)
Wrought-iron gates, Winchester College War Memorial Cloister.

It will be seen that although it is fairly easy to get a clear picture of the essential differences, it would be extremely unwise to make generalizations which were too sweeping.

The distinction between the oxides of metals and non-metals is very important and is clearly illustrated in the following experiment.

Expt. 23.   The oxides of the elements.

The following elements are burned separately in a deflagrating spoon (p. 23) in jars of oxygen.   The resulting oxide is noted, shaken up with a little water to see if it dissolves, and the resulting solution tested with a drop of litmus solution.   **Litmus goes red with acids.** **and blue with alkalis.**   An alkali is a basic substance in solution The results obtained are shown in the table:

ELEMENT	DESCRIPTION OF ELEMENT	DESCRIPTION OF OXIDE PRODUCED	DOES OXIDE DISSOLVE IN WATER?	COLOUR OF LITMUS SOLUTION
Sulphur	yellow, crystalline solid	colourless gas, choking smell	Yes	Red
Carbon (charcoal)	black, lumpy solid	colourless gas, no smell	Yes	Red
Phosphorus (white, i.e. "yellow")	yellow-white waxy solid (kept under water)	white smoke →solid	Yes	Red
Iron (filings)	dark grey metal	grey-black solid	No	—
Magnesium (ribbon)	white metal	white solid	Yes (partly)	Blue
Calcium	white metal	white solid	Yes (gives heat)	Blue
Sodium	white metal (kept under oil)	white solid	Yes (gives heat)	Blue

We may sum up these results correctly as follows:

The oxides of non-metals are often gases which give acidic solutions.

The oxides of metals are solids which, if soluble, give alkaline solutions.

Classification of the Elements—The Periodic Table

Although it is beyond the scope of this book, you will be interested to know something about the most fundamental classification of the elements—the "Periodic Table" (see fig. 14, opposite).

In 1869 Mendeleev, a Russian, found that if the elements were arranged in the order of the relative weights of their atoms (see p. 165) and divided up into periods of 8 or 18, the elements which appeared in the same vertical columns had similar properties and could be considered as "families of elements." This had been attempted before, but Mendeleev succeeded because (a) he predicted that some "atomic weights" which did not fit in the table were wrong; (b) he left blank spaces for elements then unknown (such as Germanium) and predicted their properties. When his predictions were proved by experiment to be true, the value of the scientific method was shown once more, and his ideas were accepted.

The Relative Abundance of the Elements (by weight)

By contrast with the above classification of the elements, the proportions in which the elements occur in nature seems to have neither rhyme nor reason. But their relative abundance is nevertheless important, because the uses of the elements and their compounds depend to a great extent on it.

If we include the air, the sea, and other waters, and the crust of the earth to a depth of 24 miles, we obtain the following results (due to F. W. Clarke) shown in fig. 15 (p. 50).

The surprising fact will be noted that two elements which are essential to life, carbon (0·2%) and nitrogen (0·01%), are among the "also-rans"; so are chlorine (0·2%), phosphorus (0·13%) and sulphur (0·05%). Most of the heavy metals except iron are decidedly rare (zinc, lead, copper, and uranium about 0·001%, mercury 0·00005%, and gold about one hundredth of that); the result is that the best minerals have in many cases been used up, and lead, which was nearly as cheap as cast iron fifteen years ago, is now more expensive than aluminium. At the present rates of consumption all known lead mines in the world will be worked out by 1966, and copper and zinc mines by 1976. Some "rare" elements, e.g. titanium, are abundant (0.6%).

MIXTURES AND COMPOUNDS

The difference between mixtures and compounds may be illustrated most clearly by the experiment (mentioned on p. 12)

Fig. 14.   PERIODIC TABLE OF THE ELEMENTS

Group 1	Group 2	Metals with variable valency (see p. 165) (few dealt with in this book)									Group 3	Group 4	Group 5	Group 6	Group 7	Group 0
															H	He
(Li)	(Be)	—	—	—	—	—	—	—	—	—	(B)	C	N	O	F	Ne
Na	Mg	—	—	—	—	—	—	—	—	—	Al	Si	P	S	Cl	A
K	Ca	(Ti)	(V)	(Cr)	(Mn)	Fe	(Co)	(Ni)	Cu	Zn	*	Ge	(As)	*	Br	(Kr)
*	(Sr)	*	*	(Mo)	*	*	(Rh)	*	(Ag)	(Cd)	*	Sn	(Sb)	*	I	(Xe)
*	(Ba) ⊗	*	*	(W)	*	*	*	(Pt)	(Au)	Hg	*	Pb	(Bi)	*	(At)	*
*	(Ra)	(Th)	(U etc)													

(Columns grouped as: Metals — Group 1, Group 2, Metals with variable valency; Non-Metals — Groups 3–7; Inert Gases — Group 0.)

Fig. 14 shows a version of this Periodic Table, simplified to illustrate the elements dealt with in this book.

(a) Those only mentioned, but not described in detail, are put in brackets.
(b) The places of those not mentioned are shown by a star *.
(c) A key to the symbols of the elements will be found inside the front cover (or see index).
(d) No elements are in the spaces shown by —.
(e) Atomic weights increase from left to right.

It will be seen that:

(1) All the non-metals are at the top right-hand corner of the table.

(2) Those metals which are nearest to the dividing line (aluminium, zinc, tin, lead) have oxides which can behave as acids as well as bases, i.e. show some of the properties of non-metals.

(3) The valency (pp. 165, 180) of an element is either the same as its group number e.g. Na, sodium, 1) or is 8 minus the group number (e.g. O, oxygen, $8-6=2$).

(4) Elements in the same vertical column have similar properties, e.g. sodium and potassium (group 1); magnesium and calcium (group 2); chromium, molybdenum, and tungsten, which harden steel (p. 469); copper, silver, and gold, which are used for coinage; fluorine, chlorine, bromine, and iodine (group 7, see p. 426)—to which hydrogen does not really belong; and group 0, which is the inert gases. Those who are keen on arithmetic will notice that ⊗ denotes the place of 15 exceedingly similar elements (the "rare-earths").

FIG. 15. ABUNDANCE OF THE ELEMENTS BY WEIGHT

SILICON

26%

as silicates in rocks.

OXYGEN

50%

as combined oxides in rocks,
as water in the ocean, free in
the atmosphere.

ALUMINIUM

7%

IRON	4%
CALCIUM	3%
SODIUM	$2\frac{1}{2}$%
POTASSIUM	$2\frac{1}{2}$%
MAGNESIUM	2%
HYDROGEN	1%
ALL 89 OTHERS	2%

of preparing the compound ferrous sulphide by heating a mixture of iron and sulphur, and comparing its properties with the original mixture.

Expt. 24. A mixture of about equal volumes of yellow powdered roll sulphur and grey iron filings is heated fairly strongly in a test-tube. Some of the sulphur melts to a dark liquid and boils off as a yellow vapour. When part of it becomes red-hot, the glow is seen to continue even when the tube is taken out of the flame, and to spread throughout the mixture. After cooling, the glass is cracked off the hard solid, which is then powdered. The properties are as follows:

Mixture (Iron + Sulphur)	Compound (Ferrous sulphide)
(a) No heat was given out when it was formed.	(a) Much heat was given out when it was formed.
(b) The colour is grey–yellow, depending on the relative amounts of each.	(b) The colour is blue–black, independent of the original proportions.
(c) On being heated up to 500° C. the sulphur first melts and then boils.	(c) It cannot be melted in the test-tube.
(d) Treatment with dilute sulphuric acid slowly gives hydrogen, which makes a "pop" when applied to a flame. (Only the iron reacts, leaving the sulphur unchanged.)	(d) Treatment with dilute sulphuric acid *quickly* gives hydrogen sulphide, which has a very different smell; it does not "pop," but burns quietly and gives a yellow deposit of sulphur.
(e) The iron can be separated out by means of a magnet.	(e) A magnet has no effect (or, very often, the *whole* substance is slightly magnetic).
(f) The sulphur can be dissolved out by carbon disulphide (in a fume cupboard, with all flames put out).	(f) The sulphur cannot be dissolved.

(g) In addition, it could be shown that whilst the mixture may contain any amount of sulphur from 0% to 100%, the compound (if pure) always contains 36·36% by weight of sulphur, and its composition corresponds to one atom of iron with one atom of sulphur—formula FeS.

On rearranging these results slightly, the following generalizations may be made, and used to decide whether a given substance is a mixture or a compound:

GENERAL DIFFERENCES BETWEEN MIXTURES AND COMPOUNDS

MIXTURES	COMPOUNDS
1. The constituents of a mixture can be separated by a physical change *or* by a chemical change: (e), (f), (d).	1. The constituents of a compound can *only* be separated by a chemical change: (d). This may sometimes take place when a compound is *decomposed* by heat (e.g. Expt. 11, p. 20).
2. The formation of a mixture is only a physical change, and little or no heat effect is produced: (a).	2. The formation of a compound is a chemical change, and a change of heat energy always occurs: (a).
3. The composition of a mixture is variable and need not correspond with any definite chemical formula: (g).	3. The composition of a compound is fixed and can be expressed by a chemical formula: (g).
4. The physical and chemical properties of a mixture are usually intermediate between those of its constituents, and in proportion to the amounts of each present: (b), (c), (d).	4. The physical and chemical properties of a compound need bear no relation to those of its constituents, but are characteristic of the compound: (b), (c), (d).

AIR IS A MIXTURE

Applying the above tests, we can now prove that air is a mixture of nitrogen and oxygen (etc.), and not a compound.

1. The nitrogen and oxygen (and all the other gases) can be separated from each other—either wholly or partly—by physical changes, such as:

(a) The fractional distillation of liquid air (pp. 30, 33, 35).

(b) Dissolving air in water (see Expt. 25, p. 53), when a higher proportion of the oxygen present dissolves than of the nitrogen.

(c) Allowing air to pass through a small hole (see p. 102), when the nitrogen, being lighter, diffuses slightly more rapidly; the escaping gas therefore contains more nitrogen than air.

None of these changes could take place if the air was a compound; but it should be noted that a mixture of gases is much more difficult to separate than other mixtures which contain a solid or a liquid (see p. 54).

2. If nitrogen and oxygen are mixed in the correct proportions (4 to 1 by volume), no heat is given out or taken in, yet the mixture behaves like air.

3. Although the composition of air is almost constant, because the changes brought about by breathing and photosynthesis, etc., balance one another almost exactly, it is not constant enough to satisfy the Law of Constant Composition which is obeyed by all compounds (p. 146).

The nearest possible chemical formula is N_4O, which would require $20·0\%$ oxygen by volume (p. 199) instead of $20·9\%$, and a density of 36 relative to hydrogen (p. 196) instead of $14·4$ (see below).

4. The relative density of air is $14·4$, which is what would be calculated from that of nitrogen (14) and oxygen (16).

> 4 volumes of nitrogen weigh 56 units
> 1 volume of oxygen weighs 16 units
>
> ---
>
> ∴ 5 volumes of air weigh   72 units
> ∴ 1 volume of air weighs $14·4$ units

The chemical properties of the oxygen in the air (burning, etc.) are just the same, though not so intense, as those of pure oxygen.

Expt. 25. Separating air by dissolving it in water (fig. 16).

Air is dissolved in distilled water by shaking vigorously a large, corked flask half-full of water. A 1-litre flask is completely filled with this, and also the delivery tube, by sucking with a rubber tube at B.   When the water is boiled, air bubbles out into the measuring-tube C (so long as the delivery tube does not project below the cork at A).   About 20 c.c. of gas are obtained, which can be shown to contain about 33% of oxygen by putting in yellow phosphorus on a wire (see expt. 8, p. 18).   As air normally contains 21% of oxygen, this shows that a partial separation has taken place.

NOTE: A more rapid method (2–5 minutes) of absorbing the oxygen is by using alkaline pyrogallol.   Crystals of pyrogallol and granules of sodium hydroxide are introduced into the burette by means of a burette cup, as described in Fowles's "Lecture Experiments in Chemistry," p. 72.

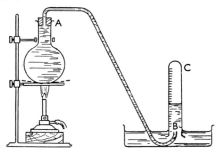

FIG. 16.   Partial separation of air by boiling it out of water.

THE SEPARATION OF MIXTURES

Most chemical substances, as obtained either naturally or in the laboratory, are in the form of mixtures. We must therefore know some of the general methods by which they can be separated into their pure constituents (see opposite).

In practice, *chemical* changes are used to a large extent, especially when only one of the substances is wanted: e.g. preparing magnesium compounds from sea-water (p. 453), or drying gases in the laboratory (p. 32), or preparing nitrogen from air commercially (p. 33).

The difficulty of separating mixtures physically is increased in two cases: (*a*) when the substances are in the same physical state, e.g. two solids; (*b*) or the particles of the substances are very small, e.g. in solutions.   The most important methods therefore depend either: (1) on making *one* only of the substances into a *gas*, the particles of which then diffuse away, e.g. nitrogen from liquid air (distillation), or ammonium chloride from a mixture with salt (sublimation); or (2) on making *one*

THE SEPARATION OF MIXTURES

	TYPE OF MIXTURE	CONSTITUENTS OF MIXTURE		DESCRIPTION OF PROCESS	CHANGE OF STATE	NAME OF PROCESS
1.	2 Solids	Sand	Salt	Dissolve salt in water, then filter	Solid→liquid	Solution+ filtration
2.	Solid+Liquid	Salt	Water	Heat to drive off water	Liquid→gas	Evaporation
3.	Solid+Liquid	Potassium chlorate	Water	Cool hot solution to obtain crystals	Liquid→solid	Crystallization+ filtration
4.	2 Solids	Sodium chloride	Ammonium chloride	Heat to drive off ammonium chloride (expt. 116, p. 319)	Solid→gas	Sublimation
5.	2 Gases	Water vapour	Air	Cool	Gas→liquid	Condensation
6.	2 Liquids	Alcohol	Water	Boil off alcohol and cool the vapours	{ Liquid→gas, Gas→liquid	Distillation+ condensation
7.	2 Gases	Oxygen	Nitrogen	Cool strongly and boil carefully	{ Gas→liquid, Liquid→gas	Liquefaction+ distillation
8.	2 Gases	Nitrogen	Carbon dioxide	Dissolve carbon dioxide in water under pressure	Gas→liquid	Solution

only of the substances into a *solid*, the particles of which are relatively large and can be filtered off, e.g. sand from a sugar solution.

In some cases, especially distillation and crystallization, the process may be only partly completed the first time; it is then called *fractional* crystallization, etc. (see p. 108).

Other methods are of use in special cases, e.g. flotation or washing for minerals (p. 9); or taking advantage of the magnetic property of iron or of iron oxide (Fe_3O_4).

Suggestions for Practical Work

Expts. 23, 24.

Finding the proportions of the constituents of mixtures such as "oxygen mixture" (potassium chlorate+manganese dioxide) both before and after use.

Also sand+salt, sodium chloride+ammonium chloride (see Expt. 116, p. 319).

QUESTIONS ON CHAPTER IV

1. What do you understand by the term *element*?

Compare in parallel columns mixtures and compounds.

To which of these classes do air, water vapour, and nitrogen belong? Justify your answer for any *one* of these. (L.)

2. Explain briefly how oxygen is produced on a large scale; manufacturing details are *not* required.

Contrast the chemical properties of oxides of metals with those of oxides of non-metals, illustrating your answer by giving *one* example of each type of oxide. (L.)

3. Describe briefly *five* experiments you would carry out to show that the product left after heating a mixture of iron filings with sulphur is different from the original mixture. State clearly the results you would expect to get in each of these five experiments. (O.)

4. Describe carefully how you would determine the proportion by volume of oxygen in a sample of air confined over water in a graduated tube. What would you expect the proportion to be?

How could you collect some of the air dissolved in tap-water? Give a diagram of the apparatus you would use. Why is the composition of this air different from that of ordinary air? (O. Gen. Sc.)

5. How has it been shown that air consists principally of a mixture of oxygen and nitrogen, and not of a compound of these two elements? (O. and C.)

6. With the aid of reference books in the library, draw up a table to show the density (*or* electrical conductivity *or* any one other physical property) of as many elements as you can. List them in order of size, illustrating by a scale diagram if possible, and writing the names of the non-metals in BLOCK CAPITALS.

7. How would you separate sandy sea-water into its three constituents?

Describe the experiments you would carry out to show that a candle contains both hydrogen and carbon in its composition. (N.)

8. Using the data inside the front cover for Zinc, Arsenic, Silicon and Tin, predict (as Mendeleev did) the approximate atomic weight, melting-point, density, and the valency of the element Germanium (Ge), which occurs in Group 4 of the Periodic Table, p. 49.

CHAPTER V

ACIDS, BASES, AND SALTS
THE CLASSIFICATION OF CHEMICAL COMPOUNDS
TYPES OF CHEMICAL REACTION

The Classification of Chemical Compounds

When various elements were burnt in oxygen (Expt. 23, p. 47), we discovered that the oxides of metals behaved differently from those of non-metals when dissolved in water and treated with litmus. This is the basis for dividing up a large number of the compounds we shall meet into three main classes: acids, salts, and bases.

It is difficult at the present stage of this book to give *definitions* which are both understandable and yet correct. (These will be given in Chapter XIV, p. 215). We can, however, give provisional definitions which will need only slight modification later on.

An acid is a substance containing hydrogen which is replaceable, directly or indirectly, by a metal. Its solution in water must turn litmus red.

EXAMPLES: (*a*) Nitric acid, HNO_3, will react with copper to give copper nitrate, $Cu(NO_3)_2$, in which the place of the hydrogen has been taken by the copper, although no hydrogen itself is formed (p. 67). (*b*) Sulphuric acid, H_2SO_4, when dilute, will not only react with iron to give ferrous sulphate, $FeSO_4$, in which the place of the hydrogen has been taken by the iron, but will actually give off free hydrogen (p. 51).

NOTE: Water (like certain other substances) is not considered to be an acid although it can have its hydrogen replaced by a metal (see p. 82). because it does not turn litmus red.

A salt is a substance in which the hydrogen of an acid has been replaced, wholly or partly, by a metal or a metallic radical.

EXAMPLES: (*a*) Copper nitrate, $Cu(NO_3)_2$, and (*b*) ferrous sulphate, $FeSO_4$, above. (*c*) Ammonium chloride, NH_4Cl, in which the ammonium group of atoms (*radical*) is behaving like a metal and has taken the place of the hydrogen of hydrochloric acid, HCl. (*d*) Sodium hydrogen sulphate, $NaHSO_4$, is classed both as an acid and as a salt, and is known as an *acid salt*, the hydrogen of the acid having been only partly replaced.

A base is a substance which reacts with an acid to give a salt and water only.

EXAMPLES: (*a*) Copper oxide reacts with nitric acid to give copper nitrate and water only:

$$CuO + 2HNO_3 = Cu(NO_3)_2 + H_2O$$

A base which dissolves in water is called an alkali.

(*b*) Sodium hydroxide solution ("caustic soda") reacts with hydrochloric acid to give sodium chloride and water only:

$$NaOH + HCl = NaCl + H_2O$$

NOTE: Many other substances which are *not* bases will react with acids to give salts, but give some other product instead of or in addition to water; e.g. metals may give hydrogen, and salts may give another acid (see below: reactions 3*a*, 4*a*, 4*d*).

Before dealing with all the reactions concerned with the preparation and properties of acids, salts, and bases, it will be convenient to divide up chemical reactions into four main types. If these are remembered, suggestions can be made as to the course of an unknown reaction, on the basis of reasonable probabilities rather than of wild guesswork.

THE TYPES OF CHEMICAL REACTION

1. *Combination*

(*a*)	Iron + Sulphur	= Iron Sulphide	(p. 51)
	Fe S	FeS	
(*b*)	Mercury + Oxygen	= Mercury Oxide	(p. 20)
	2Hg O_2	2HgO	
(*c*)	Nitric Oxide + Oxygen	= Nitrogen Dioxide	(p. 31)
	2NO O_2	$2NO_2$	

2. *Decomposition*

(a)   Mercury Oxide = Mercury + Oxygen   (p. 20)
                    $2HgO$ $2Hg$ O_2

(b)   Potassium Chlorate = Potassium Chloride + Oxygen
                    $2KClO_3$ $2KCl$ $3O_2$

(p. 29)

(c)   Ammonium Nitrite = Water + Nitrogen   (p. 33)
                    NH_4NO_2 $2H_2O$ N_2

3. *Direct Replacement*

(a)

Iron + $\begin{cases} \text{Hydrogen Sulphate} \\ \text{Sulphuric Acid} \end{cases}$ = Iron Sulphate + Hydrogen   (p. 51)

Fe H_2SO_4 $FeSO_4$ H_2

(b)

Hydrogen Sulphide + Oxygen = Hydrogen Oxide + Sulphur
        $2H_2S$ O_2 $2H_2O$ $2S$

(p. 51)

(c) Iron + Copper Sulphate = Iron Sulphate + Copper
        Fe $CuSO_4$ $FeSO_4$ Cu

(see pp. 142, 222)

4. "*Double Decomposition*" (i.e. Double Replacement)

(a) Ferrous Sulphide + $\begin{cases} \text{Sulphuric acid} \\ \text{Hydrogen Sulphate} \end{cases}$
            FeS H_2SO_4

        = Ferrous Sulphate + Hydrogen Sulphide   (p. 51)
            $FeSO_4$ $H_2S \nearrow$

(b) Magnesium Nitride + $\begin{cases} \text{Water} \\ \text{Hydrogen Oxide} \end{cases}$
            Mg_3N_2 $3H_2O$

        = Magnesium Oxide + $\begin{cases} \text{Ammonia} \\ \text{Hydrogen Nitride} \end{cases}$ (p. 33)
            $3MgO$ $2NH_3 \nearrow$

(c) Copper Sulphate + Sodium Silicate
        (soluble crystals) (5% solution of " Water Glass ")
        = Copper Silicate $\downarrow$ + Sodium Sulphate
        (growth in " Chemical Garden ") (colourless, soluble)

Similarly for other soluble crystals, especially if coloured.

Sometimes a reaction may appear to be more complex than the above, because one of the products of a double decomposition reaction may itself decompose, e.g.

(d) Sodium Carbonate + $\begin{cases} \text{Hydrogen Sulphate} \\ \text{Sulphuric acid} \end{cases}$

$\quad$ Na_2CO_3 $\qquad\qquad$ H_2SO_4

$\quad$ = Sodium Sulphate + $\begin{cases} \text{Hydrogen Carbonate} \\ \text{Carbonic acid} \end{cases}$ (p. 11)

$\qquad$ Na_2SO_4 $\qquad\qquad$ H_2CO_3

then: Carbonic acid = Water + Carbon Dioxide (p. 11

$\quad$ H_2CO_3 $\qquad$ H_2O $\qquad$ $CO_2\nearrow$

Double decomposition is the most common type of reaction. It can be made to take place if any one of the following three things is true:

(i) One of the products is a gas under the conditions chosen: e.g. hydrogen sulphide, above. If it is allowed to escape, it cannot react with the other product to make the reaction go in the reverse direction. This is often shown by an arrow pointing upwards: $\nearrow$.

(ii) One of the products is a solid which does not dissolve under the conditions chosen (see preparation of ferric hydroxide, p. 65). It is then out of the way of the substances reacting in solution. This is often shown by an arrow pointing downwards: $\downarrow$.

(iii) An acid is reacting with a base to form water and a salt (p. 59), a process known as *neutralization*. The reason is that this reaction gives out a large amount of energy—as heat; in order to make the reaction go in the *reverse* direction, this energy would have to be given back, e.g. the "electrolysis" of sodium chloride solution (p. 215).

5. *Oxidation and Reduction*

This type of reaction is described in Chapter XXIII.

Most of the reactions we meet in this book belong to one of the first *four* types.

These principles will now be applied to the preparation of acids, bases, and salts.

$\quad$ **3***

ACIDS

The Preparation of Acids

1. Combination of water with the oxide of a non-metal:

   (*a*) Sulphur Dioxide + Water = Sulphurous acid   (p. 47)
        SO_2 H_2O H_2SO_3

   (*b*) Sulphur Trioxide + Water = Sulphuric acid   (PLATE 5)
        SO_3 H_2O H_2SO_4

   (*c*) Carbon Dioxide + Water = Carbonic acid   (p. 47)
        CO_2 H_2O H_2CO_3

   (*d*) Phosphorus Pentoxide + Water = Phosphoric acid
        P_2O_5 $3H_2O$ $2H_3PO_4$ (p. 47)

These oxides of non-metals are therefore sometimes called " acid anhydrides," i.e. acids without water.

The name " oxy-gen "(=acid-maker) was invented by Lavoisier because of this property; it was not then known that some acids do *not* contain oxygen, e.g. hydrochloric, but that all contain hydrogen.

[*Photo by courtesy of Simon Carves Ltd.*

PLATE 5. PLANT FOR PRODUCING SULPHURIC ACID

Most modern plants, like the one shown here, use the Contact Process (Chapter XXII), which converts sulphur dioxide (SO_2) into sulphur trioxide (SO_3), and thence into sulphuric acid (H_2SO_4).

2. Combination of hydrogen with a non-metallic element:

(a) Hydrogen+Chlorine=Hydrogen Chloride
    H_2 Cl_2 $2HCl$

("Hydrochloric acid" when in solution in water: see p. 397.)

(b) Hydrogen+Sulphur=Hydrogen Sulphide
    H_2 S $H_2S\nearrow$

(Not a good method in this case; see p. 349.)

3. Double decomposition: action of one acid on a salt of a more volatile acid:

(a) (i) Sodium Chloride+Sulphuric acid (hot conc.)
         NaCl H_2SO_4
    =Sodium Hydrogen Sulphate+Hydrogen Chloride
              $NaHSO_4$ $HCl\nearrow$

(ii) Sodium Chloride+Sodium Hydrogen Sulphate
         NaCl $NaHSO_4$
    =Sodium Sulphate+Hydrogen Chloride
         Na_2SO_4 $HCl\nearrow$

(The hydrogen chloride is a gas which is absorbed in water; p. 397.)

(b) Sodium Nitrate+ $\left\{ \begin{array}{l} \text{Hydrogen Sulphate} \\ \text{Sulphuric acid (hot conc.)} \end{array} \right.$
    $NaNO_3$ H_2SO_4

=Sodium Hydrogen Sulphate+ $\left\{ \begin{array}{l} \text{Hydrogen Nitrate} \\ \text{Nitric acid} \end{array} \right.$
    $NaHSO_4$ $HNO_3\nearrow$

(The nitric acid is a vapour which is condensed to a liquid; p. 327.)

In both these cases the sulphuric acid must be hot and concentrated, so as to drive off the other acid which more easily goes to a gas (i.e. is more *volatile*).

The Properties of Acids

1. Their solutions change the colour of litmus (a vegetable dyestuff) to red (e.g. sulphurous acid, p. 47).

Other "indicators" behave similarly, e.g. purple cabbage goes red when "pickled" with vinegar (dilute acetic acid); methyl orange goes red except with very weak acids (p. 501); phenolphthalein remains colourless.

2. They are neutralized by the oxides (and hydroxides) of metals, i.e. bases, to give a salt+water (e.g. copper oxide, p. 59; and expt. 26, p. 65; see also "preparation of salts," pp. 69, 70).

Acid + Base = Salt + Water

3. They react at once in the cold with carbonates to give an "effervescence" of bubbles of carbon dioxide (reaction 4*d*, p. 61). Carbonic acid and "weaker" acids do not do this.

4. They often attack metals to give a salt. Many acids such as sulphuric, when in dilute solution, attack the more reactive metals such as iron, to give off hydrogen (reaction 3*a*, p. 60): nitric acid reacts but does not give hydrogen.

5. They usually have a sour taste; the three commonest acids—sulphuric, nitric, hydrochloric—all have this; also citric (from lemons), tartaric (grapes), acetic (vinegar), lactic (sour milk), formic (ants), bee stings, etc.

> "An acid is a substance which
> Turns litmus, in solution, red;
> A metal may react with it
> And give off hydrogen instead."

BASES

The Preparation of Bases

1. Combination of a metal with oxygen to form the oxide:

Magnesium + Oxygen = Magnesium Oxide   (pp. 47, 138)
$2Mg$ O_2 $2MgO$

2. Combination of a metallic oxide with water to form the *hydroxide*:

Calcium Oxide + Water = Calcium Hydroxide   (p. 47)
CaO H_2O $Ca(OH)_2$

3. Decomposition of the hydroxide or carbonate or nitrate, of any metal except potassium and sodium, by heat to give the oxide:

(*a*) Ferric Hydroxide = Ferric Oxide + Water   (p. 146)
$2Fe(OH)_3$ Fe_2O_3 $3H_2O \nearrow$

(b) Calcium Carbonate

$$CaCO_3$$
$$= \text{Calcium Oxide} + \text{Carbon Dioxide} \qquad \text{(p. 267)}$$
$$\quad CaO \qquad\qquad CO_2 \nearrow$$

(c) Lead Nitrate

$$2Pb(NO_3)_2$$
$$= \text{Lead Oxide} + \text{Nitrogen Dioxide} + \text{Oxygen} \qquad \text{(p. 335)}$$
$$\quad 2PbO \qquad\qquad 4NO_2 \nearrow \qquad\qquad O_2 \nearrow$$

4. Double decomposition of a salt, of any metal except potassium and sodium, by sodium hydroxide (another base) in solution to give the hydroxide (p. 448):

Ferric Chloride + Sodium Hydroxide

$$FeCl_3 \qquad\qquad 3NaOH$$
$$= \text{Ferric Hydroxide} + \text{Sodium Chloride}$$
$$Fe(OH)_3 \downarrow \qquad\qquad 3NaCl$$

The hydroxide is *insoluble* in water and therefore comes down as a *precipitate*. This is filtered off and washed. It must be heated very carefully if required dry, otherwise it will decompose to the oxide (see above).

The Properties of Bases

1. All bases combine with acids to give a salt and water only.

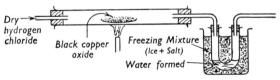

FIG. 17.   Reaction of base with acid.

Expt. 26.   The reaction of copper oxide with hydrogen chloride.

Dry hydrogen chloride gas is passed over black copper oxide (dried by heating first) in a combustion tube (fig. 17). Copper chloride sublimes as it is formed and may collect in the cool part of the tube as a brown-yellow solid. Water condenses in the cooled U-tube, and is coloured green by some of the copper chloride dissolving in it. As both the original substances were dry, the water must have been produced in the reaction.

$$CuO \; + \; 2HCl \; = \; CuCl_2 \; + \; H_2O$$

Copper	Hydrogen	Copper	Hydrogen
Oxide	Chloride	Chloride	Oxide

2. Some bases dissolve in water to form an alkali (see below). These alkalis are the hydroxides of potassium, sodium, calcium, and magnesium—KOH, NaOH, $Ca(OH)_2$, $Mg(OH)_2$ —the last two being only slightly soluble.

The Properties of Alkalis

1. Their solutions turn litmus blue (e.g. *wasp* stings).

Similarly purple cabbage goes green, methyl orange goes yellow, and phenolphthalein goes from colourless to crimson.

2. They neutralize acids to give a salt and water only, just as other bases do.

Potassium Hydroxide $+ \begin{cases} \text{Hydrogen Sulphate} \\ \text{Sulphuric acid} \end{cases}$

2KOH $\qquad\qquad$ H_2SO_4

$= $ Potassium Sulphate $+ \begin{cases} \text{Hydrogen Hydroxide} \\ \text{Water} \end{cases}$

K_2SO_4 $\qquad\qquad$ 2HOH (H_2O)

3. They react with solutions of salts by double decomposition to give hydroxides (see preparation of bases—4 above).

4. They have a soapy feel and taste (because a solution of soap contains an alkali—sodium hydroxide).

One special case of an alkali must now be mentioned: the solution of ammonia gas in water has the four properties listed above. It is therefore considered to contain an alkali, ammonium hydroxide:

Ammonia $+$ Water $=$ Ammonium Hydroxide

NH_3 $\qquad$ H_2O $\qquad\qquad$ NH_4OH

Ammonium Hydroxide $+$ Hydrogen Chloride

NH_4OH $\qquad\qquad\qquad$ HCl

$\qquad\qquad = $ Ammonium Chloride $+$ Water

$\qquad\qquad\qquad$ NH_4Cl $\qquad\qquad$ H_2O

SALTS

The Preparation of Salts

Detailed descriptions of the preparations will be given in a series of experiments on pp. 69–73. Here is a summary of the methods:

1. *Direct combination* is only of value in a few cases, especially chlorides:

$$\text{Iron} + \text{Chlorine} = \text{Ferric Chloride} \qquad \text{(p. 400)}$$
$$2\text{Fe} \qquad 3\text{Cl}_2 \qquad \quad 2\text{FeCl}_3$$

2. *Replacement of hydrogen* by metals can be used with the fairly reactive metals magnesium, zinc, and iron, with dilute sulphuric acid; concentrated hydrochloric acid will attack these metals and also aluminium and tin; nitric acid of moderate strength attacks all the common metals (except aluminium), but virtually never gives hydrogen.

$$\text{Magnesium} + \begin{cases} \text{Hydrogen Sulphate} \\ \text{Sulphuric acid} \end{cases}$$
$$\text{Mg} \qquad \qquad \text{H}_2\text{SO}_4$$
$$= \text{Magnesium Sulphate} + \text{Hydrogen}$$
$$\text{MgSO}_4 \qquad \qquad \text{H}_2 \nearrow$$

$$\text{Tin} + \begin{cases} \text{Hydrogen Chloride} \\ \text{Hydrochloric acid} \end{cases} \checkmark$$
$$\text{Sn} \qquad \qquad 2\text{HCl}$$
$$= \text{Stannous Chloride} + \text{Hydrogen}$$
$$\text{SnCl}_2 \qquad \qquad \text{H}_2 \nearrow$$

$$\text{Copper} + \text{Nitric acid}$$
$$\text{Cu} \qquad 4\text{HNO}_3$$
$$= \text{Copper Nitrate} + \text{Nitrogen Dioxide} + \text{Water}$$
$$\text{Cu(NO}_3)_2 \qquad \quad 2\text{NO}_2 \nearrow \qquad 2\text{H}_2\text{O}$$

3–5. *Double decomposition is by far the most important general method.*

3. If the salt required is soluble in water, but the oxide, hydroxide, and carbonate are insoluble (this is true in the great majority of cases), the appropriate acid is treated with an excess of the solid oxide (etc.).

$$\text{Magnesium Oxide} + \text{Hydrochloric acid}$$
$$\text{MgO} \qquad \qquad 2\text{HCl}$$
$$= \text{Magnesium Chloride} + \text{Water}$$
$$\text{MgCl}_2 \qquad \qquad \text{H}_2\text{O}$$

Ferric Hydroxide + Sulphuric acid = Ferric Sulphate + Water
$2Fe(OH)_3$ $3H_2SO_4$ $Fe_2(SO_4)_3$ $6H_2O$

Copper Carbonate + Nitric acid
$CuCO_3$ $2HNO_3$
= Copper Nitrate + Water + Carbon Dioxide
$Cu(NO_3)_2$ H_2O $CO_2 \nearrow$

4. If both the required salt and the oxide, hydroxide and carbonate are soluble (this is true for all salts of potassium, sodium—and ammonium), the amount of the hydroxide or carbonate needed to neutralize the acid must be found by the use of an indicator (usually litmus).

Potassium Hydroxide + $\begin{cases} \text{Hydrogen Nitrate} \\ \text{Nitric acid} \end{cases}$
KOH HNO_3
= Potassium Nitrate + $\begin{cases} \text{Hydrogen Hydroxide} \\ \text{Water} \end{cases}$
KNO_3 H_2O

5. If the required salt is insoluble, it must be prepared from two soluble salts or from a soluble salt and the acid:

Lead Nitrate + Sodium Sulphate
$Pb(NO_3)_2$ Na_2SO_4
= Lead Sulphate + Sodium Nitrate
$PbSO_4 \downarrow$ $2NaNO_3$

(This is so for (a) all common carbonates—except potassium, sodium, and ammonium; (b) sulphides—except of most metals ending in -ium; (c) calcium sulphate (almost insoluble); (d) the chloride and sulphate of lead; (e) silver chloride; and a number of less common salts.)

NOTES: In order to convert one insoluble salt into another, e.g. calcium carbonate into calcium sulphate (which is only slightly soluble), it is advisable first to convert it into a solution of a soluble calcium salt, e.g. the chloride, by the action of hydrochloric acid:

$CaCO_3$ + $2HCl$ = $CaCl_2$ + H_2O + $CO_2 \nearrow$;
Calcium   Hydrogen   Calcium   Water   Carbon
Carbonate   Chloride   Chloride   Dioxide

$CaCl_2$ + H_2SO_4 = $CaSO_4\downarrow$ + $2HCl$
Calcium   Hydrogen   Calcium   Hydrogen
Chloride   Sulphate   Sulphate   Chloride

Similarly, in order to convert one soluble salt into another, e.g. ferric chloride into ferric sulphate, it is usually easier to prepare an insoluble substance such as the hydroxide as an intermediate stage:

$$FeCl_3 + 3NaOH = Fe(OH)_3\downarrow + 3NaCl;$$

Ferric	Sodium	Ferric	Sodium
Chloride	Hydroxide	Hydroxide	Chloride

$$2Fe(OH)_3 + 3H_2SO_4 = Fe_2(SO_4)_3 + 6HOH$$

Ferric	Hydrogen	Ferric	Hydrogen	(Water)
Hydroxide	Sulphate	Sulphate	Hydroxide	

These points are obvious from considering the principles involved in separating mixtures (p. 55), it being much easier to separate a solid from a liquid than a solid from a solid or a liquid from a liquid.

Expt. 27A.   Preparation of Ferrous Sulphate (metal+acid).

Iron filings are gradually added to 50 c.c. of dilute sulphuric acid in a 100-c.c. beaker until no more gas is given off, the liquid being warmed at first to speed up the reaction, and brought to the boil just before filtering.

$$Fe + H_2SO_4 = FeSO_4 + H_2 \nearrow$$

The excess metal and impurities are filtered off; when the solution has been allowed to cool to room temperature, green crystals (see p. 107) of ferrous sulphate, $FeSO_4.7H_2O$, are formed.   The excess liquid (*mother liquor*) is poured off and the crystals dried between filter-papers.

In preparing zinc sulphate or magnesium sulphate it is possible to evaporate the solution if necessary until it is saturated, but ferrous sulphate is too easily oxidized by the air (see p. 470), and is liable to become "rusty."

Expt. 27B.   Preparation of Copper Sulphate (metal oxide+acid).

The method is essentially similar but, as no gas is given off, it is necessary to stir the solution with a glass stirring-rod, adding the black copper oxide until a small excess of it remains undissolved. Filter, allow to crystallize (evaporating if necessary), pour off the mother liquor, and dry the blue crystals of copper sulphate between filter-papers.

$$CuO + H_2SO_4 + 4H_2O = CuSO_4.5H_2O$$

The preparation of lead nitrate from lead oxide ("litharge") is another good example.   When a *carbonate* is used as the starting material. carbon dioxide is given off rapidly in the cold, and there is therefore a danger of frothing over.

Expt. 28. Preparation of Potassium Nitrate (alkali + acid).

Fill a burette with bench-strength nitric acid solution and allow it to run into about 25 c.c. of caustic potash solution to which a little

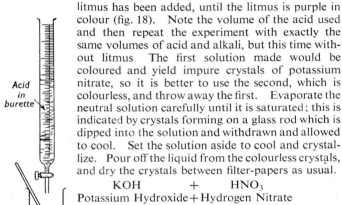

litmus has been added, until the litmus is purple in colour (fig. 18). Note the volume of the acid used and then repeat the experiment with exactly the same volumes of acid and alkali, but this time without litmus. The first solution made would be coloured and yield impure crystals of potassium nitrate, so it is better to use the second, which is colourless, and throw away the first. Evaporate the neutral solution carefully until it is saturated; this is indicated by crystals forming on a glass rod which is dipped into the solution and withdrawn and allowed to cool. Set the solution aside to cool and crystallize. Pour off the liquid from the colourless crystals, and dry the crystals between filter-papers as usual.

Acid in burette

Alkali

Fig. 18. Preparation of salt by titration.

$$KOH \quad + \quad HNO_3$$
Potassium Hydroxide + Hydrogen Nitrate
$$= \quad KNO_3 \quad + \quad HOH (H_2O)$$
Potassium Nitrate + Hydrogen Hydroxide (Water)

Sodium nitrate, sulphate, and chloride may be made by this ("titration") method and also the potassium salts. For preparing ammonium salts, either the indicator must be methyl orange or the method of expt. 113 (p. 318) may be used. No indicator is suitable for the preparation of sodium carbonate, and so a different method must be used (see p. 72).

Expt. 29. Preparation of Lead Sulphate (Precipitation of an Insoluble Salt).

Add lead oxide (litharge) to warm dilute nitric acid until no more will dissolve:

$$PbO + 2HNO_3 = Pb(NO_3)_2 + H_2O$$

Filter. To the solution of lead nitrate add dilute sulphuric acid until no further white solid settles out. Filter off the precipitate, wash with plenty of distilled water, dry the filter-paper and lead sulphate in a steam oven, and then tap off the white powder on to a watch-glass.

The Properties of Salts

Most salts are crystalline soluble compounds, and to obtain them in a high degree of purity they are recrystallized from solution in water. That is to say the impure salt is dissolved in water, and the solution, filtered if necessary, is evaporated until saturated and then allowed to cool and crystallize. (This process is explained on p. 107.) The remaining solution is poured off from the crystals, which are then dried, usually between filter-papers. To test the solution for saturation after evaporation, dip in a glass rod, and if on cooling crystals form quickly, that is an indication that the solution is saturated.

Many crystals of salts, e.g. copper sulphate, contain "water of crystallization" (see p. 86).

Expt. 30. Preparation and Recrystallization of Lead Iodide.

Potassium iodide solution is added to lead nitrate solution, and bright yellow lead iodide is precipitated, leaving potassium nitrate in solution.

$$2KI + Pb(NO_3)_2 = 2KNO_3 + PbI_2 \downarrow$$

This is filtered off and dissolved in a large beaker of boiling distilled water (it only dissolves slightly). On cooling, golden-yellow needles are obtained which are filtered off and dried as usual between filter-papers.

Lead chloride behaves similarly. With other salts very much less water is needed.

The chemical properties of salts are, in general, the sum of the properties of the metallic portion and of the acid portion (radical), see p. 214; if one knew nothing about ferrous nitrate, its chemical properties could be predicted from a knowledge of the behaviour of ferrous sulphate and of lead nitrate.

Acid Salts

When only part of the replaceable hydrogen in an acid has been replaced by a metal, the salt obtained is called an *acid salt*; e.g. sodium hydrogen sulphate, $NaHSO_4$, which is also known as acid sodium sulphate or sodium bisulphate.

By contrast, sodium sulphate, Na_2SO_4, in which all the hydrogen of sulphuric acid has been replaced, may be called "the normal salt."

The Basicity of an acid is defined as the number of replaceable hydrogen atoms in a molecule of the acid. Sulphuric acid

H_2SO_4, is a "dibasic" acid; but acetic acid, CH_3COOH, where only the final hydrogen atom is replaceable, is "monobasic." Usually, the easiest way of finding the basicity of an acid is to prepare as many different sodium salts as possible; thus there are two sodium sulphates (see above), but only one sodium acetate (CH_3COONa).

Expt. 31. Preparation of Sodium Bisulphate and of Normal Sodium Sulphate.

Prepare a neutral solution of sodium sulphate by the method described in expt. 28, p. 70, for potassium nitrate. Now add a volume of sulphuric acid equal to that already added to the solution; evaporate and crystallize out the acid salt; dry the crystals between filter-papers. Also obtain some dry crystals of the normal salt from another lot of sodium sulphate solution.

$$2NaOH + H_2SO_4 = Na_2SO_4 + 2H_2O$$
$$Na_2SO_4 + H_2SO_4 = 2NaHSO_4$$

The two salts are of different crystalline shape and have some different chemical properties. The acid salt in solution will turn litmus red, be neutralized by an alkali, and react with carbonates to give off carbon dioxide, i.e. it has many of the properties of sulphuric acid, unlike the normal salt. It resembles other sodium salts, however, in giving a persistent bright yellow colour when put in a bunsen flame; it also responds to the test for a sulphate (p. 374).

Not all "acid salts," however, are acid to litmus; sodium bicarbonate, $NaHCO_3$, is neutral or *very* slightly alkaline because carbonic acid is such a very weak acid.

Expt. 32. Preparation of Sodium Bicarbonate and of Normal Sodium Carbonate.

Carbonic acid is so weak an acid that no indicator will show when sodium carbonate has been formed (litmus is still blue). Carbon dioxide is therefore passed into a strong solution of sodium hydroxide (about 35 gm./100 c.c. of water) until sodium bicarbonate (the "acid salt") separates out; it only dissolves in water to the extent of about 10 gm./100 c.c. It can be filtered off and dried between filter-papers. The normal salt is obtained by heating the acid salt alone or by boiling the saturated solution which remains; the acid salt has a solution which is almost neutral to litmus, and decomposes to give carbon dioxide. The normal salt turns litmus blue, and does not decompose on heating; it crystallizes from water as "washing soda," $Na_2CO_3.10H_2O$.

$$CO_2 + H_2O = H_2CO_3 \text{ (Carbonic acid)}$$

$$\begin{cases} 2NaOH + H_2CO_3 = Na_2CO_3 + 2H_2O \\ Na_2CO_3 + H_2CO_3 = 2NaHCO_3 \text{ (Sodium Bicarbonate)} \end{cases}$$

$$2NaHCO_3 = Na_2CO_3 + H_2O + CO_2 \nearrow \text{ (Sodium Carbonate)}$$

$$Na_2CO_3 + 10H_2O = Na_2CO_3.10H_2O \text{ ("Washing Soda")}.$$

Basic Salts

These are substances formed by the combination of the normal salt with the oxide or hydroxide of the metal, e.g. $CuCO_3.Cu(OH)_2$, basic copper carbonate, which occurs naturally as the mineral malachite, and which is used as a green pigment in paints. The other important basic salt is $2PbCO_3.Pb(OH)_2$, basic lead carbonate, which is "white lead" used for paints (p. 521).

They are similar to acid salts in that the latter could be written in the form $Na_2CO_3.H_2CO_3$ (i.e. 2 $NaHCO_3$); also in that they can react with more *acid* to form a normal salt:

$$2PbCO_3.Pb(OH)_2 \quad + \quad H_2CO_3$$
Basic Lead Carbonate Carbonic acid
$$= \quad 3PbCO_3 \quad + \quad 2H_2O$$
Normal Lead Carbonate Water

Their two main differences from acid salts are: (*a*) they are almost always insoluble; (*b*) their composition is usually indefinite, i.e. they may be mixtures rather than true compounds.

It may help the learner to think of basic salts being part-way between bases and salts by writing such formulae as:

$Pb\begin{cases}OH\\OH\end{cases}$	$Pb\begin{cases}OH\\NO_3\end{cases}$	$Pb\begin{cases}NO_3\\NO_3\end{cases}$
Lead Hydroxide (Base)	Basic Lead Nitrate (Basic Salt)	Normal Lead Nitrate (Salt)

which are similar in form to the series:

$\begin{cases}H\\H\end{cases}SO_4$	$\begin{cases}Na\\H\end{cases}SO_4$	$\begin{cases}Na\\Na\end{cases}SO_4$
Sulphuric acid (Acid)	Sodium Hydrogen Sulphate (Acid Salt)	Normal Sodium Sulphate (Salt)

although in actual fact basic lead nitrate is almost the only basic salt which has both an OH group and a simple formula.

Suggestions for Practical Work

Expts. 27A to 32 inclusive.

QUESTIONS ON CHAPTER V

1. Give *three* characteristic properties of acids and *three* of alkalis.

Briefly describe how you would make a salt (*a*) from an acid and a soluble alkali such as potassium hydroxide; (*b*) from an acid and an insoluble base such as zinc oxide. In each case, indicate how you obtain the product free from excess of either reagent. (O.)

2. A "base" may be defined as a substance which with an acid gives a salt and water and nothing else.

Describe an experiment in detail to illustrate this definition.

3. State briefly, giving one example with the equation in each case, how you would prepare:

An acid (*a*) from an element, (*b*) from a salt;

A base (*a*) from an element, (*b*) from a salt.

Give also, with equations, two methods of preparing salts. (S.)

4. What is meant by the terms acid, base, and salt?

Starting with sulphuric acid describe three distinct methods by which specimens of zinc sulphate crystals can be obtained.

5. What do you understand by the term "double decomposition"? How would you apply this method to the preparation of (*a*) an acid, (*b*) a salt, (*c*) a base? Explain, in each case, why the reaction occurs.

6. Explain carefully what you mean by an acid salt.

Give examples, and describe the preparation of an acid salt from sulphuric acid. (O. & C.)

7. What is meant by saying that nitric acid is monobasic and sulphuric acid is dibasic? How would you show experimentally that sulphuric acid is dibasic? (O. & C.)

8. Define the terms: acid, base, acid salt, basic salt.

Starting from cupric chloride, describe briefly how you would prepare (*a*) a base, (*b*) an acid. (C.)

9. How would you attempt to obtain crystals of copper nitrate if provided with copper sulphate?

10. Starting from sodium hydroxide, describe exactly how you would prepare solid specimens of (*a*) normal sodium carbonate; (*b*) acid sodium sulphate; (*c*) neutral sodium sulphate; (*d*) acid sodium carbonate. (L.)

11. Describe in detail how you would obtain from the appropriate carbonate (*a*) calcium chloride suitable for drying gases; (*b*) crystalline sodium chloride; (*c*) crystalline lead chloride.   (C.)

12. Define the terms (*a*) acid; (*b*) basic oxide.   Name and give the formulae for (*c*) three basic oxides; (*d*) two acidic oxides.

An acid HX reacts with a basic oxide MO; give the equation for the reaction occurring.   (**C.**)

CHAPTER VI

WATER

Water is the most important of all chemical compounds as well as the most abundant. Nearly all living things contain a large proportion of it (man contains about 60%; a jellyfish over 90%), because the chemical reactions necessary to life can only be carried on in solution in water.

Apart from this, our industrial civilization is dependent on water as the source of steam for power, not only directly from coal but also when electricity is obtained from coal by means of steam turbines. In London and other large towns about 50 gallons of water are needed per inhabitant per day.

Impurities in Water

Really pure water is very uncommon, because it has such a great power of dissolving other substances. When it is evaporated from the ocean by the heat of the sun to become water vapour in the atmosphere (p. 37), it is free from solid matter, and a similar process of "distillation" is normally used to obtain it pure (see below). But when the water comes down as rain, it brings with it the dust and soot, and also the following substances in solution: (a) carbon dioxide, which—as carbonic acid—will attack many rocks, especially limestone and chalk (p. 272); (b) small quantities of oxygen and nitrogen; (c) very dilute nitric acid, a useful fertilizer, formed by the action of lightning (see p. 336); (d) in industrial districts, sulphuric acid, formed from sulphur dioxide, oxygen, and water.

The rain-water will dissolve some salts, especially those of calcium and magnesium, which make the water "hard" and react with soap (see p. 273). Also, decaying organic matter especially manure and sewage, will dissolve and carry with it a large number of bacteria, some of which may be harmful. Many rivers are heavily polluted with the waste from industrial plant and with sewage, to such an extent that nearly all the fish are killed off.

Finally the water reaches the sea, which is therefore a "dump" for all the dissolved salts; some of these, such as the calcium salts, tend to be deposited; but 3·6% by weight of sea-water consists of salts, made up as follows:

Common salt (sodium chloride) ..   2·8%
Magnesium salts ..   ..   ..   0·6% (see p. 453)
Calcium salts   ..   ..   ..   0·1%
Potassium salts   ..   ..   ..   0·1%

[*Photo by courtesy of Caird & Rayner Ltd.*

PLATE 6A. WATER DISTILLING PLANT

Three sets of the type shown here provide a " King George V " type battleship with 600 tons of distilled water (p. 79) per day.

Purification of Water

1. *Drinking-water.* Water for many large towns, such as Birmingham and Manchester, is collected in mountain reservoirs in Central Wales and the Lake District; this is almost pure rain-water (see p. 274), and so need only be filtered

through beds of sand and gravel to remove solid matter. Other towns, such as London, are dependent on river water; this must be filtered and also treated with chlorine to destroy the bacteria which would cause typhoid fever, cholera, dysentery, or other diseases. As chlorine is poisonous (see p. 407), the amount used must be small—about 1 part in 2 millions. Only in comparatively recent years have water supplies been "safe"; Albert, the Prince Consort, died of typhoid in 1861,

[*Photo by courtesy of Permutit Co., Ltd.*

PLATE 6B.   WHAT TAP WATER OFTEN CONTAINS

This pipe was removed from the hot-water system of a house. The " hard " water contained dissolved calcium salts, which were gradually deposited (p. 276) inside the pipe, and eventually choked it.

and Tchaikovski of cholera in 1893. Sea-water can be made fit to drink by distillation (PLATE 6A), but during the 1939 war life-boats were equipped with a more compact apparatus, which precipitated out the salts by double decomposition with silver nitrate, etc., and then filtered them off.

2. *Water for industry or the laboratory.* The dissolved salts (except from sea-water) are allowed to remain in drinking-water. For many other purposes they must be removed

because they would form harmful deposits (PLATE 6B) in boiler-plants and would react with other salts in the laboratory. For example, in many districts the tap-water would give a cloudy solution with silver nitrate or barium chloride, because enough silver chloride or barium sulphate would be precipitated to make the water turbid. Locomotives, laundries, etc., use "softened" water from which the harmful salts have been removed (p. 276), but the most complete method of purification is by distilling it.

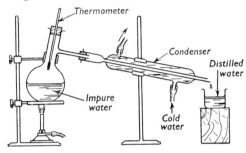

FIG. 19. Distillation of water.

Expt. 33. The distillation of water.
Tap-water, or, better, water containing a little of a coloured substance such as blue copper sulphate crystals in solution, is heated in the distilling flask. The dissolved solids remain behind, and only gaseous impurities (e.g. carbon dioxide) can escape with the steam; this is condensed in the "Liebig condenser," through the outer jacket of which a constant stream of cold water is flowing (fig. 19). The *distillate*, i.e. the liquid collecting in the beaker, is "distilled water." This is colourless and tasteless, and is pure enough for all normal laboratory purposes

Tests for Water

Three *physical* properties of water provide good tests for its purity:

(1) Freezing-point, 0° C.
(2) Boiling-point, 100° C. under 760 mm. pressure.
(3) Density, 1 gm./c.c. at 4° C.

It should be noted that the ordinary variation in atmospheric pressure from about 28·6 inches to 30·6 inches (728 to 776 mm.) corresponds with a change in the boiling-point of water from 98·8° C. to 100·6° C. (Pressure has a negligible effect on the freezing-point.)

Dissolved substances lower the freezing-point (e.g. sea-water f.p., −2° C.), and raise the boiling-point (e.g. jam, b.p., 105° C.), and may either increase the density (e.g. dilute sulphuric acid) or decrease it (e.g. ammonia solution).

The simplest test for the presence of small quantities of water is a *chemical* one: add white anhydrous copper sulphate (see p. 86), which will turn blue. *Any aqueous solution* (i.e. most laboratory reagents) *will give this test*, but not liquids such as pure alcohol, ether, or concentrated sulphuric acid.

The Chemical Nature of Water

1. Until 1781 it was thought that water was an element. Then Cavendish proved that it was a compound, hydrogen oxide, by burning hydrogen in air (and, later, also in oxygen) and showing that the product was water. This "putting together" of two elements to form a compound is known as *synthesis*. An experiment similar to this is described in the next chapter (p. 95).

2. In Chapter V it was shown that in many cases:

Metal+acid=salt+hydrogen

(e.g. Zn + H_2SO_4 = $ZnSO_4$ + H_2),
Zinc   "Hydrogen Sulphate"   Zinc Sulphate   Hydrogen

but   Metal *oxide*+acid=salt+*water*

(e.g. ZnO + H_2SO_4=$ZnSO_4$ + H_2O),
Zinc *Oxide*   Hydrogen *Oxide*

which also proves that water is hydrogen oxide.

3. Similarly, many metals act on water to give the oxide+hydrogen (see below), and others (see p. 85) have their oxides reduced by hydrogen to the metal+water:

Mg + H_2O=MgO + H_2 : CuO + H_2=Cu + H_2O
Magnesium Hydrogen Magnesium Hydrogen Copper Hydrogen Copper Hydrogen
      Oxide   Oxide   Oxide   Oxide

4. Finally, water can be decomposed electrically ("electrolysis") into hydrogen and oxygen (see below, p. 84).

This "splitting up" of a compound into its elements is known as *analysis*.

The composition of water by weight is described later in this chapter (p. 84), and the composition by volume in Chapter XIII (p. 190).

The Action of Water on Metals

This is a subject of great economic importance, and the metals can be divided into three main classes:

1. *Those which do not react:* gold, silver, mercury, copper, lead, tin. A large laboratory distillation apparatus (a "still" which runs continuously) is made of copper or tin, because these metals are not attacked by water. Lead is attacked if the water contains carbonic acid, e.g. "soft" moorland water, but not by hard water or by water in the absence of air.

2. *Those which react with steam:* iron, zinc, magnesium.
(*a*) *Iron*

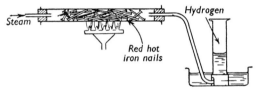

Fig 20   Action of red-hot iron on steam.

Expt. 34. Steam is passed through an iron tube, packed with iron nails and heated to redness with a long burner (fig. 20). An asbestos cloth is a useful cover to keep the heat in. Hydrogen is formed, and is collected in the gas-jar after allowing the air in the apparatus to escape. The hydrogen may be tested for by applying a light and hearing the characteristic "pop." The substance remaining in the tube is the blue-black magnetic oxide of iron; this is the coating seen on steel objects which have been "tempered" by heating in air. This reaction (with scrap iron) was much used during the war as an emergency source of hydrogen for barrage balloons.

The reaction is reversible, and if hydrogen is passed over heated iron oxide, steam and iron are slowly formed.

$$Fe_3O_4 + 4H_2 \rightleftharpoons 3Fe + 4H_2O,$$

the sign "$\rightleftharpoons$" denoting a reversible reaction.

(b) *Zinc*

Zinc oxide, used for white paint, is manufactured by heating zinc in a current of steam.

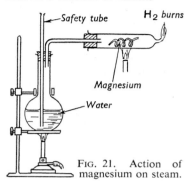

FIG. 21. Action of magnesium on steam.

(c) *Magnesium*

Expt. 35. A current of steam is passed through the small tube containing magnesium ribbon (fig. 21). When this is heated, the magnesium will catch fire and burn, although no free oxygen is present:

$$Mg + H_2O = MgO + H_2$$
$$\text{Magnesium Oxide}$$

The hydrogen may be burned as it escapes from the tube. Intense heat is given out, which very often cracks the tube after a few minutes; this also accounts for the formation of the oxide, rather than the hydroxide which might have been expected, because hydroxides are decomposed to the oxide if the temperature is high enough (see p. 64). (Those of sodium and potassium are only decomposed at white heat.)

3. *Those which react with cold water:* calcium, sodium, potassium. These metals, unlike all the preceding ones, can therefore not be used as structural materials

(a) *Calcium*

Expt. 36. A small piece of calcium metal is placed in a dish of water with a gas-jar or boiling-tube held over the top (fig. 22). Bubbles of gas are slowly given off, and may be shown to be hydrogen

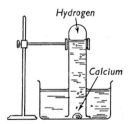

FIG. 22. Action of calcium metal on cold water.

("pop" with a flame). The water becomes cloudy because of the formation of calcium hydroxide, which only partly dissolves; the solution turns litmus blue.

$$Ca + H_2O = CaO + H_2$$
$$CaO + H_2O = Ca(OH)_2$$
$$\text{Calcium Oxide} \qquad \text{Calcium Hydroxide}$$

(b) Sodium

Expt. 37. A lump of sodium, dull in appearance owing to a coating of sodium oxide Na_2O, is taken from under oil, where it is kept to protect it from further attack by the atmosphere; a *very small* piece is cut off with a penknife, exposing a brilliantly shining surface; this is then thrown on to water in a glass dish, where it floats (density 0·97 gm./c.c.), reacting violently with the water to form a basic hydroxide (the alkali NaOH) and hydrogen, the heat of the reaction being rapidly conducted throughout the sodium, causing it to melt to a bright round globule (m.p. 97° C.), which runs rapidly to and fro until it disappears. (It is a good exercise to consider how many typically metallic properties—p. 44—are illustrated in the above description, and how many unusual ones.)

$$2Na + 2HOH = 2NaOH + H_2$$
Sodium   Hydrogen   Sodium   Hydrogen
         Hydroxide   Hydroxide

(c) Potassium

Expt. 38. An extremely small piece of potassium is treated in the same way. This time the heat of the reaction causes the hydrogen to catch fire and burn with a lilac-coloured flame. (This colour is given to a flame by potassium and all its compounds, and is a very good test for them.) If too large a piece of potassium is used it will explode.

The Decomposition of Water by Electricity—" Electrolysis "

As hydrogen burns in oxygen (or air) and gives out a great deal of heat in forming the oxide (water), this energy must be given back when water is decomposed. The most convenient way of doing this is to use electricity.

Expt. 39. "The Electrolysis of Water."

Pure water does not conduct appreciably, and so a small amount of an acid or an alkali or a salt (such as sodium chloride) must be added. This added substance serves to conduct the current (as explained in Chapter XIV (p. 217), where electrolysis is described in detail), but is not itself decomposed, and it can be shown at the end of the reaction (by titration, p. 494) that the same amount is present as before.

Direct current from a battery is passed through dilute sulphuric acid in the apparatus shown in fig. 23. The "electrodes," where the current enters and leaves the solution, are made of platinum because other metals tend to be attacked. The platinum wires are connected with the ordinary copper leads by both dipping into mercury.

The gas collected at the positive electrode ("anode") can be shown by a glowing splint to be oxygen; its volume is almost exactly half that of the gas collected at the negative electrode ("cathode"), which can be shown, by "popping" when lighted, to be hydrogen.

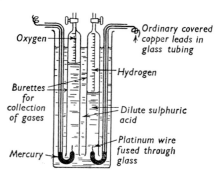

Fig. 23. " Electrolysis of water."

This is not usually regarded as the best proof that water contains 2 volumes of hydrogen to every 1 volume of oxygen (see p. 189), because of the necessity of using the acid.

$$2H_2O = 2H_2 + O_2.$$

Where electric power is cheap, both hydrogen and oxygen are manufactured by electrolysis, using sodium hydroxide solution because this reacts with the dissolved carbon dioxide, which would otherwise be given off as an impurity.

The Composition of Water by Weight ("Dumas's experiment, 1842")

Expt. 40. When dry hydrogen is passed over heated dry copper oxide, copper and water are formed. The weight of water is found by absorbing it in weighed U-tubes containing concentrated sulphuric acid (B and C in fig. 24). The weight of oxygen used up is equal to the loss in weight of the copper oxide in the combustion tube. Then, by the Law of the Conservation of Mass (p. 20), the weight of hydrogen used up must be equal to the weight of water *minus* the weight of oxygen; this is easier than weighing the hydrogen directly, though the method does not give such accurate results.

To make sure that all the water collected has been formed in the reaction, the hydrogen must be dried by passing it through the U-tube of sulphuric acid (A), and the U-tubes (B and C) must be protected from atmospheric moisture by a calcium chloride tube (D).

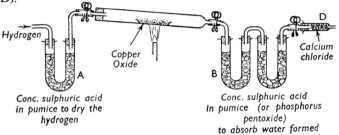

Fig. 24. Dumas's experiment

The experiment was first done by the French chemist Dumas in 1842. He did it no fewer than nineteen times in order to get the greatest possible accuracy, and prepared in all over a pound of water.

In the most accurate experiments ever done, using a different method in which the hydrogen was weighed directly,

$$\frac{\text{Wt. of hydrogen used}}{\text{Wt. of oxygen used}} = \frac{1}{7 \cdot 9385}$$

For school calculations this is taken to be $\frac{1}{8}$, and is of importance in the determination of equivalents (see p. 132).

Heavy Water

The substance known as "heavy water" occurs in ordinary water to the extent of one part in every 5000. The hydrogen in it is entirely the heavy "isotope" (p. 157) known as "deuterium", with "atomic weight" (p. 164)=2 instead of 1. It has slightly different properties from ordinary water, e.g. m.p. $3 \cdot 8°$ C., b.p. $101 \cdot 4°$ C., density $1 \cdot 107$ gm./c.c. It is prepared by the electrolysis of dilute acid (p. 84), the ordinary water being decomposed slightly more rapidly. It is of importance in connection with the use of atomic energy. It costs about £60 per pint.

Water of Crystallization

The crystals of many salts, such as copper sulphate, when obtained from solution (p. 69) can be shown to contain water; this water is known as "water of crystallization" and the salt is said to be "hydrated" or "a hydrate." If a salt or other substance has no such water, it is said to be "anhydrous."

Expt. 41. The preparation of anhydrous copper sulphate.

Some dry blue crystals of hydrated copper sulphate, $CuSO_4.5H_2O$, are powdered and placed in a test-tube. On heating, steam is given off and can be condensed by passing through a delivery tube into a cooled test-tube. The resulting liquid responds to all the tests for water (p. 79), and must have come from within the crystals, because they were perfectly dry to start with. The test-tube must be held pointing slightly downwards, or a Pyrex tube used; otherwise the condensed steam will run back into the hot part of the tube and crack it. A white, non-crystalline ("amorphous"=shapeless) solid remains behind, which is anhydrous copper sulphate. The water of crystallization of the copper sulphate is necessary both for the shape and colour of these crystals.

Most sulphates crystallize as hydrates, e.g. those of sodium, calcium, magnesium, aluminium, zinc, iron, and copper; so do many other salts, such as nitrates and chlorides. Nearly two-thirds of the weight of washing soda (sodium carbonate crystals $Na_2CO_3.10H_2O$) is water of crystallization!

Many salts, however, crystallize in the anhydrous form, i.e. without any water of crystallization. These include sodium chloride (NaCl, common salt), and *all* common salts of potassium and ammonium, e.g. potassium nitrate (KNO_3), potassium chlorate ($KClO_3$), and ammonium sulphate ($(NH_4)_2SO_4$).

Expt. 42. To find the percentage of water of crystallization in a salt.

A known weight of powdered magnesium sulphate crystals ("Epsom salt") is taken, and heated cautiously in a previously weighed crucible. When no more steam seems to be coming off, the crucible is allowed to cool and then weighed. It is then heated again for a few minutes and allowed to cool and re-weighed. If the two weights are the same, all the water has been driven off;

but if the second weight is less than the first, then the heating must be repeated until two consecutive weights are the same. The following results show how the calculation is done.

Wt. of crucible	. . . . .	= 14·700 gm
Wt. of crucible+magnesium sulphate crystals	. . . . .	= 16·476 gm
Wt. of crucible+anhydrous magnesium sulphate	. . . . .	= 15·566 gm.
Ditto, after reheating	. . . .	= 15·566 gm.
Wt. of water of crystallization	. . .	= 0·910 gm.
Wt. of magnesium sulphate crystals	. .	= 1·776 gm.

$$\therefore \text{ Water of crystallization } = \frac{0·910 \times 100}{1·776}\%$$
$$= 51·2\%.$$

Efflorescence

Some crystals, such as washing soda, tend to lose some of their water of crystallization on exposure to the atmosphere. The transparent crystals gradually turn to a white powder, especially on the surface, because the shape of the crystals is altered.

$$Na_2CO_3.10H_2O = Na_2CO_3.H_2O + 9H_2O$$

Such crystals are said to be *efflorescent*. Another example is sodium sulphate, $Na_2SO_4.10H_2O$.

Deliquescence

The reverse change, i.e. the taking up of water from the atmosphere, has already been met in Chapter III (p. 38); any substance which does this, e.g. calcium chloride or glass, is said to be *hygroscopic*. If, like calcium chloride, it absorbs so much water that the hydrate dissolves to form a saturated solution, it is said to be *deliquescent* (i.e. "turning to a liquid"). Another common deliquescent substance is caustic soda (sodium hydroxide), NaOH.

Hygroscopic substances therefore include (a) all those which are deliquescent; (b) solids, such as anhydrous copper sulphate, which absorbs water and so turns blue, but does not form a solution; (c) substances such as concentrated sulphuric acid and glycerine, which are already liquid.

Suggestions for Practical Work

Expts. 36, 41, 42.

Test various crystalline salts (prepared in Chapter V) to see which contain water of crystallization; heat them separately in test-tubes (pointed away from yourself and from your neighbours).

Write a message in "invisible ink" as follows. Use a new pen-nib and a dilute solution of cobalt chloride. The pale pink colour dries almost invisible, but when the paper is held over a bunsen-burner or near a fire, the cobalt chloride is dehydrated to a blue colour and the writing will show up clearly. (Blue "cobalt chloride paper," which must be kept in a desiccator, is used in biology as a sensitive test for moisture. If you breathe heavily upon it, the colour will fade again.)

QUESTIONS ON CHAPTER VI

1. Describe experiments by which it can be proved that air and water contain a common constituent. What reasons are there for stating that in one case this constituent is chemically combined and in the other it forms part of a mixture?

2. Give accounts of experiments which can be carried out to show that tap-water contains (*a*) dissolved oxygen, (*b*) combined oxygen. (C.)

3. How would you prove experimentally, by *three* tests, that a given liquid was pure water?

What happens when (*a*) steam is passed through a tube containing red-hot iron; (*b*) a piece of sodium is put into water? (C.)

4. What is the action of water upon the following: (*a*) sodium, (*b*) anhydrous copper sulphate, (*c*) calcium oxide, (*d*) phosphorus pentoxide? State how you would prove by experiment that what you say is correct in *two* of these cases. (O. and C.)

5. Describe fully a method for determining the composition of water by weight.

6. What do you understand by "water of crystallization"?

Write an account of the experimental method you would use to determine the percentage of water of crystallization contained in crystals of copper sulphate.

Describe and explain what is seen to happen when a crystal of copper sulphate is added to concentrated sulphuric acid. (L.)

7. Give the names and chemical formulae for two examples of each of the following:

(*a*) a salt with water of crystallization;

(*b*) a crystalline salt without water of crystallization;

(*c*) a non-crystalline salt.

8. What do you understand by *water of crystallization?* Give *three* instances each of:

(*a*) salts which contain water of crystallization;

(*b*) salts which crystallize in the anhydrous state;

(*c*) uses of substances depending on their power to take up water of crystallization.   (O.)

CHAPTER VII

HYDROGEN

Hydrogen occurs almost entirely in the form of its compounds, especially the oxide—water; compounds of hydrogen with carbon and often other elements as well are important in living animals and plants, and in coal and petroleum (see pp. 100, 264, 289).

The free element hydrogen is the chief constituent of the sun and stars (see p. 158).

Laboratory Preparation of Hydrogen

The standard method is by the action of dilute hydrochloric or sulphuric acid on a suitable metal, although hydrogen can also be obtained by the action of metals on water (p. 81) or on alkalis, or by electrolysis (p. 84).

1. *Preparation from acids.* The metal used must not be too reactive (like sodium) or too inactive (like tin). Of the four possible common metals, iron, which is much the cheapest, is the least pure and gives an evil-smelling gas. Zinc is the most commonly used because the only effect of the main impurity, lead, is the useful one of speeding up the reaction; aluminium is less reactive than *impure* zinc; and magnesium, though it reacts rapidly to give a very pure gas, is still somewhat expensive.

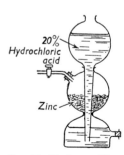

20% Hydrochloric acid

Zinc

FIG. 25. Hydrogen Kipp.

(*a*) *Standard apparatus.* Hydrogen is normally obtained in the laboratory from a Kipp's apparatus (fig. 25). The zinc is placed in the middle compartment, and fairly large lumps should be used so that they will not fall into the acid in the lower part. Hydrochloric acid, not too dilute, is poured in through the top, and reaches the zinc after filling the bottom of the apparatus. A vigorous reaction occurs with much bubbling, and some heat is given out; the zinc gradually dissolves and forms a colourless solution of zinc chloride which mixes with the acid. If the tap is open so

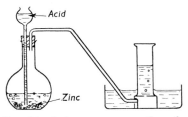

FIG. 26.   Laboratory preparation of hydrogen.

that the gas can escape the action will continue until either the zinc or the acid is completely used up. If the tap is shut, the pressure of hydrogen in the centre compartment forces down the acid, causing some to go into the upper bulb, until it no longer touches the zinc, thus effectively stopping the reaction. On opening the tap once more, hydrogen comes out, the pressure is released, and the acid again comes into contact with the zinc. Normally the acid is used up first, and the Kipp can be regenerated by removing the bung from the bottom part, allowing the zinc chloride solution to run out, replacing the bung, and refilling with acid.

Black specks of solid are often seen floating in the liquid; these are mainly lead, which is present in ordinary zinc because the ores contain both metals (p. 460). If pure zinc is used, the action has to be hastened by adding an impurity (see p. 222), usually a little copper sulphate solution, which forms a layer of copper on the surface of the zinc. The yellow colour of the liquid is due to traces of ferric chloride in the commercial acid.

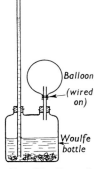

FIG. 27. Preparing hydrogen under pressure.

(b) *Occasional Preparation.* When small quantities of hydrogen are required, acid may be added through a thistle funnel to zinc in an ordinary flask or bottle (fig. 26); the gas may be collected over water. If a balloon is to be filled, a Woulfe bottle must be used as in fig. 27;

after pouring the acid in, the long tube is fitted at once; acid is forced up the tube by the gas until the pressure is sufficient to blow up the balloon.

(c) *Preparation of Pure Hydrogen.* The chief impurities in hydrogen prepared as above are: (1) hydrogen chloride, removed by passing through a wash-bottle of water; (2) moisture, removed by passing through a U-tube of calcium chloride or a wash-bottle of concentrated sulphuric acid. The dry gas must not now, of course, be collected over water; it must be collected over mercury by connecting to the tap of the burette in fig. 28, opening the tap, and allowing the mercury to fall. (A trough and gas-jar would need at least 1000 c.c. of mercury, costing £10 or more, and the bee-hive shelf would float in mercury!)

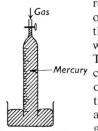

FIG. 28. Collection of dry gases.

2. *Preparation from alkalis.* Three common metals, tin, zinc, and aluminium, will dissolve slowly in solutions of sodium hydroxide or potassium hydroxide, to give off hydrogen and form a solution of a stannite, zincate, or aluminate. The action is slow except in the case of aluminium, which is attacked rapidly by hot alkalis, especially when concentrated (see expt. 154, p. 459).

$Sn + 2NaOH = Na_2SnO_2 + H_2$
Sodium Stannite

$Zn + 2NaOH = Na_2ZnO_2 + H_2$
Sodium Zincate

$2Al + 6NaOH = 2Na_3AlO_3 + 3H_2$ (Actually $NaAlO_2$ is formed.
Sodium Aluminate   see p. 459.)

It should be noted that these three metals have "amphoteric" oxides, which dissolve in acids *or* in alkalis (p. 391), according to which is present.

Commercial Preparation of Hydrogen

Large quantities of hydrogen are used, especially for the manufacture of ammonia (see p. 313), and these must be obtained from a cheap raw material, i.e. water, by means of a cheap reagent such as coke.

1. When steam is passed through a tower of red-hot coke, a mixture of hydrogen and carbon monoxide is formed, which can be used as a fuel (p. 257) under the name of *water gas.*

$$\text{Carbon} + \text{Hydrogen Oxide} = \text{Carbon Monoxide} + \text{Hydrogen}$$
$$\text{C} \qquad H_2O \qquad\qquad CO \qquad\qquad H_2$$

If the water gas is then mixed with more steam and passed over a heated catalyst (iron), twice as much hydrogen is obtained:

$$\text{Carbon Monoxide} + \text{Hydrogen Oxide}$$
$$CO \qquad\qquad H_2O$$
$$= \text{Carbon Dioxide} + \text{Hydrogen,}$$
$$CO_2 \qquad\qquad H_2$$

also the carbon dioxide can easily be removed by dissolving it in water under pressure (see p. 115).

2. Hydrogen is obtained commercially by electrolysis (p. 84) where electric power is cheap, or where it is a by-product of some other reaction (p. 405, production of sodium hydroxide).

3. Coal gas (p. 260) is about half hydrogen by volume, and hydrogen can be obtained from this if all the other constituents are liquefied by cooling with liquid air.

4. Scrap-iron reacting with steam (p. 81) was once the main method, and can still be used if required

Physical Properties of Hydrogen

Hydrogen is without colour or smell when pure. It is the lightest gas known (air being more than 14 times as heavy) and is therefore used to fill balloons for observing the weather, or in war. As mentioned above, it is not liquefied by liquid air, a temperature of $-253°$ C. being necessary. It is only very slightly soluble in water (2 volumes per 100 volumes at $0°$ C.), and so can be collected over water. It has a very great tendency to diffuse (see later in this chapter) through any porous substance, including corks, rubber tubing, and balloon fabrics.

Expt. 43. Blowing hydrogen bubbles.

If a hydrogen Kipp is connected through a wash-bottle of water (to remove acid vapours, especially hydrogen chloride) to a clay

4*

pipe, soap-bubbles* of hydrogen can be blown which rise rapidly
to the ceiling.   This shows the extreme lightness of hydrogen.
A member of the class standing on the lecture bench with a lighted
taper can catch them and show that pure hydrogen burns quietly.

If an oxygen cylinder is also connected to the clay pipe via a
T-piece, the bubbles can be blown with a mixture of hydrogen and
oxygen.   These rise much less rapidly and explode loudly when lit,
especially if the proportions of the gases are in the ratio 2 to 1 by
volume, as is required to form water; this shows the most important
chemical property of hydrogen.   Bubbles of air or oxygen will *fall*.

Expt. 44.   Pouring hydrogen upwards.

If a gas-jar full of hydrogen (A) is opened below another one full
of air (B) (fig. 29), after a moment or two the gas in the upper jar
can be lighted; this shows that the hydrogen has flowed upwards,
because it is so much lighter than air.   This property can be used
for collecting hydrogen or other gases (such as ammonia), which are
lighter than air, by putting a delivery tube right inside an inverted
gas-jar (fig. 30) and displacing the air downwards.

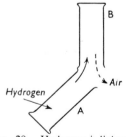

FIG. 29.   Hydrogen is lighter
than air.

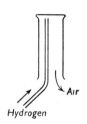

FIG. 30.   Collecting
hydrogen.

Chemical Properties of Hydrogen

1. *Combination with oxygen.*   (*a*) Hydrogen burns in air
(or oxygen) to form its oxide, water.

Expt. 45.   The Synthesis of Water.

Hydrogen from a Kipp is dried, by passing through a wash-
bottle of concentrated sulphuric acid, and allowed to displace all

* "Drene " "Dreft," or "Fairy Bubbles" are better than soap solution.

air from the apparatus. (An explosive mixture would otherwise be formed, and the whole apparatus might be blown up.)

The hydrogen is then lit at the glass jet, and the flame directed on to the cold dry surface of a retort through which cold water is flowing (fig. 31). The combination of hydrogen with oxygen makes the flame and forms water vapour which condenses as a mist, and then slowly forms drops of a colourless liquid; these drip off and are collected in a clean, dry basin.

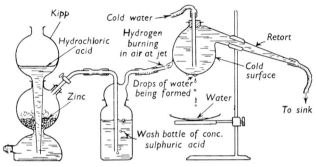

FIG. 31. Synthesis of water.

To prove that this liquid is water, the tests given on page 79 should be used; the experiment should be continued until there is enough product to do all the tests, if possible. The undried hydrogen straight from the Kipp will turn anhydrous copper sulphate blue (showing the necessity for drying it), but the dry, *unburnt* hydrogen will not (showing that the water is formed in the reaction).

(*b*) Although hydrogen burns in air, it will not allow substances to burn in it, because burning usually requires oxygen (but see p. 296 on flame).

Expt. 46. Fill an inverted gas-jar with hydrogen by putting the delivery tube right into the jar and displacing the heavier air downwards. Light the gas with a taper, and at once push the taper through the flame into the jar. The flame of the taper is put out by the hydrogen while the hydrogen is still burning in air (fig. 32).

(*c*) Hydrogen will unite with the *combined* oxygen in many metal oxides to form water and the metal. The process of removing oxygen is called *reduction*; it is the opposite of *oxidation*, which means the addition of oxygen to a substance (see pp. 380–384).

Expt. 47. A slow stream of dry hydrogen is passed through a horizontal test-tube containing a layer of black copper oxide, and is lighted (after displacing the air) at a small hole at the end of the tube (fig. 33). When the tube is heated gently, the black oxide will glow red hot and change colour quite rapidly to the red colour typical of metallic copper. During the reaction steam is produced, and so the jet issuing from the test-tube goes out; when the reaction is over, dry hydrogen escapes once more and can be re-lit.

$$\text{Hydrogen} + \text{Copper Oxide} = \text{Copper} + \text{Hydrogen Oxide}$$
$$H_2 \qquad\qquad CuO \qquad\qquad Cu \qquad\qquad H_2O$$

(This reaction has already been used to find the composition of water, p. 85.)

The oxides of lead, tin, and iron behave similarly.

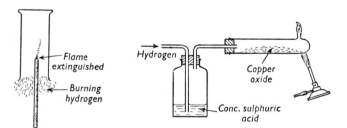

Fig. 32. Hydrogen burns but does not support burning.   Fig. 33. Hydrogen reduces copper oxide to copper.

It will be noted that in general those metals which react with water or steam (pp. 81–82) to give off hydrogen do not have their oxides reduced by hydrogen, and vice versa; only in the case of iron is the reaction reversible.

The following table shows that for many purposes the metals can be arranged in a definite order of reactivity. This order, known as the Electrochemical Series, is discussed in detail in Chapter XIV (p. 223) and will be used extensively whenever the properties of metals and their compounds are being considered.

ACTION OF HYDROGEN ON OXIDES. ACTION OF WATER AND ACIDS ON METALS

	Hydrogen on oxide	Water on metal	Hydrochloric acid on metal
Potassium	No	Cold: violent	Violent reaction to give hydrogen.
Sodium	reduction	Cold: fast	
Calcium	of	Cold: slow	
Magnesium	Oxide	Steam: burns	Moderate reaction to give hydrogen (becoming slower from magnesium to tin, and needing more concentrated acid).
Aluminium	by	Normally protected by a surface film of oxide (see p. 458)	
Zinc	Hydrogen	Steam: fairly fast	
Iron	Reversible reduction	Steam: reversible	
Tin	Reduction		Exceedingly slow reaction → Hydrogen.
Lead	Reduction	Metals unaffected by pure water	
Copper	Rapid reduction		Hydrogen never given. No attack in absence of oxidizing agents.
Mercury	Oxide decomposed by heat alone		
Silver			
Gold			
Platinum			

2. *Combination with other non-metals.* Compounds of hydrogen with all the non-metals—except of course the inert gases—are known, and many are important. Those listed below will be described later in this book.

Hydrogen combines readily with chlorine to form hydrogen chloride, and nitrogen is made to react with hydrogen under pressure (PLATE 7) to form ammonia. The other hydrides are normally prepared by indirect methods.

Element	Hydride	Common name
Chlorine	HCl	Hydrochloric acid (when in solution)
Oxygen	H_2O	Water
	H_2O_2	Hydrogen peroxide
Sulphur	H_2S	Hydrogen sulphide

[Photo by courtesy of I.C.I. Ltd.

PLATE 7.   HYDROGEN FOR MAKING AMMONIA

The machines shown here compress the hydrogen to 250 times atmospheric pressure.

Element	Hydride	Common name
Nitrogen	NH_3	Ammonia
Phosphorus	PH_3	Phosphine
Carbon	CH_4	Methane
	C_2H_4	Ethylene
	C_2H_2	Acetylene
	C_6H_6	Benzene
	$C_{10}H_8$	Naphthalene

3. *Combination with metals.* Some metals, such as sodium and calcium combine with hydrogen when heated in it. The resulting hydrides are comparatively unimportant.

$$Ca_2 + H_2 = CaH_2;$$
$$CaH_2 \quad + \quad H_2O \quad = \quad CaO \quad + \quad 2H_2$$
Calcium Hydride   Hydrogen Oxide   Calcium Oxide   Hydrogen

Lithium Deuteride is used in the "Hydrogen Bomb."

4. *Combination with Compounds.* Many naturally occurring compounds of carbon can be made to react with hydrogen, in the presence of a *catalyst*, to give useful products (see "Uses of Hydrogen") below. This process is known as *hydrogenation*.

Nascent Hydrogen

Hydrogen itself does not easily react with many compounds (except some oxides), but a reaction mixture in which hydrogen is being formed will react with many more. Such a reaction mixture (e.g. zinc and dilute hydrochloric or sulphuric acid) is called "nascent hydrogen." See also p. 340.

Expt. 48. Take two test-tubes and half fill them both with a mixed solution of potassium permanganate and dilute sulphuric acid. Into the first pass hydrogen from a Kipp; the purple colour remains. Into the second put some zinc and some more acid; the solution becomes colourless, showing that a reaction has taken place.

The explanation now generally accepted for this extra reactivity of "nascent hydrogen" (=hydrogen in the moment of birth) is as follows: some of the energy which would have been given out (as heat) by the reaction which produces the hydrogen goes instead to provide the energy required by the other reaction. This explanation accounts for the fact that those reactions which give out the most heat in forming hydrogen provide the most reactive nascent hydrogen.

In the example below, the source of the nascent hydrogen is reaction no. 1; reaction no. 2 absorbs energy and will not occur with free hydrogen; the total reaction which takes place with nascent hydrogen is given in equation no. 3 (the sum of the first two reactions), and it will be seen that free hydrogen plays no part in this.

1. Zinc + Hydrogen Chloride = Zinc Chloride + Hydrogen + much energy
2. Ferric Chloride + Hydrogen = Ferrous Chloride + Hydrogen Chloride
$$-\text{energy}$$

3. Ferric Chloride + Zinc = Ferrous Chloride + Zinc Chloride + some
energy
This reaction explains why the yellow colour of the acid in a Kipp
(p. 91) gradually fades; *ferrous* chloride is almost colourless.

Uses of Hydrogen (see fig. 34 opposite)

1. More hydrogen is used as a fuel than for any other purpose, i.e. combining with oxygen to give out heat. As purity
is not needed, it is normally used in the form of coal gas or water
gas, both of which contain 50% of hydrogen. A hydrogen-
oxygen blowpipe is also used (see p. 31).

2. The most important use of pure hydrogen is in combining
with nitrogen to form ammonia for fertilizers (p. 313). About
half a million tons per year are required for this, throughout
the world.

3. Raw materials for plastics such as *bakelite* (brown),
beetleware (bright colours; from urea), *nylon*, etc., require
large amounts of hydrogen in their manufacture from carbon
compounds which contain too little hydrogen.

4. Similar reactions occur in the manufacture of solid fats
(for *margarine*) from liquid oils (whale oil, cotton-seed oil, etc.),
and of *petrol* from coal. Petrol contains 14% by weight of
combined hydrogen, whereas coal has only 5%.

5. The reaction of hydrogen with combined oxygen is used
to prepare some metals, e.g. nickel (see p. 257) and tungsten,
from their oxides.

6. The lightness of hydrogen makes it useful for balloons.
Its ease of diffusion out of the blood accounts for its use—
mixed with oxygen, of course—by divers; other compressed
gases, such as nitrogen, form air-bubbles in the blood when the
diver comes up again, and these are very painful or even fatal.

The Diffusion of Gases

All gases tend to spread in every direction, unlike liquids
which will only move downwards, to take the shape of the
containing vessel. For example, a strong smell such as that of

HYDROGEN
Industrial Preparation and Uses

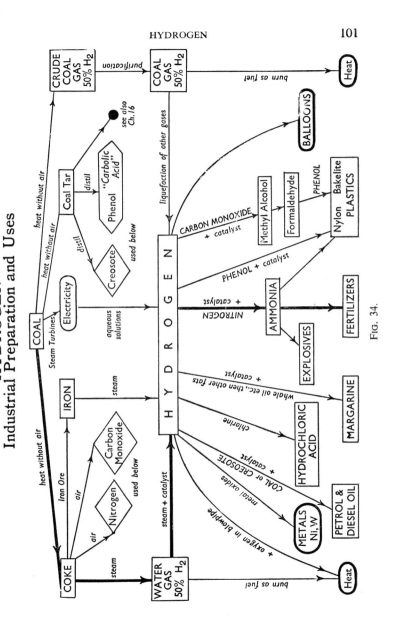

Fig. 34.

ammonia can soon be detected all over the laboratory, and
inflammable vapours like petrol or carbon disulphide are
dangerous even at a considerable distance from
a flame.   This property is not entirely due to
draughts, and is known as "diffusion."

A   Hydrogen

Expt. 49.   Hydrogen will diffuse not only upwards (expt. 44, p. 94, "pouring hydrogen") but
even *downwards*.   A jar of hydrogen (A) is inverted
over a jar of the heavy gas carbon dioxide (B), the
cover-plates removed, and left for 10 minutes
(fig. 35A).   The lower jar (B) can be shown to
contain hydrogen by putting in a lighted taper,
when the gas will "pop." Similarly, the upper
jar can be shown to contain carbon dioxide,
because lime-water goes cloudy when shaken up in it (p. 23).

B   Carbon dioxide

FIG. 35A.   Dif-
fusion of Hydro-
gen.

Gases diffuse at different speeds, as is shown in the next
experiment.

Expt. 50.   An unglazed (p. 435) porous pot is fitted on to the
end of a long U-tube containing coloured
water (fig. 35B).   When an inverted beaker
of hydrogen is placed over the pot, the
liquid rises rapidly in the right-hand tube
to a height of about 3 feet.   This excess
pressure is due to the hydrogen diffusing
in through the pores of the pot much
more rapidly than air diffuses out.

If the beaker is filled with carbon
dioxide instead, the reverse effect is seen.

In 1846 Thomas Graham, after in-
vestigating the behaviour of various
gases, put forward the following "Law"
(see below).

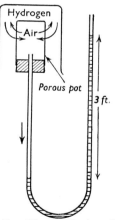

FIG. 35B.   Diffusion of
Hydrogen.

Graham's Law of Diffusion

**Gases diffuse at rates which are in-
versely proportional to the square roots
of their densities.**

For example, oxygen is 16 times as heavy as hydrogen, so
that under similar conditions hydrogen (the lighter gas) will
diffuse 4 times as fast as oxygen.

The "rate of diffusion" means the volume of gas diffusing in a given time. In practice, the times taken for a *given volume* to diffuse are measured (see below), and these will be *directly* proportional to the square roots of the densities.

Expt. 51. Illustration of Graham's Law.

An open glass tube fitted with three rubber rings and a small plug of plaster of paris at the top is placed, as shown in fig. 36, in a jar of water to the level of the top ring.

By means of a stop-clock, the time taken for the water to rise from the bottom ring to the middle ring is measured. Several readings are taken, to obtain a reliable average.

The air in the tube is now replaced by hydrogen and the average time taken for the water to rise as far as before is measured.

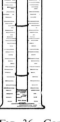

The readings give the relative times taken for equal volumes of air and hydrogen to diffuse through the porous plug at similar average pressures; these should be approximately proportional to the square roots of the densities of the two gases.

For example:

$$\frac{\text{Average time for air}}{\text{Average time for hydrogen}} = \frac{254 \text{ sec.}}{70 \text{ sec.}} = \frac{3 \cdot 6}{1}$$

$$\frac{\text{Square root of density of air}}{\text{Square root of density of hydrogen}} = \frac{\sqrt{14 \cdot 4}}{\sqrt{1}} = \frac{3 \cdot 8}{1}$$

Fig. 36. Comparing rates of diffusion.

The above results are in good agreement with Graham's Law. This, like the Law of the Conservation of Mass (p. 20) and other scientific "Laws," is an *experimental* one. That means that it is a general statement of how things behave under certain stated conditions, and it has been shown by experiment to be correct. It does not mean that there is any force or person compelling these substances to "obey" the law.

NOTE: The "densities" of the gases given above are, strictly speaking, "vapour densities": see p. 195.

The Importance of Diffusion

The above experiments can only be explained by assuming that in a gas the particles ("molecules") are constantly moving about in all directions. This behaviour is discussed in Chapter IX (p. 121).

Gases may be separated by means of diffusion, even when their chemical properties are identical. This was important in isolating the "uranium 235 isotope" (see p. 157) required for atomic energy; one of its compounds (the hexa-fluoride, UF_6) diffused 0.5% faster than the corresponding compound of ordinary uranium, and so it was separated by an elaborate process of extreme difficulty.

Suggestions for Practical Work

Examine the action of the common acids, both dilute and concentrated, on small pieces of zinc in test-tubes. Heat if necessary, and test the gas to see if it is hydrogen by "popping" it.

Repeat, using concentrated hydrochloric acid with as many different metals as possible.

Prepare several gas-jars of hydrogen and do expts. 44, 46, 47, 49, 51.

See also expt. 59 (p. 134), expt. 63 (p. 140), expt. 134 (p. 349), expt. 154B (p. 409).

QUESTIONS ON CHAPTER VII

1. "When dry hydrogen is burned in air, water is formed." Draw a labelled sketch to illustrate the apparatus you would use to show the truth of this statement. Name *two* experiments which you would perform to prove that the product so obtained is water. State how and under what conditions the following react with water: (a) iron, (b) calcium. (L.)

2. With carbon, sodium, iron, sulphuric acid, and water as starting materials, state *four* distinct ways in which hydrogen could be obtained. (Diagrams are not required in this question.)

Which of the possible ways would be suitable (a) for commercial use, (b) for the preparation of a small quantity of hydrogen in the laboratory? Give reasons for your answer. (C.)

3. Explain the difference between *analysis* and *synthesis*.

Sketch the apparatus you would use to prepare pure dry hydrogen and to show that when dry hydrogen is burned, water is produced. (A clearly labelled diagram does not need a written description.)

How would you prove your product to be water?

In what other way could you show that water contains hydrogen and oxygen? (Electrolysis of an acid solution will not be accepted.) (N.)

4. Describe and explain the construction of Kipp's apparatus. How is it used for the preparation of hydrogen? What impurities are likely to be present in the gas thus produced, and what steps would you take to remove them?

5. Describe the experiments by which you have prepared hydrogen from (*a*) water, (*b*) an acid.

For what important purposes is hydrogen used on a commercial scale?

Under what circumstances can hydrogen be made to combine directly with (*a*) chlorine, (*b*) nitrogen? (L.)

6. Explain, and illustrate by examples, the behaviour of hydrogen (*a*) in hydrogenation processes, (*b*) as a reducing agent.

Illustrate and discuss the difference between hydrogen from a Kipp and "nascent hydrogen."

7. Give an account of the characteristic properties of hydrogen, and show how these properties are made use of commercially.

8. State Graham's Law of Diffusion of gases, and describe any experiments you have witnessed relating to the diffusion of gases.

In 50 seconds 300 c.c. of oxygen diffuse through a porous plate. How long will it take 500 c.c. of chlorine to diffuse through the same plate? (Assume that the vapour densities of oxygen and chlorine are 16 and 36 respectively.) (L.)

9. In the "fusion" type of nuclear energy, as produced on the sun, 4 hydrogen atoms (weight 1·0080 units each) are converted into 1 atom of helium (weight 4·003 units). Assuming Einstein's equation $E = MC^2$, i.e. Energy set free = Matter destroyed × (Velocity of Light)^2, calculate:

(*a*) How much energy (in calories) will be set free by the nuclear reaction of 1 gram of hydrogen;

(*b*) How many times more powerful such a nuclear charge is than a chemical charge.

(Assume (i) the velocity of light = 30,000,000,000 cm./sec., (ii) 1 calorie = 42,000,000 gm. cm^2/sec^2, (iii) 1 gram of hydrogen, if completely burned to water, gives 28,000 calories.)

CHAPTER VIII

SOLUTION AND SOLUBILITY

Solutions and Suspensions

When a little salt is stirred into a beaker of cold water, the salt slowly dissolves to form a *solution* in which no solid particles can be seen. If more salt is gradually added, a limit is reached beyond which the salt no longer dissolves, but remains as visible solid particles; while the liquid is being stirred, these particles remain in *suspension*, but if they are left undisturbed they will settle out on the bottom. If this suspension is poured on to a filter-paper in a funnel, the suspended particles will be too large to pass through the pores of the paper and so will remain behind; the salt which has dissolved into solution will pass through the filter as the *filtrate*, because its particles are very much smaller—being in fact of similar size to the gas molecules which can diffuse through a porous pot (p. 102), and to the water molecules which also pass through the filter-paper.

A solution is a homogeneous mixture of two or more substances, i.e. it appears to be all "of the same kind," unlike (say) a mixture of iron and sulphur.

The dissolved substance (*solute*) may be a solid, or a liquid, e.g. sulphuric acid, or a gas, e.g. ammonia.

The liquid which does the dissolving (*solvent*) is usually water, but other liquids may be used (e.g. pp. 51, 414). "Rubber solution" for mending punctures is a solution of rubber in benzene; paints (p. 284) will dissolve in turpentine; "tincture" of iodine is a solution in alcohol; lacquers for motorcars may contain nitrocellulose dissolved in other kinds of alcohols.

A solution in which no more solute will dissolve under the same conditions is said to be *saturated*, and the proportion of solute in such a solution (the *solubility*) is defined below.

Solutions of Solids in Liquids

The solubility of a substance in a solvent, at a given temperature and pressure, is defined as the maximum weight of it in grams which will dissolve, under those conditions, in 100 gm. of the solvent, in the presence of excess of undissolved substance.

NOTE: In the absence of undissolved solid, a *supersaturated* solution may be obtained, which contains an amount of solid in excess of its true solubility (see p. 113).

Effect of Temperature on the Solubility of a Solid (see p. 108)

The value given for the solubility of a solid is meaningless unless the temperature is stated. (Pressure is relatively unimportant.)

As we saw in the preparation of salts (p. 69), a hot solution if fairly concentrated will usually deposit crystals on cooling. This means that the solubility in hot water is greater than that in cold water. For example, 100 gm. of water will dissolve about 50 gm. of ferrous sulphate crystals ($FeSO_4.7H_2O$) at 50° C., but only half that amount when cooled to room temperature (say 20° C.); the other 25 gm. can no longer remain in solution and so come out as a solid.

Most solids are similar to this, in being more soluble in hot water than in cold; a few common substances, however, such as calcium sulphate, calcium hydroxide, and *anhydrous* sodium sulphate, are exceptions to this rule and are *less* soluble in hot water.

Some compounds, such as sodium chloride (common salt), show little change in solubility with temperature. Most potassium salts, on the other hand, have a fairly steep solubility curve (fig. 37) and are therefore crystallized more easily than the corresponding sodium salts; this explains their frequent use as laboratory reagents (e.g. iodide, dichromate, permanganate).

The solubility curves of a number of common substances, illustrating the above points, are given overleaf; they may be constructed as described in the next section.

Substances with different solubility curves may be separated by *fractional crystallization*: e.g. a mixture of 30 gm. of

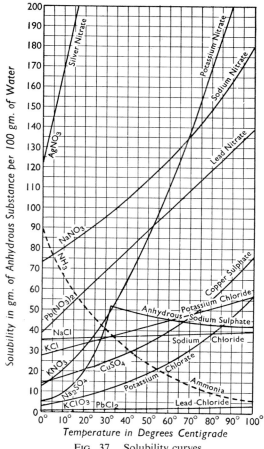

FIG. 37. Solubility curves.

potassium chlorate with 30 gm. of potassium chloride will all dissolve in 100 gm. of water at 80° C. or above; on cooling to 10° C. all the potassium chloride will remain in solution, but 25 gm. of pure potassium chlorate will crystallize out, free from the chloride. This is a very widely used method for the separation of mixtures. See also potassium nitrate (p. 333).

Measuring the Solubility of a Solid in Water

Expt. 52. To find the Solubility of Potassium Nitrate at 40° C.
Heat about 200 c.c. of distilled water to a temperature of about 50° C. in a beaker. Stir gradually into this more of the powdered potassium nitrate crystals than will dissolve, so that a little remains undissolved in the beaker. Allow the solution to cool slowly, and when its temperature is 40° C. decant about 25 to 30 c.c. into a clean, weighed evaporating basin and re-weigh. In pouring the solution from the beaker, care must be taken to avoid getting any of the undissolved solid, which by now will be at the bottom of the beaker. The contents of the basin must now be very cautiously evaporated to dryness. This is much less easy than it might appear, because of the tendency of the solution to "spit." The final stages are preferably carried out on a water-bath or in a steam oven. The weight of dry solid and basin is then found. The basin is then re-heated and re-weighed until the weight is found to be constant. The following typical set of results shows how the calculation is carried out:

Weight of basin	$= 53 \cdot 51$ gm.	(W_1)
,, ,, ,, +saturated solution . .	$= 92 \cdot 66$ gm.	(W_2)
,, ,, ,, +dry potassium nitrate .	$= 68 \cdot 46$ gm.	(W_3)
,, ,, , +dry potassium nitrate .	$= 68 \cdot 46$ gm.	(repeat)
∴ Weight of potassium nitrate .	$= 14 \cdot 95$ gm.	$(W_3 - W_1)$
Weight of water in saturated solution	$= 24 \cdot 20$ gm.	$(W_2 - W_3)$

24·20 gm. of water dissolve 14·95 gm. of potassium nitrate at 40° C.

∴ 100 gm. of water dissolve $14 \cdot 95 \times \dfrac{100}{24 \cdot 20}$ gm. of potassium nitrate at 40° C.

∴ *Solubility* of potassium nitrate in water at 40° C. $= 14 \cdot 95 \times \dfrac{100}{24 \cdot 20}$
$$= 61 \cdot 6 \text{ gm.}$$

In order to plot a solubility curve, the process must then be repeated at other temperatures.

This method is not suitable for salts which contain water of crystallization (see p. 86), because they would be decomposed by heat in the course of the evaporation.

Expt. 53.   To find the solubility of potassium chlorate at various temperatures.

A less accurate but much quicker method is possible for salts which crystallize well.

A weighed amount (4·8 gm.) of potassium chlorate ($KClO_3$) is put into a boiling-tube fitted with a cork, a thermometer, and a piece of copper wire as a stirrer (fig. 38). 10 c.c. of water (10 gm. approx.)

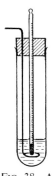

are added from a burette, and the tube heated in a mug of boiling water until all the solid has dissolved.

The tube is then allowed to cool in the air, and the solution is vigorously stirred up and down until white crystals just begin to appear, and the temperature (about 90° C.) is at once written down. At this temperature 10 gm. of water are saturated by 4·8 gm. of solid, i.e. 100 gm. would be saturated by $4·8 \times \dfrac{100}{10}$ gm. = 48 gm. of potassium chlorate, which is therefore the solubility.

Another 2 c.c. of water are then added from the burette, and the process repeated to find the (rather lower) temperature at which the solubility is

FIG. 38. Apparatus for finding the solubility of potassium chlorate.

$4·8 \times \dfrac{100}{12}$, i.e. 40 gm. per 100 gm. of water.

Other readings are then taken, e.g. with the quantity of water *totalling* 16 gm. (solubility 30 gm.), 20 gm., 24 gm., 30 gm., etc., until the tube is full (48 gm.). The various results are then plotted on a graph paper, and a *smooth* curve drawn through them. From this the solubility at definite temperatures (between 90° C. and 30° C.) can be read off, but it is unwise to extend ("extrapolate") the curve as far as 100° C. or 0° C. because figures obtained from this part would only be guesswork.

The major cause of inaccuracy in this experiment is evaporation of the water. It is therefore unsuitable for advanced work.

"Insoluble substances"

Substances whose solubility at room temperature is less than about 1 gm. per 100 gm. water are generally called "insoluble"; that is to say, the amount which dissolves does not matter from one particular point of view. Thus lead chloride, $PbCl_2$, is classed as insoluble because it is normally prepared by precipitation (p. 71), but drinking 2 pints of a solution of it saturated at room temperature would produce symptoms of lead poisoning. On the other hand, lime-water is a saturated solution of calcium hydroxide, $Ca(OH)_2$, containing only 0·2 gm. of solid per 100 gm. of water; but as this is quite strong enough to act as a test for carbon dioxide, no one would normally say that calcium hydroxide was "insoluble," although its solubility is in fact less than one-fifth of that of lead chloride.

The Preparation of Crystals

A crystal is a substance which has solidified in a definite geometrical form. Common salt consists of tiny cubes, as can be seen by looking at the solid grains through a good magnifying-glass (PLATE 8). One of the best examples is sodium sulphite ($Na_2SO_3.7H_2O$). which is in the form of perfectly

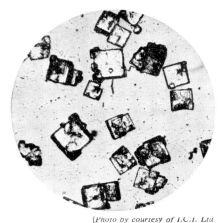

[*Photo by courtesy of I.C.I. Ltd*

PLATE 8. CRYSTALS OF COMMON SALT.
These are magnified 20 times.

regular hexagonal prisms, about $\frac{1}{2}$ cm. across, easily visible to the naked eye when picked out of the bottle.

The shapes of crystals depend on the regular arrangement of the atoms (p. 153) inside these solids, which can be shown by means of X-rays; the atoms (actually "ions," see pp. 181, 213) of sodium and of chlorine in sodium chloride being at the corners of a cubical network (fig. 39).

The growing of a single well-shaped large crystal will therefore demand three conditions for its success: (1) the particles of the solid must have enough time to diffuse through the solution to the correct positions on the growing crystal; (2) there must be no other crystals, or dust, present on which the particles can grow; (3) the "parent" crystal must be suspended in solution so that the particles can grow on to it regularly from all sides (including from below).

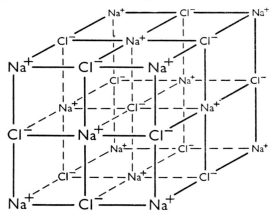

FIG. 39. The structure of a sodium chloride crystal.

Normally, crystals look rather different from the ideal shapes because these conditions are not fulfilled; thus crystals obtained from the bottom of a dish will have been prevented from growing evenly by the glass and by the nearness of their neighbours. Also, if a hot, saturated solution of copper sulphate is cooled rapidly by holding it under the tap, a large number of small crystals are formed, because the particles of solid have been deposited on dust, etc., rather than on to any one crystal which could only grow slowly. Even so, the angles between corresponding faces of a crystal will be the same in all crystals of the same substance

Expt. 54. Growing a large crystal.

A cold, saturated solution of the substance (e.g. copper sulphate) in distilled water is prepared, by warming to dissolve it and allowing it to cool overnight. It is then filtered into three or four clean beakers, to provide a greater chance of success than if only one experiment were done. In each of these a single well-formed crystal (obtained from the saturated solution above) is hung by a piece of cotton from a glass rod as shown in fig. 40. A piece of paper is put on top to exclude dust, and the beakers are put away in an even temperature, free from vibration, for several days.

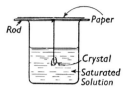

FIG. 40. Growing a crystal.

With luck, it is not difficult to get crystals 1 inch across, and exhibition crystals of potash alum have been prepared more than 3 feet across. The largest single crystal of a mineral ("spodumene," a lithium aluminium silicate) found in nature was 42 feet long and weighed 65 tons.

Supersaturation

It will now be fairly easy to understand how supersaturated solutions can occur when a saturated solution is cooled in the complete absence of solid or dust particles. The reason is that there is no "nucleus" round which the crystals can be formed.

Expt. 55. Crystals of photographic "hypo" (sodium thiosulphate, $Na_2S_2O_3.5H_2O$) are gently heated in a boiling-tube with a few c.c. of water until they all dissolve to form a saturated solution. This does not crystallize out when allowed to cool. On adding one tiny speck of the solid to the cold, supersaturated solution, crystals will grow rapidly from this point until the solution sets almost solid.

Colloidal Solutions

Colloidal solutions contain particles which are small enough to pass through a filter-paper, but are larger than ordinary molecules. Milk is a colloidal solution or "emulsion" of fat in a liquid which is mostly water; under the influence of gravity the fat particles slowly rise to the top, being lighter than water. Silicic acid, obtained by treating water-glass (p. 435) with dilute acid, easily forms colloidal solutions; and so does sulphur (see p. 348), especially when prepared by the action of dilute acid on sodium thiosulphate solutions, as in the "sunset" physics experiment.

$$Na_2S_2O_3 + 2HCl = 2NaCl + SO_2 + S \downarrow + H_2O$$

Such solutions show the *Tyndall effect* of scattering light, in the same way that fine dust particles do in a beam of sunlight; true solutions do not do this, because the particles (molecules or ions) are too small.

Colloids may be separated from "crystalloids" (salts and other substances with small molecules) by *dialysis*. The mixture is placed in a parchment bag with a stream of water flowing past the outside. The crystalloids diffuse through the parchment and are washed away, but the colloids remain behind.

Very many of the substances, e.g. proteins (p. 303) dealt with in the chemistry of living things are colloids, which are therefore very important. Colloidal particles usually carry negative electrical charges which cause the particles to repel one another. If therefore these charges are neutralized the particles will stick together. This may be done by adding aluminium sulphate, which gives Al^{+++} ions (p. 213), and so is widely used for treating sewage (also as a "styptic pencil" for clotting blood). Smokes and other gaseous colloids are treated by "electrostatic precipitation" (see Contact Process, p. 362).

Solutions of Gases in Liquids

These differ from solutions of solids in three main ways:

1. As gases are normally measured by volume, the most convenient definition of the solubility is **"the volume of gas in c.c., measured under the given conditions of temperature and pressure, which will saturate 1 c.c. of liquid under these conditions."**

TABLE OF SOLUBILITIES OF COMMON GASES IN WATER

(in c.c. per 1 c.c. of water)

		0° C.	15° C.	
NH_3	Ammonia	1200	800	Extremely soluble (solutions used as reagents)
HCl	Hydrogen Chloride	500	450	
SO_2	Sulphur dioxide	80	50	Fairly soluble (not collected over cold water)
H_2S	Hydrogen sulphide	4·5	3	
Cl_2	Chlorine	4·5	2·5	
CO_2	Carbon dioxide	1·8	1	
N_2O	Nitrous oxide	1	0·8	
NO	Nitric oxide	0·07	0·05	Very slightly soluble (may be collected over cold water)
O_2	Oxygen	0·05	0·035	
CO	Carbon monoxide	0·035	0·025	
N_2	Nitrogen	0·023	0·017	
H_2	Hydrogen	0·019	0·015	

2. The effect of increased temperature is in all cases to *decrease* the solubility (see table above). We have already seen how heating tap-water to boiling-point drove out completely the oxygen and nitrogen which had dissolved in the cold water (p. 53). All other common gases, except hydrogen chloride (p. 398), behave similarly.

The graph in fig. 37, p. 108, shows the solubility of ammonia in *grams* of gas per 100 gm. of water under a pressure of 760 mm. of *ammonia*. If the pressure of gaseous ammonia is less, the solubility—as *thus* expressed— is far less (see (3) below).

3. An increase of pressure causes a greater *mass* of gas to dissolve, as might be expected. "Soda water" and fizzy drinks contain carbon dioxide dissolved under pressure, and the same principle is used to remove carbon dioxide from a mixture of it with nitrogen (p. 33).

When air dissolves in water, each gas dissolves separately, and the amount dissolved is directly proportional both to its pressure and to its solubility. Now the total pressure of air is the sum of the "partial" pressures of its constituents (see p. 128), the pressure of the nitrogen in air being 4 times that of the oxygen; the solubility of the nitrogen, however, is only half that of the oxygen (see table above).

$$\therefore \frac{\text{Vol. of dissolved } O_2}{\text{Vol. of dissolved } N_2} = \frac{\text{Pressure of } O_2 \times \text{Solubility of } O_2}{\text{Pressure of } N_2 \times \text{Solubility of } N_2}$$

$$= \frac{1}{4} \times \frac{2}{1} = \frac{1}{2}$$

The volume of the dissolved oxygen is therefore about *one-half* that of the nitrogen, i.e. 33% of the total gas, as is actually found (p. 53).

Henry's Law states that the mass of gas dissolved by a given volume of liquid is proportional to the pressure of the gas; i.e. if the pressure is doubled, the *mass* is doubled; but the *volume*, measured under the doubled pressure, remains the same (p. 122), and therefore the solubility *as defined on p. 114* also remains constant.

Suggestions for Practical Work

Expts. 52–55. A good co-operative experiment is to plot a solubility graph, using the method of expt. 52, with different pupils obtaining the results at different temperatures.

QUESTIONS ON CHAPTER VIII

1. What would you do if asked to find out whether a given solid is soluble in alcohol?

2. Define the terms (a) saturated solution, (b) solubility. when applied to the solution of a salt in water.

Describe *in detail* how you would determine the solubility of sodium chloride in water at room temperature. (C.)

3. Explain and illustrate the terms: solute, solvent, so'ution, supersaturated solution.

Describe with all necessary details how you would determine the solubility of potassium nitrate in water (a) at room temperature and (b) at 60° C. (B.)

4. 100 parts of water dissolve the following parts by weight of potassium chlorate at the given temperatures:

Temperature (°C.)	10°	20°	30°	40°	50°	60°
Solubility		5·0	7·1	10·1	14·5	19·7	26·0

Draw a solubility curve for this salt and deduce from it:

(a) the solubility of potassium chlorate at 45° C.;

(b) the weight of water required to dissolve 40 gm. of potassium chlorate at 25° C.

5. The following data were obtained in experiments on the solubility of sodium sulphate:

Temperature (° C.)	0°	10°	20°	30°	32·7°	35°	50°	100°
Solubility ..	..	4·8	8·3	16·3	29·0	33·6	33·4	31·8	29·8

From these figures draw the solubility curve of sodium sulphate. Point out any abnormal characteristics your curve possesses, with such explanations as you can give. (L.)

6. Describe, giving essential experimental details, how you would determine the solubility of sodium chloride at room temperature.

The solubility of ammonium chloride is 64 at 80° C. and 32·8 at 10° C. Ammonium chloride was added to 50 gm. of water at 80° C. until no more would dissolve. What weight of ammonium chloride will crystallize out on cooling this solution to 10° C.? (C.)

7. The following table gives the solubility (in gm. per 100 gm. of water) of potassium nitrate at various temperatures:

Temperature (° C.)	20°	30°	40°	50°	60°	70°	80°	90°
Solubility ..	..	32	46	64	86	110	138	169	202

Draw the solubility curve of potassium nitrate, on squared paper and use it to answer the following questions:

(a) What are the solubilities of potassium nitrate at 26° C. and 85° C.?

(b) What weights of potassium nitrate and water must be used to make 100 gm. of a saturated solution at 85° C.?

(c) If the solution in (b) is cooled to 26° C., what weight of potassium nitrate will crystallize? (B.)

8. The solubilities of oxygen and nitrogen in water, under 760 mm. pressure, at 0° C. are 48·9 c.c. and 23·5 c.c. respectively. Assuming that air consists of 21% of oxygen and 79% of nitrogen by volume, calculate the percentage composition by volume under these conditions of the gas dissolved by water from air.

9. Explain what is meant by the term "saturated solution."

State *two* ways in which colloidal solutions differ from ordinary solutions. What solvents, one in each case, would you use (a) to dissolve fats, (b) to remove paint from your hands?

Describe *one* important chemical action in nature of a solution of a gas in a liquid. (C.)

PART 2

THE THEORETICAL FOUNDATIONS

CHAPTER IX

THE GAS LAWS

In the previous section we have made some progress towards understanding some of the simpler chemical phenomena, and we have learned to classify certain materials into types. Further progress must involve quantitative work, i.e. investigation of the weights of various substances which take part in chemical reactions.

Many of the most important substances, however, are gases which are inconvenient to weigh; and so we more often measure their volumes, and then convert these into weights, using a knowledge of their densities.

The Behaviour of Gases

It is a matter of everyday experience that a volume of gas can be compressed to occupy a smaller space, and that in this respect gases differ from solids and liquids. Again, in blowing up a cycle or motor tyre, even when the tyre has already reached its full size, more air may be blown in if the pressure is increased.

For this and other reasons (see Diffusion, p. 103) gases are supposed to consist of very great numbers of tiny particles ("molecules"), moving continuously in empty space; the volume of this empty space must also be very large compared with the space actually occupied by the molecules themselves. The regular bombardment of these molecules on the walls of a containing vessel constitutes the pressure of the gas.

If heat energy is applied to a gas so as to raise its temperature, then the molecules are supposed to move more quickly; if the walls of the vessel prevent the expansion of the gas, then they will be hit more frequently, and so an increased pressure is observed.

In chemical experiments a gas is usually collected and its volume measured under the conditions of temperature and

pressure in the laboratory at the time of the experiment.   In
order to calculate the weight of gas, it is necessary to know
what this volume would be under standard conditions of
temperature and pressure; this may be worked out from the
following Gas Laws.

Boyle's Law

Robert Boyle in 1664 carried out a series of experiments,
applying pressure to a gas, and discovered the law that:

**The volume of a fixed mass of any gas at constant temperature
is inversely proportional to its pressure.**

This means that if we double the pressure of a fixed mass of
gas, then its volume will be halved; or, in general, if V is the
volume of gas and P its pressure, then:

$$P \propto \frac{1}{V}, \text{ i.e. } P \times V = \text{constant, if the temperature is constant ;}$$

or $P_1V_1 = P_2V_2$ where P_1 and P_2 are the two pressures corresponding to the volumes V_1 and V_2 of the same mass of gas.

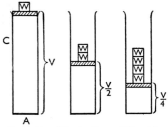

FIG. 41.   Illustration of Boyle's
Law.

A simple illustration will
make the meaning of this expression clear.   In fig. 41, C
represents a cylinder, of cross-
sectional area A, in which a
quantity of gas is enclosed by
means of a piston of weight
W.   (The piston is assumed to
give a gas-tight joint, but yet
to be frictionless.)   If an additional weight W equal to that
of the piston is now placed
upon it, the gas will be compressed to occupy half its original
volume, since the pressure has been increased from $\frac{W}{A}$ to $\frac{2W}{A}$.

Pressure is defined as weight per unit area, e.g. the pressure
due to the atmosphere on the earth's surface is normally
about 14 lb. per sq. inch (which is obviously the same as 28 lb.
on 2 sq. in., etc.), i.e. about 1030 gm. per sq. cm.   This is
equivalent to a column of mercury 76 cm. high, because this

represents 76 c.c. of mercury on 1 sq. cm., i.e. $76 \times 13.56 =$ 1030 gm. per sq. cm. (the density of mercury being 13.56 gm. per c.c.). The same pressure would be exerted by 76×2 c.c. of mercury on 2 sq. cm., and so we see that the pressure $\left(= \dfrac{\text{weight}}{\text{area}} \right)$ is fixed by the height of the mercury, and is not affected by the area of cross-section of the tube containing it.

Expt. 56. Experimental proof of Boyle's Law.

In proving Boyle's Law experimentally, it is convenient to use a column of mercury rather than weights and pistons as the source of pressure. A simple form of apparatus is shown in fig. 42, and consists of a closed tube A, containing air or some other gas, connected by thick-walled rubber tubing with an open tube B.

The tube A is uniform, so that the volume of gas is proportional to the length of tube occupied. The pressure on the mercury surface in the open tube is that of the atmosphere (measured by a barometer), and that on the gas is equal to the atmosphere + that due to the height by which the mercury in the tube B is above that in the tube A.

The pressure can be varied by raising or lowering the tube B and the corresponding lengths of column of gas in A are measured.

FIG. 42. Boyle's Law apparatus.

The levels of the mercury are read on a scale attached to the apparatus.

Results may be tabulated as follows (barometer 76 cm.):

LENGTH OF ENCLOSED AIR (L)	DIFFERENCE OF MERCURY LEVELS (D)	PRESSURE OF AIR IN CM. OF MERCURY	PRODUCT— PRESSURE × LENGTH OF AIR
20·5 cm.	12·8 cm.	$76 + 12.8$ $= 88.8$	1820
22·6 cm.	4·4 cm.	$76 + 4.4$ $= 80.4$	1817
25·0 cm.	− 3·2 cm.	$76 - 3.2$ $= 72.8$	1820

The products in the fourth column are found to be approximately constant, showing that at constant temperature, pressure × volume = constant.

EXAMPLE: The volume of a certain mass of gas at 15° C. and 745 mm. pressure is 125 c.c.; what will its volume become if the temperature remains the same, but the pressure becomes 760 mm.?

Volume of gas at 745 mm. pressure $=$ 125 c.c.
,,   ,,   ,,   1 mm.   ,, $= 125 \times 745$ c.c.
,,   ,,   ,,   760 mm.   ,, $= 125 \times \dfrac{745}{760} = 122 \cdot 6$ c.c.

Charles's Law

Ordinary experience would lead us to expect that any gas would expand in volume if its temperature is raised, e.g. if a balloon is heated, the gas expands, thus stretching the balloon until it bursts; the quantitative relation between volume and temperature was investigated in about 1782 by Charles, and also by Gay-Lussac, who discovered that:

If the pressure remains constant, the volume of a given mass of gas increases by $\frac{1}{273}$ of its volume at 0° C. for every 1° C. rise in temperature.

Absolute Scale of Temperatures

If the temperature is lowered, then the volume of gas decreases by $\frac{1}{273}$ of its volume at 0° C. for every 1° C. fall in temperature. Hence, theoretically, at −273° C. the decrease in volume would be 273/273, i.e. the whole of the volume would have disappeared and no lower temperature would be possible. (This, of course, does not really occur, because at low temperatures gases become liquids, and so Charles's Law can no longer apply.) −273° C. is therefore called the Absolute Zero, and temperatures are often written as Absolute Temperatures, i.e. reckoning from absolute zero instead of from 0° C.

The relation between temperatures expressed on the Centigrade scale and on the Absolute scale is therefore as follows:

° Centigrade	° Absolute
−273	0
0	273
100	373
t	$273 + t$

When temperatures are expressed on the absolute scale, Charles's Law becomes:

The volume (V) of a given mass of gas at constant pressure is proportional to its Absolute Temperature (T).

$V \propto T$ (°Abs.), i.e. $\dfrac{V}{T} =$ constant, if P is constant.

The gases produced by an explosion (see p. 330) expand to about ten times their volume as their temperature is raised from 300° Abs. to 3000° Abs. by the heat of the reaction (PLATE 9, p. 126).

Expt. 57. Experimental proof of Charles's Law.

The law can be verified by using the very simple form of apparatus shown in fig. 43.

A volume of air is enclosed in it by means of a pellet of mercury, and a glass scale is attached to the tube. A small pellet of mercury is put at the closed end of a uniform tube to fill up any irregularity due to the sealing off of the tube.

The apparatus, together with a thermometer, is immersed in a bath of water whose temperature is gradually raised. At various recorded temperatures the length of the air column (proportional to volume) between the two pellets of mercury is measured. These lengths are found to be proportional to the corresponding temperatures expressed on the absolute scale.

The General Gas Equation

FIG. 43.
Charles's Law apparatus.

The above laws may be combined together so as to connect the volume of a given mass of gas when under certain conditions of temperature and pressure with the volume of the same mass of gas under other conditions of temperature and pressure.

Thus, if the volume is V_1 when the absolute temperature is T_1 and the pressure P_1, then the volume V_2 when the absolute temperature is T_2 and the pressure P_2 is given by the equation:

$$\frac{P_1 \times V_1}{T_1} = \frac{P_2 \times V_2}{T_2}, \quad \text{i.e. } PV = RT \text{ (where R is constant).}$$

Densities of gases (i.e. weights per unit volume) are usually recorded under "Normal Temperature and Pressure" (often called Standard Temperature and Pressure), i.e. 0° C. (273° Abs.) and 760 mm. Volumes of gases measured under other conditions must therefore be converted to the volumes at N.T.P. (S.T.P.) before their weights can be obtained.

5*

[Photo by courtesy of Prof. John Read, F.R.S., and Fox Photos

PLATE 9.   EXPANSION OF HOT GASES

Successive phases in the firing of a naval gun, showing how
the hot gases expand (p. 125) and so propel the missile.

EXAMPLE: A certain mass of gas is found to occupy a volume of 225 c.c. when measured at 17° C. and 770 mm. What will this volume become if reduced to N.T.P.?

$$0° C. = 273° Abs. \qquad 17° C. = 290° Abs.$$

$$\frac{P_1 V_1}{T_1} = \frac{P_2 V_2}{T_2}$$

∴
$$\frac{770 \times 225}{290} = \frac{760 \times V_2}{273}$$

∴
$$V_2 = \frac{770 \times 225 \times 273}{760 \times 290} = 214 \cdot 6 \text{ c.c.}$$

Many students will find it easier and safer to make this calculation in stages thus:

225 c.c. at 290° Abs. will become less at the lower temperature of 273° Abs., i.e. $225 \times \dfrac{273}{290}$ c.c.; this volume at 770 mm. will become more at the lower pressure of 760 mm.,

i.e. $225 \times \dfrac{273}{290} \times \dfrac{770}{760} = 214 \cdot 6$ c.c.

The Effect of Temperature on Pressure

It follows from the General Gas Equation that if the volume is kept constant, then the pressure of a given mass of gas will be proportional to its absolute temperature. This may be demonstrated experimentally by the constant-volume air thermometer:

Expt. 58. Constant-Volume Air Thermometer.

A glass bulb C containing air is connected by a narrow tube and a length of pressure tubing to an open tube D as shown in fig. 44.

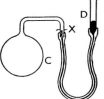

FIG. 44. Constant-volume air thermometer.

The bulb is immersed in a bath of water whose temperature is gradually raised. At each temperature the volume of the gas is compressed to a fixed value by adjusting the level of the right-hand tube until the mercury in the left-hand tube is at the fixed scratch X.

The pressure corresponding to each temperature is found from the difference in mercury levels, as in the Boyle's Law experiment. These pressures are found to be proportional to the absolute temperatures, i.e. $\frac{P}{T}$ = Constant, if V is constant.

Mixtures of Gases—Partial Pressures

The partial pressure of a gas, in a mixture of gases, is defined as that pressure which it would exert, if it alone occupied the total volume of the mixture. *Dalton's Law of Partial Pressures* states that:

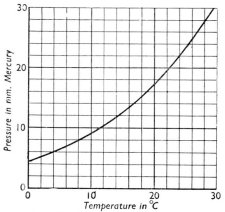

FIG. 45. Pressure of water vapour.

"The total pressure exerted by a mixture of gases is the sum of the partial pressures of each gas, providing that there is no chemical reaction between them."

Thus in ordinary air, $\frac{4}{5}$ of the volume is nitrogen and the remaining $\frac{1}{5}$ is oxygen. If the total pressure of the air is one atmosphere (760 mm. of mercury), then the nitrogen present would, if it occupied the whole volume of the air, exert a pressure of $\frac{4}{5}$ atmosphere; this is therefore its partial pressure. This fact is used in calculating the composition of air dissolved in water (p. 115).

Again, when a gas is collected over water (as is often the

case, see next section), after the water-levels have been adjusted to be the same inside and outside the container, the pressure of the atmosphere is balanced by that of the mixture of dry gas and water vapour:

$$\text{Atmospheric pressure (A)} = P_{\text{water vapour}} + P_{\text{gas}}$$
$$\therefore \qquad P_{\text{gas}} = A - P_{\text{water vapour}}$$

To obtain the pressure of the dry gas, it is therefore necessary to subtract from the recorded atmospheric pressure that of the water vapour with which the gas is assumed to be saturated. This "pressure of aqueous vapour" depends on the temperature, and its value may be obtained from the graph (fig. 45). (At 100° C. it is, of course, equal to 760 mm., because at the boiling-point the pressure is equal to that of the atmosphere.)

EXAMPLE: Some gas has been collected over water, and its volume after adjusting the water-levels is found to be 120 c.c., on a day when the temperature is 14° C. and the mercury barometer shows 755 mm.

From the graph (fig. 45), the pressure due to the water vapour at 14° C. is 12 mm. The pressure of the dry gas is therefore 755−12=743 mm., and the volume of the gas reduced to N.T.P. is

$$120 \times \frac{273}{287} \times \frac{743}{760} = 111\cdot6 \text{ c.c.}$$

In calculations set in examination questions, the student should only allow for water vapour pressure when the necessary data are given in the question.

Measurements of Volumes of Gases in Ordinary Apparatus

When a gas is collected in a graduated tube "over water," as shown in fig. 46, at the conclusion of the experiment the water-level in the tube will still be higher than in the basin. Now this means that the pressure of the gas is less than that of the atmosphere, otherwise the level would be depressed to that of the outside, which is obviously open to the effect of the atmosphere. The simplest method of finding the volume which this quantity of gas would occupy at atmospheric pressure is to place the thumb under the open end of the tube, transfer it to a tall cylinder of water, release the thumb, and depress the tube until the water-levels outside and inside are the same (see fig. 47). (Allowance must be made—as above—for the pressure of water vapour.)

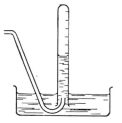 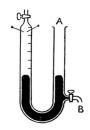

FIG. 46.   FIG. 47.   FIG. 48.
Collecting gases over water.   Measuring gases collected over mercury.

It is also often necessary to measure volumes of gases contained in apparatus of the type shown in fig. 48. Mercury is the liquid usually enclosing the gas, and the quantity of mercury can be adjusted by pouring more mercury into the open limb of the tube (A), or by running some out of the tap (B) until the levels in the two limbs are the same. The pressure on each is then atmospheric, and its value can be measured by the reading of the laboratory barometer.

The volume thus measured is then reduced to N.T.P. in the usual way.

Suggestions for Practical Work
Expts. 56–58.

QUESTIONS ON CHAPTER IX

1. The volume of a given mass of gas at 15° C. and 740 mm. pressure is 175 c.c. Calculate what its volume would be at N.T.P. (0° C. and 760 mm.)

2. Four cubic feet of oxygen are contained in a "hospital size" cylinder, the pressure being 120 atmospheres. What volume will the gas occupy at atmospheric pressure, assuming that the temperature remains constant?

3. A mass of air at 15° C. and at a pressure of 63 cm. of mercury occupies 25 c.c. On raising the pressure to 80 cm. the volume occupied is found to be 21 c.c. What is now the temperature of the air? (L.)

4. Two equal flasks are connected by a narrow tube with a tap which is closed. The pressure of the air in one flask is double that in the other. After opening the tap the common pressure is 80 cm. of mercury. What are the original pressures? (N.)

5. 144 c.c. of gas are collected over water at 17° C. and 770 mm. Find the volume of this gas dry at N.T.P.
(Pressure of aqueous vapour at 17° C. = 14·4 mm.)

6. State (*a*) Boyle's Law, (*b*) Charles's Law. Give a full account of an experiment to verify *one* of these laws. (L. Gen. Sc.)

CHAPTER X

EQUIVALENTS

After the nature of burning had been successfully explained by Lavoisier as chemical combination with oxygen (p. 21), a great deal of accurate quantitative experimental work was done on the combining weights ("equivalents") of elements; this led to the discovery of the Laws of Chemical Combination, and so to the establishment of Dalton's Atomic Theory (see Chapter XI) in the early years of the nineteenth century.

Equivalents, i.e. Relative Combining Weights

In distinguishing between mixtures and compounds (p. 52), it has been seen that compounds always have a fixed composition. Thus ferrous sulphide contains its two elements in the proportion of 7 gm. of iron to 4 gm. of sulphur. Similar results are found for other compounds, e.g., 3 gm. of magnesium are united to 2 gm. of oxygen in magnesium oxide. In order to compare the combining weights of various substances it is necessary to have some common standard or unit. For this purpose unit weight of hydrogen, the lightest element, is often chosen, because then all other combining weights are greater than one.

Then by definition:

The equivalent of an element is the number of units of it, by weight, which will combine with or replace one of the same units of hydrogen: e.g. the equivalent of oxygen is 8, because 8 gm. of oxygen combine with 1 gm. of hydrogen (p. 85).

A list of equivalents gives the weights of different elements which have the same exchange or combining weight as unit weight of hydrogen; in the same way, we could compile a list of goods showing the different quantities of each which could be bought with the same unit amount of money.

Strictly speaking, the *equivalent* is a pure number, i.e. a ratio, not a weight. If x lb. of an element combine with 1 lb. of hydrogen, then the equivalent of the element is x, and x gm. of it combine with 1 gm. of hydrogen. *The Gram equivalent*, or *gram equivalent weight*, means the weight of an element *in grams* which combines with or displaces *1 gm.* of hydrogen, e.g. the *gram* equivalent of oxygen is *8 gm.* (The expression *equivalent weight*, usually taken to mean the same as equivalent, is best avoided.)

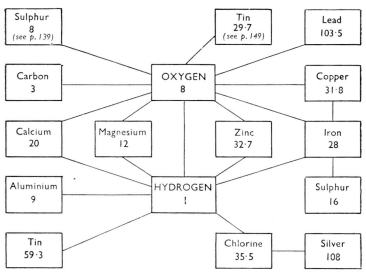

Fig. 49. The equivalents of the elements.

As an equivalent of one element will normally combine with one equivalent of another element (see "The Law of Equivalent Proportions," p. 148), it is often simpler to find an equivalent by combining the element with oxygen or some other element. The equivalent of an element is then taken as the number of units of it by weight which combine with or replace 8 units of weight of oxygen.

The Oxygen Standard for Equivalents

Accurate determinations of the composition of water show that the equivalent of oxygen is about 7·94 (p. 85). Actually, as stated above, it is often more convenient to find equivalents by combination with oxygen; therefore the standard for equivalents is nowadays taken to be oxygen $= 8 \cdot 00$, and so hydrogen $= \dfrac{8 \cdot 00}{7 \cdot 94} = 1 \cdot 008$, instead of $1 \cdot 00$ (see p. 195). In elementary work this distinction may be ignored.

The accompanying diagram (fig. 49) shows the equivalents of the more important elements as determined by the methods described in this chapter; the lines show reactions in which the one element combines with or replaces the other.

Determination of Equivalents

1. *Hydrogen displacement method.* Several metals (e.g. calcium, magnesium, aluminium, zinc, iron, tin) will displace hydrogen when acted upon by a suitable acid. Hydrogen is a very light gas, and for that reason it is difficult to collect and weigh it accurately. Its volume, however, can be measured and then corrected to N.T.P. (see p. 125); knowing that at N.T.P. a litre of hydrogen weighs $0 \cdot 09$ gm., the measured volume can then be converted into weight.

$$\underset{\text{Magnesium}}{\text{Mg}} + \underset{\substack{\text{Sulphuric} \\ \text{acid}}}{\text{H}_2\text{SO}_4} = \underset{\substack{\text{Magnesium} \\ \text{Sulphate}}}{\text{MgSO}_4} + \underset{\text{Hydrogen}}{\text{H}_2}$$

$$\underset{\text{Aluminium}}{\text{2Al}} + \underset{\substack{\text{Hydrochloric} \\ \text{acid}}}{\text{6HCl}} = \underset{\substack{\text{Aluminium} \\ \text{Chloride}}}{\text{2AlCl}_3} + \underset{\text{Hydrogen}}{\text{3H}_2}$$

Various types of apparatus are possible for measuring the volume of hydrogen evolved when a known weight of metal is dissolved in acid (or, in some cases, alkali, see p. 92); the one which is perhaps the commonest is shown in fig. 50.

Expt. 59. A small test-tube A is weighed empty, and then again when it contains some small pieces of metal (about $0 \cdot 2$ gm. of magnesium, $0 \cdot 5$ gm. of zinc or iron, etc.). This is lowered by a thread into a flask B containing a shallow layer of the acid (dilute hydrochloric or sulphuric for magnesium, and hydrochloric acid of increasing strength for the others—see p. 97).

The flask B is connected to a "gas burette" (C) of capacity about 300 c.c., and water is run out of the open limb at E until the levels in C and D are equal. The original level in C is then noted.

The flask is then shaken to bring the metal into contact with the acid.   The hydrogen which is given off pushes water from C into D. Water is run out of E to keep the levels in C and D approximately equal.   When the reaction has finished, the flask is allowed to cool to room temperature, the water-levels in C and D are exactly

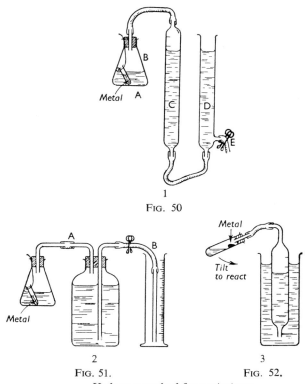

FIG. 50

FIG. 51.   FIG. 52.

Hydrogen method for equivalents.

equalized by adding or running out water from D   The difference between the original and final levels in C is the volume of hydrogen which has been evolved.

Other variations of this apparatus are shown in figs. 51 and 52, which are self-explanatory.   The student should be quite certain that he can draw a neat diagram from memory, quickly and accurately, of the particular form of apparatus which he has used for this experiment.

EXAMPLE:

Weight of test-tube . . .	= 5·24 gm.
Weight of test-tube + zinc . .	= 5·76 gm.
∴ Weight of zinc	= 0·52 gm.
Original level in C. . . .	= 5 c.c.
Final level in C	== 200 c.c.
∴ Volume of gas	= 195 c.c.
Temperature.	= 14° C.
Vapour pressure of water at 14° C. .	= 12 mm.
Atmospheric pressure . . .	= 750 mm.

(i) The pressure of dry gas = 750 − 12 = 738 mm.

∴ Volume of hydrogen at N.T.P.

$$= 195 \times \frac{273}{287} \times \frac{738}{760} = 180 \text{ c.c.}$$

(ii) Now 1000 c.c. of hydrogen at N.T.P. weigh 0·09 gm.

∴ Weight of hydrogen displaced by 0·52 gm. of zinc

$$= \frac{180 \times 0·09}{1000} = 0·0162 \text{ gm.}$$

(iii) Weight of zinc which displaces 1 gm. of hydrogen

$$= \frac{0·52}{0·0162} = 32·1 \text{ gm.}$$

∴ **Equivalent of zinc = 32·1.**

Effects of Errors

No experiment is perfect (see "Inert Gases," p. 34, and PLATE 10A) and so the answer must not pretend to imaginary accuracy by being given to a large number of decimal places, e.g. 32·098.

(1) The inaccuracy of weighing the zinc is 0·005 gm. on 0·5 gm.; this means that there is a possible error of $\frac{0·005}{0·5} \times 100 = 1\%$. The result is therefore 32·1 ± 0·3, i.e. somewhere between 31·8 and 32·4.

(2) Similarly the inaccuracy of measuring the hydrogen (2 c.c. on 200 c.c.) also gives a possible error of 1%, which may be in the same direction as the previous error.

As the true equivalent of zinc is 32·69, the above result of 32·1 ± 0·6 is just within *experimental error*.

[*Photo by courtesy of G.E.C. Ltd.*

PLATE 10A. EXPERIMENTAL ERROR PROVES USEFUL

This aircraft beacon uses neon, which was discovered by looking into the cause of an experimental error (p. 34).

Effects of Mistakes

(1) If some of the hydrogen is allowed to escape, the equivalent will be too high. Similarly, if not enough acid is used to react with all the metal, the same result will follow. This can easily be seen by working out the above example on the assumption that only half the true volume of hydrogen was obtained.

(2) Failure to correct the volume of hydrogen for temperature and pressure in the above example would give the answer 29·6, i.e. an error of as much as 8%.

2. *Direct Combination with Oxygen.* The hydrogen displacement method can only be used for the elements listed above (and sodium and potassium, and rarer elements), so that in many cases other methods, such as those based on the composition of oxides, must be used.

(*a*) *Solid oxides (from metals).* In some cases, the oxide is a solid obtainable by heating the element in the air (suitable for calcium and magnesium):

$$2Mg + O_2 = 2MgO$$

Expt. 60. A crucible and lid are carefully weighed, and then re-weighed after a small quantity of magnesium has been placed in the crucible.

The crucible is then placed on a pipeclay triangle on a tripod and heated, the lid being raised occasionally to allow air to enter. After a time the lid may be removed and the heating continued.

A certain amount of magnesium nitride will be formed in addition to the oxide. Therefore it is advisable to allow the crucible to cool, to add a few drops of water, and to re-heat so as to convert any nitride into oxide (see p. 33). The crucible and its contents are allowed to cool and weighed, and should be reheated until the final weight is constant.

The use of dilute nitric acid instead of water has the advantage of converting any unchanged magnesium to oxide.

EXAMPLE:

Weight of crucible and lid . . . = 10·35 gm.
Weight of crucible and lid+magnesium . = 10·91 gm.
Weight of crucible and lid+magnesium oxide = 11·28 gm.

$(11·28 - 10·91) = 0·37$ gm. oxygen combine
with $(10·91 - 10·35) = 0·56$ gm. magnesium.

8 gm. oxygen combine with $\dfrac{0·56 \times 8}{0·37} = 12·1$ gm. magnesium.

∴ **Equivalent of magnesium = 12·1.**

The equivalent of calcium may be found by a precisely similar method.

(*b*) *Gaseous oxides* (*from non-metals*). In cases where the oxide is a gas, this must be collected in absorption tubes containing a suitable alkaline chemical to absorb the acid gas (suitable for carbon or sulphur).

Expt. 61. For example, the equivalent of carbon may be determined by heating a few small pieces of charcoal, weighed in a porcelain boat, in a combustion tube through which a current of dry oxygen is slowly passed (fig. 53).

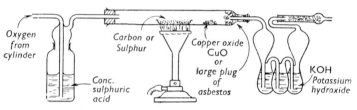

FIG. 53. Equivalent of carbon or sulphur.

The carbon dioxide is absorbed in two absorption tubes containing a strong solution of potassium hydroxide. These are weighed before and after the experiment.

(i) $C + O_2 = CO_2$; $\underset{\text{Carbon Dioxide}}{CO_2} + 2KOH = \underset{\text{Potassium Carbonate}}{K_2CO_3} + H_2O$

(ii) $S + O_2 = SO_2$; $\underset{\text{Sulphur Dioxide}}{SO_2} + 2KOH = \underset{\text{Potassium Sulphite}}{K_2SO_3} + H_2O$

Greater accuracy will be obtained if some dry copper oxide is placed in the combustion tube between the boat and the absorption tube. This will convert any carbon monoxide present into carbon dioxide.

$$\underset{\text{Copper Oxide}}{CuO} + \underset{\text{Carbon Monoxide}}{CO} = \underset{\text{Copper}}{Cu} + \underset{\text{Carbon Dioxide}}{CO_2}$$

Similarly the equivalent of sulphur may be determined, but in this case it is advisable to weigh the whole combustion tube, as some sulphur will vaporize and condense on the tube without burning. A large plug of asbestos wool to retain sulphur vapour should be inserted in place of the copper oxide.

3. *Conversion to Oxide by Nitric Acid.* This method may be used with metals such as calcium, magnesium, zinc, tin, lead, and copper.

(Aluminium does not dissolve in nitric acid; iron only in dilute acid, which requires much boiling; mercury and silver dissolve, but are of course too expensive.)

Expt. 62. A clean, dry test-tube is weighed empty, and then again after a few small pieces of clean copper (not more than 1 gm.) have been placed in it.

Concentrated nitric acid is now cautiously added, a few drops at a time (with many metals the action is rather violent). It is important to add only the *minimum* amount of acid required to convert the metal into a solution of its nitrate, because the excess of acid must be boiled off without loss of solution. Brown fumes of nitrogen dioxide, and steam, are given off.

The tube is then carefully heated, whilst held in a holder, pointing away from the experimenter or anyone else, and being moved continuously to and fro through the flame to avoid bumping and spitting. The blue solution of copper nitrate becomes deeper in colour, and eventually the solid greenish nitrate is obtained. On further heating this decomposes, giving off more brown fumes (and oxygen, which can be tested by a glowing splint) leaving the black oxide. The tube and its contents are weighed, when cool, and then reheated until no further change in weight occurs.

$$Cu + 4HNO_3 = Cu(NO_3)_2 + 2NO_2 + 2H_2O$$

Copper   Nitric acid   Copper Nitrate   Nitrogen Dioxide   Water

$$2Cu(NO_3)_2 = 2CuO + 4NO_2 + O_2$$

The equations for the other metals are similar, except that tin gives SnO_2 with hardly any nitrate as an intermediate product.

4. *Reduction of Oxide to Metal.* Suitable for copper, lead, (tin), iron.

Expt. 63. This experiment with copper oxide has twice been described already (expt. 40, p. 84, to determine the composition of water; expt. 47, p. 96, to show the reducing power of hydrogen). For the present purpose it is convenient to use coal gas from the mains instead of hydrogen, but it must be purified from ethylene and sulphur compounds and dried, by passing through potassium permanganate and concentrated sulphuric acid, contained in wash-bottles (fig. 54). The test-tube alone, the test-tube+oxide, and the test-tube+metal must all be weighed.

All air must be driven out of the apparatus by the coal gas before heat is applied, to prevent any risk of an explosion; and the metal must be allowed to cool in the gas, to prevent oxidation by the air.

$$PbO \quad + \quad H_2 \quad = \quad Pb \quad + \quad H_2O$$
Lead Oxide   Hydrogen   Lead   Hydrogen Oxide
("Litharge")

Tin oxide is reduced to the metal, but the quantitative results are not very accurate because the reaction is slow

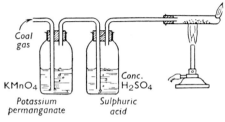

Coal gas

$KMnO_4$
Potassium permanganate

Conc. H_2SO_4
Sulphuric acid

Fig. 54   Reduction of copper oxide.

5. *Replacement of one metal by another.* Elements replace one another in relative weights which are proportional to their equivalents (see the "Law of Equivalent Proportions," p. 148). Thus the equivalent of iron will replace the equivalent of copper (a less active metal, p. 222) from a solution of copper sulphate (PLATE 10B). If the equivalent of iron is known, then that of the copper can be found (or vice versa):

$$Fe \quad + \quad CuSO_4 \quad = \quad FeSO_4 \quad + \quad Cu$$
Iron   Copper Sulphate   Iron Sulphate   Copper
("Ferrous Sulphate")

Expt. 64. A length of iron wire (about 0·4 gm.) is cleaned with emery paper, weighed, and placed in a basin containing copper sulphate solution. The iron may be rubbed occasionally to accelerate the reaction, which may only be complete after a day or two. The copper is then filtered off (a filter-paper whose weight is the same as the one used being put aside), washed thoroughly with water, and dried in the oven. The filter-papers are placed on opposite pans of the balance and the weight of the copper found.

As the equivalents of copper and iron are very close together (31·8 and 28), it is difficult to obtain a result which is far out, even though the innermost parts of the iron wire have not all reacted.

Similar experiments may be carried out using zinc, or magnesium, and copper sulphate solution or silver nitrate solution, but the replacement method is of theoretical interest rather than of practical value for finding equivalents.

[Photo by courtesy of the Rio Tinto Co. Ltd

PLATE 10B.   IRON REPLACES AN EQUIVALENT AMOUNT OF COPPER

In Spain a 0·1% solution of copper sulphate is formed by treating copper-bearing iron pyrites for two years with air and water.   8000 tons of scrap-iron are added each year to this from the overhead magnetic transporter, precipitating 5000 tons of copper which is usually worth at least 10 times as much.   The excess of iron over the theoretically equivalent amount (p. 141) is used in reacting with impurities such as free sulphuric acid.

6. *Other Methods.* (*a*) Nearly all elements, including hydrogen, *combine directly with chlorine*, so that these reactions can also be used for determining equivalents.

(*b*) Similarly many metals, such as iron and copper, *combine directly with sulphur* (see pp. 51, 151).

(*c*) A method in which a metal is treated with dilute acid and the amount of unchanged acid is estimated by reacting with an alkali (*titration*) is described in expt. 180 (p. 505).

(*d*) Methods depending on *Faraday's Laws of Electrolysis* (see pp. 212, 225).

(*e*) The most important equivalent of all, that of oxygen, was obtained (p. 85) by direct *combination with hydrogen*, but very few other elements will undergo this.

Suggestions for Practical Work

Expts. 59, 60, 62–64. In all quantitative experiments, the results obtained by the whole class should be discussed, to see which ones are within experimental error (p. 136) and which ones must be explained away by mistakes or accidents.

QUESTIONS ON CHAPTER X

(N.B.—1000 c.c. of hydrogen at N.T.P. weigh 0·09 gm.)

1. Explain, by means of a labelled diagram, the apparatus you would use to find the volume of hydrogen given off when a known small weight of a suitable metal is dissolved in excess of dilute sulphuric acid. State any necessary precautions.

If you found that 1 gm. of the metal liberated 935 c.c. of hydrogen, measured at 13° C. and 760 mm., calculate the weight of that metal which would liberate 1 gm. of hydrogen.

(1 c.c. of hydrogen at S.T.P. weighs 0·00009 gm. You may leave your answer as a compound fraction if you please.) (O.)

2. 0·385 gm. of iron liberated from hydrochloric acid 169 c.c. of hydrogen measured over water at 20° C. and 755 mm. The vapour pressure of water at 20° C. is 18 mm.

Calculate the equivalent of iron.

3. A metal has an equivalent of 12; calculate the weight of this metal required to liberate from an acid 525 c.c. of hydrogen at 15° C. and 760 mm. pressure.

4. Ordinary zinc dust is a mixture of zinc and zinc oxide. One gm. of such a mixture gave 180 c.c. of hydrogen at 0° C. and 760 mm. when dissolved in dilute sulphuric acid. What was the percentage of free metal present in the zinc dust? (C.)

5. Calculate the equivalent of lead from the following data: 488 c.c. of dry hydrogen, measured at 13° C. and 730 mm. pressure, were required to set free 2·07 gm. of lead from one of the oxides of lead. (D.)

6. Describe, with a labelled diagram, how the composition of water by weight can be found.

Water contains $88 \cdot 8\%$ of oxygen by weight. What is the equivalent weight of oxygen? ($H = 1$.) (O. Gen. Sc.)

7. Hydrogen was passed over heated cupric oxide and the latter was converted into metal. When $5 \cdot 2$ gm. of the oxide were completely changed $1 \cdot 2$ gm. of water were obtained. What is the equivalent of the metal? How would you confirm your result using the metal obtained? (O. and C.)

8. A metallic oxide contains 36% of oxygen: what is the equivalent weight of the metal? (N.,

9. $2 \cdot 11$ gm. of a metal oxide were found to give 150 c.c. of oxygen at $27°$ C. and 750 mm. pressure. Calculate the equivalent of the metal from these data. (32 gm. of oxygen at N.T.P. occupy $22 \cdot 4$ litres.) (L.)

10. A specimen of copper has been partially oxidized. $3 \cdot 78$ gm. of this specimen when heated in hydrogen until no further loss of weight occurred weighed $3 \cdot 18$ gm. What proportion of the original specimen was metallic copper? (Equivalent of copper $= 31 \cdot 5$.)

11. Stas found that for every 100 parts by weight of silver dissolved in nitric acid and precipitated as silver chloride he obtained $132 \cdot 845$ parts of the latter. If the equivalent of silver is taken as $107 \cdot 943$, calculate that of chlorine.

12. $4 \cdot 213$ gm. of platinum chloride when heated leave $2 \cdot 438$ gm. of platinum. What is the equivalent weight of the metal? (Equivalent of chlorine $= 35 \cdot 5$.) (A.)

13. $1 \cdot 656$ gm. of lead were dissolved in nitric acid and precipitated as sulphate by the addition of dilute sulphuric acid. The weight of lead sulphate obtained was $2 \cdot 424$ gm. If the equivalent of sulphuric acid is 49, calculate that of lead.

14. $0 \cdot 31$ gm. of a certain metal when acted upon by dilute hydrochloric acid set free 287 c.c. of hydrogen measured at $0°$ C. and 760 mm. pressure. The same weight of this metal when placed in a solution of copper sulphate disappeared and $0 \cdot 82$ gm. of copper took its place. Calculate the equivalent weight of copper. (A.)

15. Three metals, A, B, and C, were separately reacted with dilute hydrochloric acid. The volumes of hydrogen (measured at $0°$ C. and 760 mm. pressure) set free by $0 \cdot 30$ gm. of each metal were respectively 277 c.c., 370 c.c., 166 c.c. Calculate the equivalents of A, B, C.

CHAPTER XI

THE LAWS OF CHEMICAL COMBINATION AND THE ATOMIC THEORY

1. The Law of Conservation of Mass

Matter is neither created nor destroyed in a chemical reaction.

This law was first stated by Lavoisier in 1774 (p. 20), and we have already seen (p. 17) how its truth can be illustrated by burning phosphorus in air in a sealed flask. It has been shown that whenever a chemical reaction occurs the total weight of the final products is equal to the total weight of the original substances. Another experiment to illustrate this is as follows:

Expt. 65. A chemical reaction is chosen which does not produce a gas or generate great heat, but which shows an obvious change such as the formation of a precipitate in a double decomposition reaction, e.g.

$$\underset{\text{Silver Nitrate}}{AgNO_3} + \underset{\text{Sodium Chloride}}{NaCl} = \underset{\text{Silver Chloride}}{AgCl \downarrow} + \underset{\text{Sodium Nitrate}}{NaNO_3}$$

The solutions are run in separately, by means of pipettes, into the two sides of a divided flask (fig. 55). The apparatus is securely corked and accurately weighed. By tilting the flask, the two clear, colourless solutions are mixed and a white precipitate is formed. When it is weighed again, no change in weight can be detected.

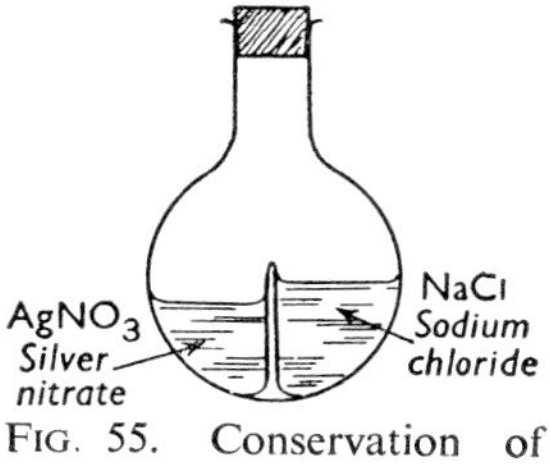

FIG. 55. Conservation of mass.

Very accurate experiments of this kind were carried out by Landolt in the U.S.A., who found the law to hold to an accuracy of 1 part in 10,000,000.

From time to time experimental results have been quoted in an attempt to prove that the law is not always strictly true but eventually discrepancies have been shown to be due to the fact that many reactions give out heat which disturbs the film of moisture on the surface of a glass vessel and also causes variations in the buoyancy due to the expansion of the vessel.

By Einstein's principle of relativity, matter can be converted into energy (and vice versa).   This happens when the nuclei of atoms are split (see p. 157), as in the atomic bomb, but the amount of energy in such a "nuclear change" is many millions of times greater than in the *chemical* changes which we consider in this book.   The alterations in mass in chemical changes are of the order of 1 part in 1,000,000,000,000, and therefore quite negligible.

2. The Law of Constant Composition (or Law of Definite Proportions)

A pure compound always contains the same elements united in the same proportions by weight, no matter how it is made.

This law was enunciated by Proust in 1799, but its truth was questioned by Berthollet, who said that it appeared that a metal, such as lead, when heated in the air could combine with continuously increasing amounts of oxygen.   It is now realized that although several different oxides of lead are known, the products obtained in Berthollet's experiments were mixtures of these, and of course mixtures may have variable compositions.

Experimental illustrations of the Law of Constant Composition

Expt. 66.   Several pure specimens of the black oxide of copper may be prepared by different methods, as follows:

Method 1.   Some copper foil is dissolved in concentrated nitric acid, and so converted into copper nitrate; this is decomposed, by further heating, into copper oxide.   (See expt. 62, p. 140.)

Method 2.   Copper nitrate solution, obtained as in method 1, is converted into copper hydroxide by the addition of sodium hydroxide solution.   The light blue hydroxide of copper, being an insoluble precipitate, is filtered off, washed, and converted into oxide by heat

$$Cu(NO_3)_2 \quad + \quad 2NaOH \quad = \quad Cu(OH)_2 \downarrow \quad + \quad 2NaNO_3$$
Copper Nitrate   Sodium Hydroxide   Copper Hydroxide   Sodium Nitrate

$$Cu(OH)_2 \quad = \quad CuO \quad + \quad H_2O \nearrow$$
Copper Hydroxide   Copper Oxide   Water

Method 3. The solution of copper nitrate gives a thick, blue-green precipitate of copper carbonate when a solution of sodium carbonate is added to it. This precipitate is filtered, washed, and dried, and on heating decomposes into copper oxide and carbon dioxide.

$$Cu(NO_3)_2 \quad + \quad Na_2CO_3 \quad = \quad CuCO_3 \downarrow \quad + \quad 2NaNO_3$$
Copper Nitrate   Sodium Carbonate   Copper Carbonate   Sodium Nitrate

$$CuCO_3 = CuO + CO_2 \nearrow$$

Analysis of these Specimens of Copper Oxide

The specimens obtained by different methods should be well washed and dried. A weighed quantity of each specimen is then analysed by heating in a current of dry hydrogen or coal gas, which converts it to the metal (expt. 63, p. 141).

In each case it is found that, in the pure black oxide of copper, 31·8 gm. of copper are combined with 8 gm. of oxygen.

The Composition of Silver Chloride

Similar but more expensive experiments on the composition of silver chloride were performed by Stas in 1865 to verify this law.

Thus silver and chlorine were combined directly; silver was dissolved in nitric acid and precipitated as silver chloride by the addition of hydrochloric acid and also by ammonium chloride. In each case a known weight of silver was taken and the silver chloride obtained was washed and dried and weighed.

$$AgNO_3 \quad + \quad HCl \quad = \quad AgCl \downarrow \quad + \quad HNO_3$$
Silver Nitrate   (Hydrogen Chloride)   Silver Chloride   (Hydrogen Nitrate)

The most up-to-date chemical analysis has shown that silver and chlorine combine in the proportion, by weight, of 107·880 : 35·457 (these being the accurate equivalents of the two elements on the oxygen standard) no matter how the silver chloride is made, provided that it is pure.

It must be realized that the above two laws are assumed to be true whenever any ordinary chemical calculation is made; without them, the additions and subtractions made in chemical arithmetic would be meaningless.

Also, the Law of Constant Composition of Compounds means that man-made "synthetic" compounds are equally as good as "natural" compounds prepared from plants. Thus the blue dyestuff indigo is the same substance whether it is made by a chemical manufacturer in steel vessels in Manchester or by the woad plant grown by an Ancient Briton on Salisbury Plain And vitamin C is equally effective when obtained from a tablet as from a tomato.

3. The Law of Equivalent Proportions

This law was first put forward by Richter, in about 1793, and states that:

The ratio of the weights of substances which combine with or replace each other in a chemical change is the same as, or a simple multiple of, the ratio of their equivalents.

A slight variation of the same law is known as the Law of Reciprocal Proportions, which says that:

The ratio of the weights of two substances A and B which separately react with a given weight of a substance C is the same as, or a simple multiple or fraction of, the ratio of the weights of A and B which will react with each other.

Examples will make the meaning of this law clear.

EXAMPLE (*a*): The equivalent of magnesium as determined by the hydrogen displacement method is 12; i.e. 12 gm. of magnesium replace 1 gm. of hydrogen from a dilute acid.

Further, the equivalent of oxygen on the hydrogen standard is 8: i.e. in the determination of the composition of water it is found that 8 gm. of oxygen combine with 1 gm. of hydrogen.

Finally, the two elements magnesium and oxygen (A and B) are found to combine with each other to form magnesium oxide in the ratio of 12 : 8, i.e. in the ratio of their equivalents (fig. 56).

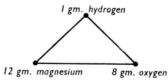

FIG. 56.   Equivalent proportions.

This clearly illustrates the above law and some students may prefer to memorize it in the form:

Elements combine with one another in the proportion of their equivalents or of a simple fraction of them.

EXAMPLE (b): 59·3 gm. of tin replace 1 gm. of hydrogen from hydrochloric acid.

8 gm. of oxygen combine with 1 gm. of hydrogen to form water.

When tin is acted upon by strong nitric acid to form tin oxide, the higher oxide of tin is obtained, and the ratio of the weights of tin and oxygen which combine together is $\dfrac{59·3}{16}$, i.e. a simple fraction ($\frac{1}{2}$) of the former ratio, $\dfrac{59·3}{8}$.

Thus the experimental results already obtained for equivalents are sufficient to illustrate this law, yet it is interesting to note that the data on which Richter originally based the law were the equivalents of compounds and not elements.

EXAMPLE (c).   (See "Titrations," Chapter XXIX.)

20 c.c. of a solution of sulphuric acid, *or*

15 c.c. of a solution of nitric acid

} neutralize 10 c.c. of a given solution of *sodium* hydroxide.

16 c.c. of the same solution of sulphuric acid, *or*

12 c.c. of the same solution of nitric acid

} neutralize 20 c.c. of a given solution of *potassium* hydroxide.

Thus $\dfrac{20}{15}=1·33=\dfrac{16}{12}$, i.e. the acids react in equivalent proportions.

The law is important in that it provides a method for finding the equivalent of one substance when that of another, with which it reacts, has already been determined (see p. 133)

4. The Law of Multiple Proportions

This was predicted by Dalton in 1804 as a consequence of his Atomic Theory (see p. 153).

We have seen that the Law of Constant Composition (or Definite Proportions) refers to the combination of A and B to form one compound, and the Law of Equivalent Proportions to the reaction of A and B with each other and with C; the Law of Multiple Proportions deals with cases in which A and B form more than one compound with each other.

This law may be stated as follows:

When two elements A and B combine in more than one proportion, then the different weights of A which separately combine with a fixed weight of B are in the ratio of small whole numbers.

E.g. in water (H_2O) 8 gm. of oxygen are combined with 1 gm. of hydrogen;

    in hydrogen peroxide (H_2O_2) 16 gm. of oxygen are combined with 1 gm. of hydrogen;

∴   the weights of oxygen, 8 and 16 gm., which combine with a fixed weight of hydrogen. are in the ratio of small whole numbers ($\frac{1}{2}$).

Experimental illustrations

Expt. 67A. The two Oxides of Copper.

Specimens of the black and the red oxide of copper are obtained as pure and dry as possible and weighed amounts are contained in weighed test-tubes. These are then separately reduced to copper by heating in hydrogen or coal gas, as described on p. 140 (expt. 63).

A final weighing will give the weights of copper obtained from known weights of the oxides

It will be found that in the black oxide 8 gm. of oxygen combine with 31·8 gm. of copper; and in the red oxide, 8 gm. of oxygen combine with 63·6 gm. of copper.

Thus the weights of copper which combine with 8 gm. of oxygen are as 31·8:63·6 or, as 1:2; in other words, the equivalent of copper in the black oxide is 31·8 and in the red oxide it is 63·6.

The Law of Multiple Proportions may therefore be remembered (but should not be stated for examinations!) in the form:

"If an element has two or more equivalents, they are in the ratio of small whole numbers."

$$CuO \quad +H_2=Cu+H_2O$$
Cupric Oxide (black)

$$Cu_2O \quad +H_2=2Cu+H_2O$$
Cuprous Oxide (red)

A similar experiment may be carried out with the three oxides of lead (litharge, red lead, and lead dioxide), but in this case the oxygen represents only a small proportion of the weight of each oxide. The losses in weight are small and therefore difficult to measure accurately.

Expt. 67B. The two Sulphides of Copper.

(1) A crucible is weighed empty and then again after adding a small amount of copper turnings. Some powdered sulphur is added and the crucible and contents carefully heated, and finally any sulphur not required for combination with the copper is boiled off. After being allowed to cool, the crucible and contents are again weighed. Some more sulphur may be added, and the heating repeated until the final weight is constant. The compound so obtained is cuprous sulphide, and the relative weights of copper and sulphur in it are thus determined:

$$2Cu + S = Cu_2S$$

(2) Another sulphide of copper, cupric sulphide, is obtained by passing hydrogen sulphide into a solution of any copper salt. This may be filtered off, washed, and carefully dried in a steam-oven:

$$CuSO_4 \quad + \quad H_2S \quad = \quad CuS \downarrow \quad + \quad H_2SO_4$$
Copper Sulphate Hydrogen Sulphide Cupric Sulphide   Sulphuric acid

A second crucible is weighed alone and after adding some of the prepared cupric sulphide. On heating, the cupric sulphide decomposes, giving off sulphur and leaving cuprous sulphide, which can be weighed. The composition of this is already known, and the calculations below will show how the Law of Multiple Proportions is illustrated by this experiment:

$$2CuS \quad = \quad Cu_2S \quad + \quad S \nearrow$$
Cupric Sulphide Cuprous Sulphide Sulphur

(a) *Cuprous Sulphide*

(1) Wt. of crucible . . . . =	10·22 gm.
(2) Wt. of crucible+copper . . =	11·06 gm.
(3) Wt. of crucible+cuprous sulphide =	11·27 gm.
(2)−(1) Wt. of copper . . . =	0·84 gm.
(3)−(2) Wt. of sulphur . . . =	0·21 gm.

i.e. $\frac{4}{5}$ of the weight of cuprous sulphide is copper, and $\frac{1}{5}$ of the weight is sulphur.

Wt. of copper which combines with 1 gm. of sulphur

$$= \frac{0·84}{0·21} = 4 \text{ gm.}$$

(b) *Cupric Sulphide*

(1) Wt. of crucible . . . . = 9·14 gm.
(2) Wt. of crucible+cupric sulphide . = 11·04 gm.
(3) Wt. of crucible+cupr*ous* sulphide . = 10·72 gm.
(3)—(1) Wt. of cupr*ous* sulphide . = 1·58 gm.
From expt. (a), above, $\frac{4}{5}$ of this is copper = 1·26 gm.
$\frac{1}{5}$ is sulphur . = 0·32 gm.
(2)—(3) Wt. of additional sulphur in
cupric sulphide . . . . = 0·32 gm.

1·26 gm. copper are combined with 0·64 gm. sulphur.
Wt. of copper which combined with 1 gm. of sulphur

$$=\frac{1·26}{0·64}=2 \text{ gm. (approx.)}$$

Thus in the two sulphides of copper, the weights of copper which combine with a given weight (1 gm.) of sulphur are in the ratio of $\frac{4}{2}$, i.e. $\frac{2}{1}$, which are small whole numbers.

As in the case of the Law of Equivalent Proportions, so with the Law of Multiple Proportions, it should be realized that such relationships do not only apply to the combinations of elements.

Thus to check the Law of Multiple Proportions, in 1808 Wollaston measured the volume of carbon dioxide evolved when a known weight of sodium bicarbonate was (a) heated and (b) acted upon by dilute acid.

After reducing the two volumes to similar conditions of temperature and pressure, he found that the volumes of gas obtained from equal weights of bicarbonate were as 1:2.

The following equations illustrate this result:

(a) $\underset{\text{Sodium Bicarbonate}}{2NaHCO_3} = \underset{\text{Sodium Carbonate}}{Na_2CO_3} + H_2O + \underset{\text{Carbon Dioxide}}{CO_2}\nearrow$

(b) $2NaHCO_3 + \underset{\text{Sulphuric Acid}}{H_2SO_4} = \underset{\text{Sodium Sulphate}}{Na_2SO_4} + 2H_2O + 2CO_2\nearrow$

THE ATOMIC THEORY

We have already seen (p. 51) how all compounds and mixtures are made up of elements, but the problem remains "What are elements made of?" The above laws of chemical combination provided the evidence necessary to solve this problem.

If a lump of an element is divided up into halves, and then into quarters, eighths, sixteenths, and so on, one might imagine it to be possible to go on subdividing it for ever, supposing that matter was like a jelly; this was the view of the Greek thinker Aristotle (350 B.C.), who regarded matter as continuous.

Alternatively, one might imagine that at last a stage would be reached when there was a minute piece of matter remaining which could not be divided up any further; this was the view of Demokritos (500 B.C.) and of the Roman Lucretius (50 B.C.), who thought that matter was *dis*continuous, and consisted of small "seeds" or "atoms" separated by empty spaces. (The Greek word *atomos* means "a thing which cannot be cut.")

Many famous thinkers such as Bacon, Boyle (p. 122), and Newton held the "atomic" view, which is supported by the behaviour of gases. If matter is continuous it is difficult to explain how it is that the application of pressure will force a gas to occupy a smaller space. Even in the case of liquids, there are several examples where a contraction in total volume occurs when two liquids are mixed. Also, a large quantity of solid may be dissolved in a liquid without altering the volume appreciably.

Dalton's Atomic Theory, 1803

It was John Dalton, however, a Manchester Quaker (1766–1844), who was the first man to put forward any *quantitative* ideas which were capable of being tested by experiment. He suggested that the atoms of the elements had fixed and different weights which determined their combining proportions ("equivalents": Chapter X).

Important points in his theory are:

1. All matter is made up of a great number of extremely small particles, called "atoms."

2. Atoms cannot be created or destroyed or divided.

3. All the atoms of any one element are alike, especially in weight ; the atoms of different elements have different weights.

4. In a chemical change, small whole numbers of atoms combine with or replace one another, e.g. 1 atom A + 1 atom B, or 1 atom A + 2 atoms B, etc.

5. In a physical change, the atoms are merely rearranged without the addition or subtraction of other atoms.

Explanation of the Laws of Chemical Combination

Dalton's hypothesis (now invariably referred to as a theory, because it was proved to be true—but see p. 158) explained these laws as follows:

The Law of Conservation of Mass.   (See p. 145)

As atoms cannot be created or destroyed either in chemical or physical changes, their weights will remain constant; and

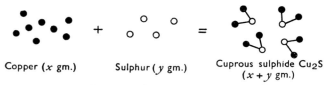

Copper (x gm.)   Sulphur (y gm.)   Cuprous sulphide Cu_2S
($x + y$ gm.)

FIG. 57.   Conservation of mass.

although the atoms may be regrouped or rearranged, the *total weight must remain unchanged* (see fig. 57).

The Law of the Constant Composition of Compounds. (See p. 146)

If one atom of sodium combines with one atom of chlorine to form one "compound atom" (known as a "molecule")

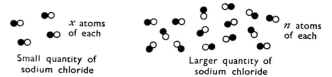

x atoms of each n atoms of each

Small quantity of sodium chloride   Larger quantity of sodium chloride

FIG. 58.   Constant composition of compounds.

of sodium chloride (common salt), then a larger quantity of sodium chloride will consist of n molecules, i.e. n atoms of sodium combined with n atoms of chlorine (fig. 58). The relative weights of sodium and chlorine present will then be as the weight of one sodium atom (all alike) to that of one chlorine atom (all alike).   This will always be true, no matter how much sodium chloride is present and no matter how it is made, provided that it is pure, as the Law states. If a molecule could exist which contained one atom of sodium combined with *two* atoms of chlorine, it would not be the same substance as the sodium chloride above.

$$\frac{\text{Wt. of sodium}}{\text{Wt. of chlorine}} = \frac{\text{Wt. of } x \text{ atoms of sodium}}{\text{Wt. of } x \text{ atoms of chlorine}}$$
$$= \frac{\text{Wt. of 1 atom of sodium}}{\text{Wt. of 1 atom of chlorine}}$$
$$= \text{constant} = \frac{\text{Wt. of } n \text{ atoms of sodium}}{\text{Wt. of } n \text{ atoms of chlorine}}$$

The Law of Equivalent Proportions.   (See p. 148)

If two elements A and C combine to form a substance whose molecules (compound atoms) each contain one atom of A and

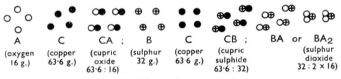

FIG. 59.   Equivalent proportions.

one atom of C, then the weights of A and C present will be in the proportion $\frac{\text{Wt. of 1 atom of A}}{\text{Wt. of 1 atom of C}}$ (fig. 59).

Similarly, when elements B and C combine, the result may be a compound whose molecules also contain one atom of each element, and the ratio of the combining weights will be

$$= \frac{\text{Wt. of 1 atom of B}}{\text{Wt. of 1 atom of C}}.$$

Now if atoms of A combine with atoms of B, they may form a compound with molecules AB (i.e. one atom of each), in which case the ratio of the combining weights will be

$$= \frac{\text{Wt. of 1 atom of A}}{\text{Wt. of 1 atom of B}},$$

which is the same as the ratio of the weights of these two elements which combine with a fixed weight (i.e. one atom) of C.

If A and B should combine in some other way (such as two atoms of A with one atom of B), then the ratio of their combining weights will be a simple multiple of that above (in this case twice), as is required by the Law (see fig. 59).

The Law of Multiple Proportions.   (See p. 149)

Finally, two elements may combine to form more than one compound, but even then their molecules (compound atoms)

Cupric sulphide
CuS

Cuprous sulphide
Cu_2S

Fig. 60.   Multiple proportions.

must be represented as AB or A_2B or AB_2 or A_3B, etc. (fig. 60). The relative weights of the elements in these cases will be

$$= \frac{\text{Wt. of 1 atom of A}}{\text{Wt. of 1 atom of B}} \quad or \quad \frac{\text{Wt. of 2 atoms of A}}{\text{Wt. of 1 atom of B}}, \text{ etc.}$$

and the weights of one element which combine with a fixed weight of the other element are in the ratio of small whole numbers (e.g. 2: 1).

$$\frac{\text{Wt. of copper}}{\text{Wt. of sulphur}} = \frac{\text{Wt. of } x \text{ atoms copper}}{\text{Wt. of } x \text{ atoms sulphur}}$$
$$= \frac{\text{Wt. of 1 atom copper}}{\text{Wt. of 1 atom sulphur}} = \frac{1}{2} \times \frac{\text{Wt. of } 2y \text{ atoms copper}}{\text{Wt. of } y \text{ atoms sulphur}}$$

Although compounds like carbon monoxide (CO) and carbon dioxide (CO_2), in which the same two elements combine in different proportions, were already known before Dalton's hypothesis, no one had put forward the Law of Multiple Proportions.   Dalton deduced the law as a logical consequence of his hypothesis, and his prediction was then tested by a large number of accurate analyses of suitable compounds.   These experiments proved the truth of the law, and hence also confirmed the truth of the atomic hypothesis, thus very clearly illustrating the Scientific Method (p. 21).

The Size of Atoms

Atoms are now known to be even smaller than imagined by Dalton. The mass of the hydrogen atom is $1 \cdot 66 \times 10^{-24}$ gm., i.e. a million million million million hydrogen atoms weigh just over a gram. One illustration of the meaning of this size is that the earth is as much bigger than a model globe (melon-sized), as a globe is bigger than an atom. Atoms are too small to be seen even with the most powerful microscope (see PLATE 13, p. 192), but the *effects* caused by a single atom can be seen.

Modern Atomic Theory

Dalton's Theory explained all the known facts for nearly a hundred years, but the remarkable advances in experimental physics in the past fifty years make some alterations necessary.

In 1896 it was found that certain "*radioactive*" atoms (uranium, etc.) were destroying themselves and creating other atoms (e.g. lead, helium, etc.). In 1897 J. J. Thomson showed that all atoms contain *electrons*, which were found to have only about $\frac{1}{2000}$th of the weight of a hydrogen atom. In the next thirty years or so it was proved that the atoms of all elements are built up of the same three kinds of particles: electrons, protons and neutrons; an *electron* has unit negative charge, a *proton* has unit positive charge, and a *neutron* has no charge; both the proton and the neutron have a weight almost equal to that of the hydrogen atom. The protons and neutrons (possibly "stuck together" by *mesons*) form a "nucleus," which is extremely small and contains practically all the weight of the atom; the electrons rotate in orbits around this, like planets round the sun. The number of neutrons in the atom has no effect on the chemical properties, and so an element can have "*isotopes*," i.e. atoms with different numbers of neutrons and hence different atomic weights but the same chemical properties (e.g. chlorine has two isotopes, with atomic weights of 35 and 37; as these always occur in the proportion of about $3:1$, the average atomic weight is $35 \cdot 5$). Finally, it has been found possible to change small quantities of one element into another artificially (PLATE 11)—at immense cost—and even to create elements, e.g. plutonium, which do not occur in nature; some of these changes involve the conversion of small amounts of mass into tremendous quantities of energy (i.e. "atomic" or "nuclear" energy).

From all this it might be thought that Dalton's Theory had been so completely "exploded" that it was no longer worth studying, but this is not so. There has indeed been a complete revolution in ideas, as can be judged from Dalton's confident statement that "we might as well attempt to introduce a new planet into the solar system or to annihilate one already in existence, as to create or destroy a particle of hydrogen." In actual fact, the creation of a particle of hydrogen was first done by

6*

Rutherford in 1919 (from nitrogen); and the destruction of particles of hydrogen (by conversion into helium) has been going on for three thousand million years or more, ever since before the earth took shape, because this provides the atomic energy which gives the sun its heat.

But with a few small changes, Dalton's statements still hold good:

1. All matter is composed of a great number of extremely small atoms (*which are themselves made up of electrons, protons, and neutrons*).

2. Atoms cannot be created or destroyed (*in a chemical change*). (The addition of or removal of electrons from an atom gives the atom an

[*Crown copyright reserved*

PLATE 11. APPARATUS FOR CHANGING ONE ELEMENT INTO ANOTHER

The 770-ton magnet of the cyclotron being set up at the Harwell Atomic Energy Research Establishment (see p. 157).

electrical charge, and accounts for "valency"—Chapter XII, p. 181, and electrolysis—Chapter XIV).

3. The *average* weight of the atoms of any one element is constant, and different from that of any other element.

4. Statement no. 4, that *small* whole numbers of atoms combine together, still holds good (as does no. 5), so long as it is realized that in compounds like $C_{20}H_{42}$ (a constituent of vaseline) or $C_{16}H_{18}O_3N_2S$ (Penicillin X) each carbon atom is joined to only four other atoms (see p. 290), each hydrogen atom to only one other atom, etc.

So we see that Dalton's Theory still provides an excellent explanation of all but the most advanced chemistry, and is perfectly adequate for the purposes of this book, even though it has needed modification in the light of further facts. Scientists rarely need to discard theories as being "untrue," but they are always learning *more* of the truth.

Suggestions for Practical Work

Expts. 66–67B, with different pupils preparing the copper oxide of expt. 66 by different methods.

QUESTIONS ON CHAPTER XI

1. "A chemical compound always contains the same elements combined together in the same proportions." Choose any compound and give experiments which would support this statement. (L.)

2. 10 gm. of one specimen of black copper oxide when reduced by hydrogen yielded 8 gm. of copper.

2 gm. of another specimen of black copper oxide (made by an entirely different method) when reduced by hydrogen yielded 1·6 gm. of copper.

State the law which these facts illustrate and show how they illustrate it.

Draw a labelled diagram to show how the reduction named above can be carried out.

Name another compound which can be used to illustrate the law, and briefly outline *two* different ways of preparing it. (C. Gen. Sc.)

3. Various quantities of lead were dissolved in nitric acid and precipitated as lead sulphate by the addition of dilute sulphuric acid.

Show that the following figures illustrate the Law of Definite Proportions:

(i) 2·07 gm. of lead gave 3·03 gm. of lead sulphate.

(ii) 2·76 gm. of lead gave 4·04 gm. of lead sulphate.

(iii) 1·78 gm. of lead gave 2·60 gm. of lead sulphate.

4. Carbon dioxide contains 27·27% of carbon and 72·73% of oxygen. Marsh gas contains 75% of carbon and 25% of hydrogen. Water contains 11·11% of hydrogen and 88·89% of oxygen.

State the important law which is indicated by these figures, and show from them that the law is satisfied. (W.)

5. Explain how the three results given below illustrate a certain law and state the law:

(*a*) 1 gm. of magnesium when oxidized gives 1·67 gm. of the oxide;

(*b*) 0·54 gm. of magnesium liberates from an acid 505 c.c. hydrogen at N.T.P.;

(*c*) 5·36 gm. copper oxide are heated in hydrogen. When reduction is complete 4·72 gm. copper remain, while 0·72 gm. of water has been produced.

Describe in detail, emphasizing important precautions, how you would carry out either (*b*) or (*c*) of the above experiments. (S.)

6. Richter showed experimentally that 859 parts of soda and 1605 parts of potash respectively would neutralize 1000 parts of sulphuric acid. He also showed that 321 parts of potash would neutralize 281 parts of nitric acid.

How many parts of soda would be required to neutralize 843 parts of nitric acid?

7. State the Law of Multiple Proportions. How would you prove by experiment that the law is true for the oxides of copper?

The two chlorides of tin contain respectively 62·6% and 45·5% of the metal. Show that these numbers are in accordance with the Law of Multiple Proportions. (D.)

8. Three oxides of a certain element contained respectively 7·15, 9·35, 13·4% of oxygen. Calculate the equivalent of the element in each case and show how these results obey the Law of Multiple Proportions. (C.)

9. A certain salt forms two crystalline compounds with water; the composition of these compounds is:

	(*a*)	(*b*)
Anhydrous salt .	63·86	89·83
Water . . .	36·14	10·17

Show that these numbers illustrate the Law of Multiple Proportions. (O. and C.)

10. 3·6 gm. of the puce-coloured oxide of lead were heated gently in a stream of hydrogen. The substance became yellowish in colour and on cooling was found to weigh 3·359 gm. The residue was then more strongly heated in the stream of hydrogen, and metallic beads were formed which weighed 3·118 gm. Interpret these results as fully as you can. (S.)

11. Has Dalton's Atomic Theory been "exploded" by the atomic bomb?

Explain why it is still taught in schools.

CHAPTER XII

CHEMICAL SYMBOLS AND EQUATIONS

N.B.—Chemical names are explained on pp. 528–529.

CHEMICAL SYMBOLS

Early chemists used symbols instead of words to describe their substances and processes, partly as a kind of shorthand, but largely in order to keep their knowledge secret (fig. 61).

FIG. 61.   Alchemical symbols.

Then, in 1803, Dalton invented a new system of symbols to represent his atoms as round indivisible particles, and attempted to show the atomic composition of compounds by the symbols which he gave to them (fig. 62).   As the knowledge of the composition of various substances accumulated, it soon became clear that this was not a shorthand, and that a substance such as alum (whose formula has 96 atoms in it) would be a printer's nightmare.

⊙	○	⊙○	⊜	⊜○
Hydrogen	Oxygen	Water	Carbon	Carbon monoxide
⊕	①	⊙①	©	○⊜○
Sulphur	Nitrogen	Ammonia	Copper	Carbon dioxide

FIG. 62.   Dalton's atomic symbols.

Dalton's symbols were therefore soon replaced by those of Berzelius (1818), which are the ones still used to-day. In this system, an atom of an element is represented (when possible) by the first letter of its name:

161

TABLE OF COMMON ELEMENTS AND THEIR SYMBOLS

H	Hydrogen	
O	Oxygen	
N	Nitrogen	
C	Carbon	
P	Phosphorus	
S	Sulphur	
Cl	Chlorine	
K	Potassium	"Kalium" (from al*kali*)
Na	Sodium	"Natrium" (from "natron")
Ca	Calcium	
Mg	Magnesium	
Al	Aluminium	(not known until 1827)
Zn	Zinc	
Fe	Iron	"Ferrum" (compare "ferrous")
Sn	Tin	"Stannum" (compare "stannous")
Pb	Lead	"Plumbum" (compare "plumber")
Cu	Copper	"Cuprum" (French *cuivre*)
Ag	Silver	"Argentum" (French *argent*)
Hg	Mercury	"Hydr-argyrum" (quick-silver)
Au	Gold	"Aurum" (French *or*)
Pt	Platinum	

As there are far more elements (101) than there are letters of the alphabet, a second letter is often added: this may be the next letter, e.g. Calcium=Ca (Carbon=C), or some other one if this would be ambiguous, e.g. Chlorine=Cl (Chromium =Cr), Magnesium=Mg (Manganese=Mn), Silver, i.e. "Argentum"=Ag (Argon=A). See also table inside front cover.

Those metals which had been known for many hundreds or even thousands of years and which therefore had different names in every language, were referred to by their Latin names, e.g. Gold ("Aurum")=Au (see PLATE 12); Iron ("Ferrum")= Fe—compare the French *chemin-de-fer* (railway). The two alkali metals potassium and sodium, recently discovered by Davy (1807), were treated similarly; Sodium ("Natrium")= Na, being named after "natron" which is a form of sodium carbonate occurring naturally in Egypt. In this way, chemical symbols were made into a completely international language which is understood everywhere; a scientific paper written in Dutch or Russian or Chinese may be difficult to translate, but the same chemical symbols are used in it, and their meaning causes no difficulty, when once they have been learned

Symbols of Compounds

A compound is formed by the atoms of two or more elements combining together, and the product is known as a " molecule " (Dalton called it a " compound atom "). Thus when magnesium burns in oxygen equal numbers of atoms of each combine together to form molecules of magnesium oxide, which is written as MgO. A molecule of water has two atoms

[*Photo by courtesy of the British Museum and the Baghdad Museum*

PLATE 12. GOLD HELMET, FIVE THOUSAND YEARS OLD

Helmet of Meskalam-dug, found at Ur of the Chaldees.

of hydrogen united with one of oxygen (H_2O), and a molecule of carbon dioxide has one atom of carbon united with two of oxygen (CO_2). The way in which these formulae are determined is described on pp. 197–199.

For many elements, the atoms do not normally exist separately, but are joined together in pairs, e.g. oxygen (O_2)—see Chapter XIII, p. 193. Thus there are not only molecules of compounds to be considered, but also molecules of elements:

A molecule of an element or compound is the smallest part of it which can exist as a free and separate substance,
whilst

An atom of an element is the smallest part of it which can take part in a chemical change.

The very important difference between O_2 and $2O$ is represented in fig. 63:

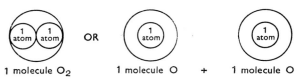

FIG. 63.   Real molecule and imaginary molecules.

Most of the other common gaseous elements are also "diatomic" (having two atoms per molecule), and are written as hydrogen H_2, nitrogen N_2, chlorine Cl_2, fluorine F_2.

The gas ozone (O_3) is triatomic; phosphorus *vapour* is P_4; sulphur *vapour* may be S_8 or S_2, depending on the temperature.

There are very few monatomic molecules; mercury *vapour* is simply Hg, and the inert gases are argon (A), helium (He), etc.

The molecules of solid elements are usually written as being monatomic, both for simplicity and for the still better reason that we do not know the "atomicity" (number of atoms per molecule) of elements in the solid state (see p. 193).

ATOMIC WEIGHTS

As the actual weight of an atom is very small indeed (about 10^{-24} gm., see p. 157), for practical purposes the weight of a hydrogen atom is taken as a unit, and the

$$\text{"Atomic Weight" of an element} = \frac{\text{Wt. of 1 atom of the element}}{\text{Wt. of 1 atom of hydrogen}}$$

Now the equivalent of an element has already been defined (p. 132) as

$$\frac{\text{Wt. of an element reacting}}{\text{Wt. of hydrogen combining with or displaced by it}}$$

At first sight, the atomic weight would seem to be the same as the equivalent, but this is only so when one atom of the element combines with one atom of hydrogen, e.g.

by experiment, 1 *gram* of hydrogen will combine with 35·5 gm. of chlorine, and therefore the equivalent of chlorine is 35·5;

now if the equation for the reaction is

1 atom hydrogen + 1 atom chlorine (atomic weight 35·5)
                              = hydrogen chloride (HCl),

then the atomic weight is the same as the equivalent, i.e. 35·5.

The chemical compound water contains 8 times as much oxygen by weight as it does hydrogen (p. 85). Supposing that the molecule of water consisted of one atom of oxygen and one atom of hydrogen, then the oxygen atom would be 8 times as heavy as the hydrogen atom. Actually we know nowadays (p. 193) that water contains two atoms of hydrogen to every one atom of oxygen (H_2O), and therefore the one oxygen atom must be 8 times as heavy as *two* hydrogen atoms, i.e. 16 times as heavy as one hydrogen atom; this means that the "atomic weight" of oxygen is 16.

Thus we see that the Atomic Weight = Equivalent × n, where n is a small whole number representing **the number of hydrogen atoms which combine with or replace one atom of the element**; this whole number is called the **Valency** (pronounced "Vāy-len see"), e.g. 1 for Cl (in HCl), 2 for O (in H_2O).

Atomic weight = Equivalent × Valency is a very important relationship and must be memorized. (The word "valency" has the same derivation as "value," from the Latin *valere* = to be strong.)

The Determination of Atomic Weights

Dalton had no means of knowing the number of atoms of the elements in even a simple compound, and therefore could not determine the atomic weight from the known equivalent. A good scientist always accepts the simplest hypothesis until it is shown to be untrue. Dalton therefore assumed (incorrectly) that the formula of water was ⊙○ (HO), and as his value for the equivalent of oxygen was 7 (not 8), he gave 7 as the atomic weight of oxygen. Similarly, he assumed the formula of ammonia (incorrectly) to be ①⊙ (NH), and so obtained a value for the atomic weight of nitrogen which was about one-third of the correct figure.

In 1818 the Swedish scientist Berzelius published a list of his symbols for elements (p. 162) with his suggestions for their atomic weights; these were often better guesses than those of Dalton. In the next year two French scientists, Dulong and Petit, found a method which did not require guesswork. They investigated the connection between these atomic weights and the results obtained by contemporary physicists for the specific heats (see below) of the elements; they were then able to formulate the following law:

Dulong and Petit's Law
For solid elements, Atomic Weight × Specific Heat = approximately 6·4.

(N.B.—The specific heat of a substance is the number of calories required to raise the temperature of 1 gm. of the substance by 1° C.; the specific heat of water is 1.)

A few examples, using modern results, are given in the following table:

TABLE ILLUSTRATING DULONG AND PETIT'S LAW

ELEMENT		ATOMIC WEIGHT	SPECIFIC HEAT	AT. WT. × SP. HT. ("ATOMIC HEAT")
Potassium	K	39·1	0·166	6·5
Magnesium	Mg	24·3	0·245	6·0
Zinc	Zn	65·4	0·093	6·1
Iron	Fe	56	0·112	6·2
Lead	Pb	207·2	0·031	6·4
Copper	Cu	63·6	0·095	6·0
Mercury	Hg	200·6	0·033	6·6
Phosphorus	P	31	0·202	6·3
Sulphur	S	32	0·188	6·0

Using this law, Dulong and Petit were able to correct some of Berzelius's atomic weights, notably silver, for which he had chosen the wrong valency.

There are, however, some important *exceptions*, notably carbon, for which the law does not hold at room temperature; carbon would appear to have an atomic weight of 36 if it were true, whereas the equivalent was known to be 3 or 6. For fifty years the atomic weight of carbon remained uncertain, and hence also the formulae of carbon compounds, until Cannizzaro's method was developed (p. 203).

Use of Dulong and Petit's Law

It must be realized that the value obtained for the atomic weight of an element from the expression $\dfrac{6\cdot4}{\text{Specific heat}}$ will only be approximate, because Dulong and Petit's Law is only roughly true.

This value will, however, be good enough to give the valency of the element, because

$$\text{Valency} = \frac{\text{Approximate Atomic Weight}}{\text{Equivalent}} \quad \text{(to the nearest whole number).}$$

The equivalent is an accurate experimental value, and hence the accurate atomic weight can then be calculated from the fact that

Accurate atomic weight = Valency × Equivalent

An example will make this method clear.

EXAMPLE: 1·68 gm. of a metallic powder gave 2·40 gm. of oxide when heated in a current of oxygen.

The specific heat of the metal was 0·11.

Calculate the atomic weight of the metal.

$2\cdot40 - 1\cdot68 = 0\cdot72$ gm. of oxygen combine with 1·68 gm. of metal

∴   8 gm. of oxygen combine with $\dfrac{1\cdot68 \times 8}{0\cdot72} = 18\cdot67$ gm.

∴   Equivalent of metal = 18·67.

By Dulong and Petit's Law, approx. atomic weight = $\dfrac{6\cdot4}{0\cdot11} = 58$.

∴   Valency = $\dfrac{\text{Approx. at. wt.}}{\text{Equivalent}} = \dfrac{58}{18\cdot67} = 3$ (nearest whole number to 3·1)

∴   *Accurate Atomic Weight* = Valency × Equivalent
$$= \quad 3 \quad \times \quad 18\cdot67 \quad = \mathbf{56\cdot01}$$

(the element being iron).

VALENCIES OF ELEMENTS

Once the atomic weight of an element is known, its valency (p. 165) can be calculated, and hence the formulae of its compounds. Thus:

The atomic weight of sulphur is 32 (by Dulong and Petit's Law)

16 gm. of sulphur are combined with 1 gm. of hydrogen in hydrogen sulphide (by experiment)

∴ 32 gm. of sulphur are combined with 2 gm. of hydrogen

∴ 1 atom of sulphur is combined with 2 atoms of hydrogen.

So the valency of sulphur is 2 in the compound hydrogen sulphide; and the formula of the latter is H_2S.

The elements hydrogen, oxygen, nitrogen, carbon have respectively valencies of 1, 2, 3, 4; the following are therefore the formulae of their compounds with hydrogen:

H—H hydrogen (H_2);

$$\begin{matrix} H \\ \diagdown \\ \end{matrix} O \text{ water } (H_2O);$$

$$\begin{matrix} H \\ | \\ H—N—H \end{matrix} \text{ ammonia } (NH_3);$$

$$\begin{matrix} H \\ | \\ H—C—H \\ | \\ H \end{matrix} \text{ methane } (CH_4)$$

Similarly, hydrogen chloride has the formula HCl, in which the chlorine is "monovalent," i.e. it has a valency of 1. As the valency of sodium is also 1, sodium chloride has the formula NaCl. Calcium, valency 2, forms $CaCl_2$, calcium chloride.

Elements with Variable Valency

Elements which have two or more different equivalents (see Law of Multiple Proportions, p. 149) must have correspondingly different valencies.

In black copper oxide, CuO, the copper atom is in the place of the two hydrogen atoms of H_2O, and therefore has a valency of 2 (atomic weight $63 \cdot 6 = 2 \times$ equivalent $31 \cdot 8$); but in red copper oxide, Cu_2O, each copper atom is in the place of *one* hydrogen atom and has therefore a valency of 1 (atomic weight $63 \cdot 6 = 1 \times$ equivalent $63 \cdot 6$).

In the same way, phosphorus shows valencies of 3 and 5 in the *tri*chloride PCl_3 and the *penta*chloride PCl_5.

Iron shows valencies of 2 and 3 in *ferrous* chloride $FeCl_2$ and *ferric* chloride $FeCl_3$.

Valencies of Radicals

Certain groups of atoms, known as *radicals*, normally occur together, and have their valencies, just as do single atoms.   For example:

—NO_3 nitrate, valency 1, from nitric acid HNO_3,

$>SO_4$ sulphate, valency 2, from sulphuric acid H_2SO_4,

$>CO_3$ carbonate, valency 2, from carbonic acid H_2CO_3,

—OH hydroxide, valency 1 (from water H—OH),

NH_4— ammon*ium*, valency 1, from ammonium hydroxide NH_4OH.

Sodium (valency 1) therefore forms sodium nitrate, $NaNO_3$; sodium sulphate, Na_2SO_4; sodium carbonate, Na_2CO_3; sodium hydroxide, $NaOH$.

When more than one radical of the same type occurs in the formula, it is usual to write them in brackets, e.g. $(NH_4)_2SO_4$ for ammonium sulphate rather than $N_2H_8SO_4$; similarly, calcium nitrate is written as $Ca(NO_3)_2$ rather than CaN_2O_6, in order to show its similarity with ammonium nitrate, NH_4NO_3, and aluminium nitrate, $Al(NO_3)_3$, etc.

A solution of ammonia (NH_3) in water is called ammonium hydroxide because it has the properties both of ammonium salts and of metallic hydroxides (see p. 66), and is therefore given the formula NH_4OH which shows this, rather than NH_5O which tells us nothing.

The metallic part of a compound (or hydrogen or the ammonium radical) is normally placed first, e.g. NH_4Cl, ammonium chloride, rather than $ClNH_4$; although O_3CCa would represent calcium carbonate $CaCO_3$, it is not conventionally correct and is therefore more difficult to recognize.

Many crystalline salts are compounds of the anhydrous salt with water of crystallization, and their formulae are written to indicate this fact—for example magnesium sulphate crystals are $MgSO_4.7H_2O$ the dot (.) meaning "combined with" (see also "double salts," e.g. p. 174, example *b*).

A table showing the valencies of the common elements and radicals is given opposite. The time spent on learning this table by heart now will save endless trouble and difficulty later on.

Formulae of Compounds

Elements combine with or replace one another in such a way that their valencies (combining powers) are satisfied, as will have been clear from earlier examples, e.g.:

In hydrogen chloride the hydrogen and chlorine are each monovalent, giving the formula HCl. Now when an atom such as sodium, which is also monovalent, replaces the hydrogen from hydrogen chloride, one atom of sodium will take the place of one atom of hydrogen, forming sodium chloride (NaCl):

$$\begin{matrix} H\!-\!Cl \\ + \\ H\!-\!Cl \end{matrix} \quad \begin{matrix} Na \\ \\ Na \end{matrix} = \begin{matrix} Na\!-\!Cl \\ \\ Na\!-\!Cl \end{matrix} + \begin{matrix} H \\ | \\ H \end{matrix}$$

(i.e. $2HCl + 2Na = 2NaCl + H_2$).

Similarly, the metal zinc has an atomic weight 65, which is twice its equivalent, and so is di-valent. Therefore an atom of zinc will take the place of two hydrogen atoms

$$\begin{matrix} H\!-\!Cl \\ + \\ H\!-\!Cl \end{matrix} \quad Zn = Zn\!\!\begin{matrix} {\diagup}Cl \\ {\diagdown}Cl \end{matrix} + \begin{matrix} H \\ | \\ H \end{matrix}$$

Zinc Chloride ($ZnCl_2$)

and aluminium (trivalent) will form aluminium chloride

$Al\!\!\begin{matrix} {\diagup}Cl \\ {-}Cl \\ {\diagdown}Cl \end{matrix}$ (i.e. $6HCl + 2Al = 2AlCl_3 + 3H_2$).

TABLE OF VALENCIES

VALENCY	1 (Mono-) (Uni-)	2 (Di-) (Bi-)	3 (Tri-) (Ter-)	4 (Tetra-) (Quadri-)	5 (Penta-) (Quinque-)	6 (Hexa-) (Sexa-)
Non-Metals	H (HCl) Cl (HBr) Br (HI) I (HF) F	O (H₂O) C (CO) S (H₂S)	N (NH₃) P (PH₃)	C (CO₂) S (SO₂) Si (SiO₂)	N (N₂O₅) P (P₂O₅)	S (SO₃)
Metals	Na (NaCl) K NH₄ Ag Cu (-ous) Hg (-ous)	Ca (CaCl₂) Ba Mg Zn Fe (-ous) Sn (-ous) Pb (-ous) Cu (-ic) Hg (-ic)	Al (AlCl₃) Fe (-ic)	Sn (-ic) Pb (-ic)		
Acid Radicals	OH (NaOH) HCO₃ (NaHCO₃) HSO₄ (NaHSO₄) NO₃ (-ate) NO₂ (-ite) ClO₃ (-ate)	CO₃ (-ate) SO₄ (-ate) SO₃ (-ite)	PO₄ (-ate)			

The following points will help in remembering these valencies:

(a) The most important valency of an element is shown in heavy type.
(b) The valencies of the non-metals are obvious from the formulae of their important compounds, e.g. HCl, H_2S, NH_3, CH_4, P_2O_5.
(c) The metals with valency 1 are sodium (and potassium and "ammonium") and silver.
(d) The metals with valency 3 are aluminium and iron (ferric).
(e) All other common metals have 2 as their most important valency.
(f) The formulae of the acids (HCl, HNO_3; H_2CO_3, H_2SO_3, H_2SO_4; H_3PO_4) and also of water (H_2O. i.e. $H—OH$) should be remembered. as these will show the valencies of the corresponding radicals

Sodium and sulphuric acid give two salts, i.e.

$\genfrac{}{}{0pt}{}{Na}{H}{>}SO_4$ (NaHSO$_4$, sodium bisulphate, sodium hydrogen sulphate), and

$\genfrac{}{}{0pt}{}{Na}{Na}{>}SO_4$ (Na$_2$SO$_4$, sodium sulphate), the sulphuric acid being "dibasic" (p. 72).

With a divalent metal and a dibasic acid, the following salts are obtained:

Ca=CO$_3$ calcium carbonate; $Ca\genfrac{}{}{0pt}{}{>CO_3}{>CO_3}$ calcium bicarbonate $Ca(HCO_3)_2$

Ca=SO$_4$ calcium sulphate   (the bisulphate does not exist).

Aluminium sulphate is Al$_2$(SO$_4$)$_3$, i.e.

$Al\genfrac{}{}{0pt}{}{/SO_4}{\setminus SO_4}$
$Al\genfrac{}{}{0pt}{}{<SO_4}{\setminus SO_4}$ and calcium phosphate is $Ca\genfrac{}{}{0pt}{}{\setminus PO_4}{/}$ $Ca\genfrac{}{}{0pt}{}{}{>PO_4}$

$Ca_3(PO_4)_2$

In some compounds the valency of an element appears at first sight to be not a whole number. For example, in red lead, Pb$_3$O$_4$, the equivalent of lead is 77·6 (i.e. the number of units of it which are combined with 8 units of oxygen). The atomic weight of lead is 207, and hence its valency in this compound appears to be $\frac{207}{77·6}=2·67$, which is not a whole number. This apparent absurdity is due to red lead being a "mixed oxide" (p 392), the lead showing valencies of 2 and 4 in the same formula: its structure is probably

$$Pb\genfrac{}{}{0pt}{}{O}{O}Pb\genfrac{}{}{0pt}{}{O}{O}Pb$$

Similarly, the magnetic oxide of iron, Fe_3O_4, is probably

$$Fe\begin{matrix} \diagup O \\ \diagdown O \end{matrix}$$
$$Fe\begin{matrix} \diagup \\ \diagdown O \end{matrix}$$
$$Fe\begin{matrix} \diagup O \\ \diagdown O \end{matrix}$$

the iron showing valencies of both 2 and 3.

Modern ideas of valency and of the forces holding atoms together in a compound are given at the end of this chapter (pp. 180–183).

The Quantitative Meaning of Chemical Formulae

Strictly speaking, the symbol H stands for one single atom of hydrogen, i.e. a weight of $1 \cdot 66 \times 10^{-24}$ gm. In practice, it is taken to mean 1 unit weight, e.g. 1 gm. of hydrogen, and the symbol Cu (atomic weight $63 \cdot 6$) to mean $63 \cdot 6$ gm. of copper. In any case, if the atomic weights are known, it is possible to determine the formula from the percentages of the various elements by weight, or vice versa.

EXAMPLE (*a*). *Calculation of Formula.* A substance contains $29 \cdot 1\%$ of sodium, $40 \cdot 5\%$ of sulphur, and $30 \cdot 4\%$ of oxygen. Calculate its simplest formula, given the atomic weights: sodium $Na = 23$; sulphur $S = 32$; and oxygen $O = 16$.

	SODIUM	SULPHUR	OXYGEN
Relative weights	$29 \cdot 1$	$40 \cdot 5$	$30 \cdot 4$
Relative numbers of atoms $= \dfrac{\text{Relative weight}}{\text{Atomic weight}}$	$\dfrac{29 \cdot 1}{23} = 1 \cdot 26$	$\dfrac{40 \cdot 5}{32} = 1 \cdot 26$	$\dfrac{30 \cdot 4}{16} = 1 \cdot 9$
Divide by the smallest number	$\dfrac{1 \cdot 26}{1 \cdot 26} = 1$	$\dfrac{1 \cdot 26}{1 \cdot 26} = 1$	$\dfrac{1 \cdot 9}{1 \cdot 26} = 1 \cdot 5$
Multiply to make whole numbers	2	2	3

Therefore the simplest formula for this substance is $Na_2S_2O_3$ (photographic "hypo"). It is clear that a formula $Na_4S_4O_6$ or $Na_6S_6O_9$, etc., would agree equally well with the given composition. Unless more evidence is provided, the formula is written in its simplest form, $Na_2S_2O_3$, and this is called the *empirical formula*.

The true *molecular formula* can be derived from this only if it is possible to find the molecular weight (see pp. 200–202).

EXAMPLE (*b*). *Calculation of Composition.* Calculate the percentage of iron by weight in ferrous ammonium sulphate crystals, $FeSO_4.(NH_4)_2SO_4.6H_2O$. The atomic weights are: $H=1$, $N=14$, $O=16$, $S=32$, $Fe=56$.

This formula represents a "double salt" consisting of ferrous sulphate, ammonium sulphate and 6 molecules of water of crystallization. The complete formula weight of this is therefore:

$$\begin{array}{ccccccc} Fe & S & O_4 & (NH_4)_2 & S & O_4 & 6H_2O \\ 56+32+ & (4\times16) & +2(14+4) & +32+ & (4\times16) & +6(2+16) \\ =56+32+ & 64 & + \;\;\;36 & +32+ & 64 & + \;\;108 & =392 \end{array}$$

Hence there are 56 parts by weight of iron in 392 parts of compound:

$$\therefore \% \text{ Fe by weight} = \frac{56 \times 100}{392} = \mathbf{14 \cdot 3}\% \text{ (exactly one-seventh).}$$

EXAMPLE (*c*). *Calculation of Chemical Requirements.* In the same way, a blast-furnace manager can calculate that in order to prepare 1000 tons of iron from a mineral $Fe_2O_3.2H_2O$ (assumed to be pure), he will need

$$\frac{Fe_2O_3.2H_2O}{2Fe} \times 1000$$
$$= \frac{(2\times56)+(3\times16)+(2\times18)}{2\times56} \times 1000$$
$$= \frac{196000}{112}$$
$$= 1750 \text{ tons of mineral.}$$

CHEMICAL EQUATIONS

A chemical equation is an attempt to write in shorthand form what happens in a chemical reaction. Very many such equations have already been given in this book (e.g. pp. 59–69), but now we must look more closely at the principles underlying them.

How to Construct an Equation

1. The *formulae of the reacting substances* are written down on the left-hand side. These formulae are determined by chemical analysis, as in example (*a*) above; they can be worked out by the student from a knowledge of the valencies of the elements and radicals (p. 171).

Thus if the reaction is between black copper oxide (CuO, the valencies of copper and oxygen both being 2) and hydrogen chloride (HCl, the valencies of hydrogen and chlorine both being 1), we write:

$$CuO + HCl \rightarrow$$

2. Similarly, the *formulae of the products* of the reaction are written on the right-hand side, the nature of these products having been found by chemical analysis (see p. 480, 490).

In the example chosen (see expt. 26, p. 65) the products are copper chloride (formula $CuCl_2$ from copper, valency 2, and chlorine, valency 1), and water (H_2O).

We therefore write:

$$\rightarrow CuCl_2 + H_2O$$

3. Now the Law of Conservation of Mass must be obeyed, and hence any atom which appears on one side of the equation must also appear on the other, because atoms can be neither created nor destroyed.

An equation must therefore be *balanced*, and this is done by inserting whole numbers, usually small, in front of the appropriate molecular formulae.

In the reaction being considered, there are two atoms each of hydrogen and chlorine on the right-hand side, but only one atom of each on the left. Two molecules of hydrogen chloride (each containing one atom of hydrogen and one atom of chlorine) are thus required to react with one molecule of copper oxide. The two chlorine atoms appear in the one molecule of copper chloride on the right-hand side, and the two hydrogen atoms in the molecule of H_2O.

The equation now balances, and an "equals" sign $(=)$ is put in place of the arrow:

$$CuO + 2HCl = CuCl_2 + H_2O.$$

4. The equation should then be carefully *checked* to make sure that for every element the same numbers of atoms are present on either side:

$$Cu=O \ + \ \begin{matrix} H-Cl \\ H-Cl \end{matrix} \quad = \quad Cu\!\!\begin{matrix} Cl \\ Cl \end{matrix} \ + \ \begin{matrix} H \\ H \end{matrix}\!\!O$$

On the left-hand side there is one atom of copper, one of oxygen, two of hydrogen and two of chlorine; on the right-hand side the same atoms are again present, though combined in a different way. The equation is therefore correct.

Equations Involving Gaseous Elements

As most of the common gaseous elements occur as molecules containing two atoms (pp. 192–194), e.g. oxygen $= O_2$, equations which involve them must be written to show this fact.

Thus, in the decomposition of potassium chlorate, a 2 must be placed before the $KClO_3$ in order that the oxygen on the other side may be written as O_2:

$$\underset{\text{Potassium Chlorate}}{2KClO_3} \quad = \quad \underset{\text{Potassium Chloride}}{2KCl} \quad + \quad \underset{\text{Oxygen}}{3O_2} \quad \text{(expt. 18, p. 29).}$$

The balancing of such equations should be done in stages: e.g. aluminium (valency 3) dissolving in hydrochloric acid to give aluminium chloride + hydrogen $(Al + HCl \rightarrow AlCl_3 + H_2)$. $AlCl_3$ requires $3HCl$, which gives 3H atoms; but $3H_2$ *molecules* must be formed, and so the whole equation is doubled to give:

$$2Al + 6HCl = 2AlCl_3 + 3H_2.$$

An excellent example for the student to try to balance is the burning of the mineral "iron pyrites" in air (or oxygen) to form ferric oxide and sulphur dioxide $(FeS_2 + O_2 \rightarrow Fe_2O_3 + SO_2)$. The answer is given on p. 355.

Dangers of Writing Equations

(*a*) Balanced equations can be written for many reactions which do not in fact take place, e.g. there is nothing wrong with $Cu+H_2SO_4=CuSO_4+H_2$ *except* that it doesn't happen! Similarly, one might write $H_2SO_4+Zn=ZnSO_3+H_2O$, but nature does not "obey" statements merely because they are down in black and white.

(*b*) The products shown in the right-hand side of an equation must not react with the starting materials shown on the left, e.g. on p. 200, equation 5, it would be wrong to put

$$3Cl_2+2NH_4OH=N_2+6HCl+2H_2O$$

because the hydrogen chloride would react with the ammonium hydroxide to form ammonium chloride and water, as shown in the correct equation.

The Information given by a Chemical Equation

If the atomic weights of all the elements concerned are known, a chemical equation tells us the composition of various compounds and the quantity of one substance obtainable from a given quantity of another:

$$Mg \quad + \quad 2HCl \quad = \quad MgCl_2 \quad + \quad H_2 \nearrow$$
24 gm.   2(1+35·5) gm.   24+(2×35·5) gm.   2 gm.

A detailed example, (*c*), is given below.

If an upward-pointing arrow is inserted by the side of a formula, it indicates that the substance is volatile and goes off as a gas *under the conditions of the experiment.*

$$H_2SO_4 \quad + \quad NaNO_3 \quad = \quad NaHSO_4 \quad + \quad HNO_3 \nearrow$$
Sulphuric acid   Sodium   Sodium   Nitric acid
(hot. conc.)   Nitrate   Bisulphate

Similarly a downward-pointing arrow indicates that a substance is a solid which is insoluble under the conditions of the experiment and is therefore precipitated:

$$Fe+CuSO_4=Cu \downarrow +FeSO_4 \quad \text{(pp. 141–142).}$$

Normally, however, a plain chemical equation will *not* indicate whether the various substances are solids, liquids or gases, *nor* whether they are in solution or otherwise, *nor* whether acids are dilute or concentrated; this latter fact has a very important bearing on the nature of the products obtained (see pp. 366, 369).

Similarly, a plain chemical equation will *not* usually state whether a reaction gives out heat or whether it absorbs it, *nor* what conditions are necessary for the reaction to proceed (see Chapter XV), *nor* whether it is a quick or slow reaction.

For these reasons, a chemical equation such as $Mg+2HCl= MgCl_2+H_2$ (p. 177) is *not* by itself a good enough description of the reaction in expt. 59 (p. 134). The following shows what is necessary: "Small pieces of magnesium metal react rapidly at room temperature with a dilute solution of hydrogen chloride gas in water; hydrogen gas is given off, heat is given out, and magnesium chloride (which is a solid) remains dissolved in the water"—and the equation is *also* given.

Calculations from Equations

EXAMPLE (*d*). What weight of sodium carbonate will be obtained on heating 5 gm. of sodium bicarbonate?

The equation for this action is:

$$2NaHCO_3 \quad = \quad Na_2CO_3 \quad +CO_2+H_2O$$
$$2[23+1+12+(3\times16)] \quad [(2\times23)+12+(3\times16)]$$
$$2\times84 \qquad\qquad 106$$

It is only necessary to take notice of the formula weights of the substances mentioned in the question.

Thus:

168 gm. of $NaHCO_3$ give 106 gm. of Na_2CO_3

∴   5 gm. of $NaHCO_3$ give $\dfrac{106\times5}{168}$ gm. of Na_2CO_3

$$=3\cdot155 \text{ gm. of } Na_2CO_3.$$

N.B.—It is equally true that 5 lb. of $NaHCO_3$ would give $3\cdot155$ lb. of Na_2CO_3. In general, the formula weights of substances in an equation may be expressed in any units, provided that the same units are used throughout.

Calculation of Volumes of Gases Obtained

EXAMPLE (*e*). In the above equation two formula weights of sodium bicarbonate give one molecular weight of carbon dioxide, i.e. 168 gm. of bicarbonate give CO_2 or $12+(2\times16)=$ 44 gm. of carbon dioxide.

It is known from density measurements that 1000 c.c. of carbon dioxide at N.T.P. weigh 1·96 gm. Hence the 44 gm. of gas occupy 44/1·96 litres=22·4 litres at N.T.P.; and this in turn may be converted into the volume it would occupy at the temperature and pressure of the experiment.

We shall prove in the following chapter that the molecular weight in grams of *any* gas occupies a volume of 22·4 litres at N.T.P. Hence **whenever one gram-molecule of a gas appears in an equation we can write down 22·4 litres at N.T.P.,** and for two gram-molecules 44·8 litres at N.T.P., etc.

EXAMPLE (*f*). Calculate the volume of oxygen at 17° C. and 740 mm. pressure to be obtained from the complete decomposition of 10 gm. of potassium chlorate.

The equation is:

$$2KClO_3 = 2KCl + 3O_2$$

i.e. $2[39+35\cdot5+(3\times16)]$ gm. give $3\times22\cdot4$ litres at N.T.P.

245 gm. $KClO_3$ give 67,200 c.c. oxygen at N.T.P.

10 gm. $KClO_3$ give $\dfrac{67,200\times10\times290\times760}{245\times273\times740}$ c.c. at 17° C. and 740 mm.

$$= \textbf{2993 c.c. of oxygen.}$$

Calculations on Water of Crystallization

The composition by weight of a crystalline salt may give a result such as $CuSO_9H_{10}$ or $Na_2CO_{13}H_{20}$ as its formula. In writing these formulae the structure of the compound is better represented if the formula of the anhydrous salt is put first, followed by the number of molecules of water of crystallization combined with one molecule of anhydrous salt.

Thus copper sulphate crystals are $CuSO_4.5H_2O$, and washing soda or sodium carbonate crystals are $Na_2CO_3.10H_2O$.

EXAMPLE (*g*). Epsom salt (magnesium sulphate crystals) is found to contain 51·2% of water of crystallization (expt. 42, p. 86). Calculate n in the formula $MgSO_4.nH_2O$.

The formula weight of the crystalline salt is:

$$\text{Mg} \quad \text{S} \quad \text{O}_4 \quad n\text{H}_2\text{O}$$
$$24 \cdot 4 + 32 + (4 \times 16) + n(2 + 16) = 120 \cdot 4 + 18n$$

Now $(100 - 51 \cdot 2)$

$$= 48 \cdot 8 \text{ gm. of } MgSO_4 \text{ combine with } 51 \cdot 2 \text{ gm. } H_2O$$

$$\therefore 120 \cdot 4 \text{ gm. of } MgSO_4 \text{ combine with } 51 \cdot 2 \times \frac{120 \cdot 4}{48 \cdot 8} \text{ gm. } H_2O$$

$$= 126 \cdot 3 \text{ gm. } H_2O$$

But $120 \cdot 4$ gm. of $MgSO_4$ combine with $18n$ gm. H_2O

$$\therefore \quad 18n \quad = \quad 126 \cdot 3$$
$$\therefore \quad n \quad = \quad 7 \cdot 016, \text{ but it must be a whole number,}$$
$$\therefore \quad n \quad = \quad \textbf{7.}$$

The Accurate Determination of Atomic Weights

It has already been stated (p. 167) that accurate atomic weights may be calculated from equivalents, after approximate values have been obtained by using Dulong and Petit's Law or by other methods which will be referred to in Chapter XIII. A final accurate value for the atomic weight of an element is usually found by a very careful analysis of one of its pure compounds or by a quantitative investigation of a reaction of one of these. The atomic weights of the other elements concerned must already be accurately known, and also the formulae of all the compounds concerned. (This amounts, in fact, to finding the equivalent.)

EXAMPLE (h). $3 \cdot 064$ gm. of potassium chlorate ($KClO_3$), after strong heating to drive off all the oxygen, gave a residue of $1 \cdot 864$ gm. of potassium chloride (KCl). Given the atomic weights $O = 16 \cdot 00$, $Cl = 35 \cdot 46$ and the formulae above, find the atomic weight of potassium. Let it $= x$.

$$2KClO_3 = 2KCl + 3O_2$$
$$(x + 35 \cdot 46 + 48) \text{ gm.} \qquad\qquad (x + 35 \cdot 46) \text{ gm.}$$

$$\frac{x + 83 \cdot 46}{x + 35 \cdot 46} = \frac{3 \cdot 064}{1 \cdot 864} \quad \therefore 1 + \frac{48}{x + 35 \cdot 46} = 1 + \frac{1 \cdot 2}{1 \cdot 864}$$

$$\frac{x + 35 \cdot 46}{48} = \frac{1 \cdot 864}{1 \cdot 2} \quad \therefore x + 35 \cdot 46 = \frac{1 \cdot 864 \times 48}{1 \cdot 2} = 74 \cdot 56.$$

$$x = 74 \cdot 56 - 35 \cdot 46 = 39 \cdot 10.$$

$$\therefore \textit{Atomic weight of potassium} = \textbf{39} \cdot \textbf{10}.$$

The Modern Idea of Valency

The reason for an element having a definite combining power (valency is now known to be connected with the internal structure of its atom (see p. 157). This resembles an extremely small-scale solar system, with electrons (unit negative charges of electricity) rotating in orbits around the central nucleus (which has a positive charge, known as its *atomic number*; see the table inside front cover).

If the elements are arranged in order of increasing atomic number—which is very nearly the order of increasing atomic weight (see chart of Periodic Table, p. 49)—each succeeding element has one electron more than the element before it: e.g. H has 1, He 2, Li 3, Be 4, B 5, C 6, N 7, O 8, F 9, Ne 10, Na 11, etc.

The inert gases, helium, neon, argon, etc., which form no chemical compounds whatever, are considered to have specially stable arrangements of their electrons. Other elements usually undergo chemical reactions in order to gain or lose enough electrons to get the stable structure of an inert gas. The two main ways in which this can be done are by the use of electrovalency or covalency

Electrovalency

The sodium atom has one electron more than the inert gas neon. If it loses this in order to acquire a stable structure, it will be left with one *positive* charge (the atom was originally electrically neutral, and the electron had a negative charge), thus becoming a sodium *ion*, Na^+.

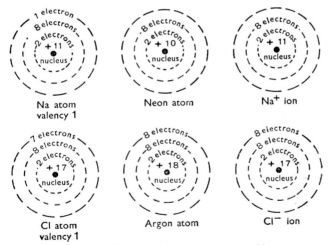

FIG. 64.   Electrovalency—sodium chloride.

The chlorine atom has one electron less than the inert gas argon. By combining with a sodium atom, it can obtain the latter's surplus electron, thus becoming a stable chlorine ion Cl^- with one negative charge (fig. 64).

The compound sodium chloride therefore consists of equal numbers of sodium ions and chlorine ions, held firmly together by the electrical attraction of their opposite charges (fig. 39, p. 112), and *not* consisting of separate molecules. Such *electrovalent* compounds (e.g. all salts) have high melting-points (NaCl, m.p. 800° C.), because much heat energy is needed to separate the ions; also, when molten or when dissolved in water, these ions will move and carry an electric current, showing the phenomenon of electrolysis (Chapter XIV, p. 211).

It will be noticed that the valency of the sodium and of the chlorine is equal to the number of electrons exchanged (1). In the case of magnesium chloride, the magnesium has two electrons more than the inert gas neon. Two chlorine atoms must accept one electron each to form $Mg^{++}Cl^-Cl^-$ ($MgCl_2$), the magnesium having a valency of 2 and chlorine of 1.

Covalency

Another way in which atoms may combine so as to obtain the stable structure of an inert gas is by sharing electrons.

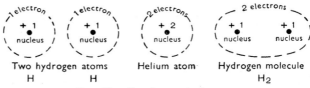

Two hydrogen atoms   Helium atom   Hydrogen molecule
H   H H_2

FIG. 65. Covalency—hydrogen.

A hydrogen atom has only one electron, whereas the inert gas helium has two. If two atoms of hydrogen combine to form a molecule H_2, each atom acquires a share in the electron which previously belonged only to the other (fig. 65), and thus obtains a structure similar to that of the helium atom.

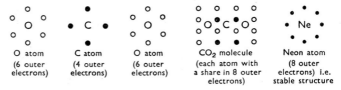

O atom   C atom   O atom CO_2 molecule   Neon atom
(6 outer   (4 outer   (6 outer   (each atom with   (8 outer
electrons)   electrons)   electrons)   a share in 8 outer   electrons) i.e.
                                          electrons)   stable structure

FIG. 66. Covalency—carbon dioxide.

This type of valency link is known as a *covalent* link and is characteristic of compounds between the non-metals, e.g. H_2O, NH_3, CO_2, CCl_4. This does not link charged particles, and so the molecules are quite separate and independent; as the forces between *molecules* are only weak, covalent compounds have low melting-points and boiling-points

(H_2, b.p. $-253°$ C.; carbon tetrachloride, CCl_4, b.p. 77° C.) Also they do not conduct electricity when liquid, nor when in solution unless they react, e.g.

$$NH_3 \quad + \quad H_2O \quad = \quad NH_4{}^+OH^-$$

Ammonia   Water   Ammonium
Hydroxide

The valency of the atom is equal to the number of new electrons in which it acquires a share, e.g. carbon 4, oxygen 2: see fig. 66 in which the outermost electrons only are shown.

Suggestions for Practical Work

(*a*) Find the specific heat of copper, and hence the atomic weight (knowing the equivalent).

(*b*) Expt. 42 (p. 86) can be used to find x in the formula $MgSO_4.xH_2O$, as shown on p. 179.

(*c*) A similar experiment on borax ($Na_2B_4O_7.10H_2O$) can be used to find the atomic weight of boron, assuming all other atomic weights (compare example (*h*), p. 180).

(*d*) Find the formula of a basic carbonate, e.g. $xPb(OH)_2.yPbCO_3$ (p. 73)—or the corresponding copper or zinc compounds—by finding the loss in weight when it is heated to form the oxide.

(*e*) Find the strength of a solution of sodium hydroxide by titration (pp. 70, 494) against hydrochloric acid whose strength is known. The equation shows what quantities react together (compare p. 177).

QUESTIONS ON CHAPTER XII

1. State Dulong and Petit's Law.

0·5 gm. of a metal produced, when heated in air, 0·62 gm. of the oxide of the metal. The specific heat of the metal is 0·09. What is the valency of the metal? Calculate the accurate atomic weight of the metal. (D.)

2. 0·1089 gm. of metal of specific heat 0·245 when dissolved in hydrochloric acid gave 109·1 c.c. of hydrogen collected over water at 15° C. and 755 mm. pressure. Find the atomic weight of the metal.

Explain the following points in connection with the above experiment:

(i) a method by which the metal and acid might be brought into contact;

(ii) a way in which the volume of hydrogen might be measured;

(iii) the reason for introducing absolute degrees of temperature into the calculation. (Navy.)

3. Distinguish between the chemical equivalent and the atomic weight of an element, illustrating your answer by reference to any suitable metallic element.

In an experiment, 0·49 gm. of a metal was dissolved in hydrochloric acid and found to displace 295 c.c. of dry hydrogen at a temperature of 22° C. and a pressure of 752 mm. of mercury. The specific heat of the metal was found to be 0·152. Calculate the atomic weight of the metal. (S.)

4. Explain the meaning of the term "valency."

An anhydrous metallic chloride was found to contain 20·2% of the metal. Calculate the equivalent of the metal.

The specific heat of the metal was 0·225. Determine the atomic weight of the metal. (C.)

5. An element has two equivalent weights, 18·67 and 28. Its specific heat is 0·12. What are (a) its exact atomic weight, (b) its two valencies, (c) the formulae of its two chlorides? (O.)

6. A metal X has an atomic weight of 60 and valencies of 2 and 3. What are its equivalents? Write the formulae of its oxides, hydroxides, chlorides, and sulphates.

7. The equivalent of oxygen is 8. What would be its atomic weight if the formula for water were (a) HO, (b) H_3O?

8. The compositions by weight of certain gaseous compounds are:

Carbon .	. 75	81·8	92·3
Hydrogen .	. 25	18·2	7·7

Deduce their simplest formulae.

9. What is the simplest or empirical formula of a substance which contains: carbon 40·67%, nitrogen 23·73%, oxygen 27·13%, and hydrogen 8·47%?

10. A hydrated salt contains 14·29% of sodium, 9·94% of sulphur, 19·87% of oxygen and 55·90% of water. Calculate the formula of the salt. (N.)

11. When the water of crystallization is driven off from 2·56 gm. of washing soda, 0·95 gm. of sodium carbonate remains. Calculate the number of molecules of water of crystallization in one molecule of the hydrated salt. (A.)

12. Crystallized zinc sulphate, $ZnSO_4.xH_2O$, is found to contain 44·3% of water of crystallization. Calculate the value of x.

13. 10 gm. of a substance when strongly heated give off 2·55 gm. of CO_2, 0·525 gm. of H_2O and leave a residue of CuO. What is the simplest formula of the substance? (O. and C.)

14. A substance containing only the elements carbon, hydrogen, and oxygen was heated with copper oxide in a stream of oxygen. The water formed was absorbed in calcium chloride tubes and the carbon dioxide in potash bulbs. 0·45 gm. of the substance gave 0·86 gm. of carbon dioxide and 0·53 gm. of water. Deduce the simplest formula for the substance.

15. A compound containing only carbon, hydrogen, and oxygen gave the following results on analysis: 0·81 gm. of substance gave 1·32 gm. of carbon dioxide and 0·45 gm. of water. Find its simplest formula. (D.)

16. What is the weight of oxygen in 100 gm. of each of the oxides HgO, MnO_2, Pb_3O_4?

17. Calculate the weight of iron required to give 10 gm. of (a) $FeSO_4.7H_2O$, (b) $FeSO_4.(NH_4)_2SO_4.6H_2O$.

18. Determine the percentage of water of crystallization in (a) $CuSO_4.5H_2O$, (b) $Na_2B_4O_7.10H_2O$.

19. How many grams of zinc sulphate crystals $ZnSO_4.7H_2O$ can be obtained theoretically from (a) 5 gm. of zinc, (b) 5 gm. of zinc oxide, (c) 5 gm. of zinc carbonate?

20. *Example.* The statement "a monovalent metal, M, burns in oxygen to form its oxide" may be represented by the equation $4M + O_2 = 2M_2O$.

Construct equations, as in this example, to represent the following reactions: (a) a monovalent metal, M, reacts with water, forming its hydroxide and liberating hydrogen; (b) a nitrate $x(NO_3)_2$ is decomposed by heat to give the oxide of the metal x, oxygen, and an ox.de of nitrogen; (c) a solution of sodium sulphate is added to a solution of the chloride of a bivalent metal, x, which forms an insoluble sulphate. (L.)

21. Complete the following chemical equations so that they obey the Law of Conservation of Mass:

(a) $C_2H_2 + O_2 \rightarrow CO_2 + H_2O$
(b) $FeS_2 + O_2 \rightarrow Fe_2O_3 + SO_2$
(c) $H_2S + SO_2 \rightarrow S + H_2O$
(d) $KClO_3 \rightarrow KCl + O_2$
(e) $K_2SO_3 \rightarrow K_2S + K_2SO_4$
(f) $NaOH + P + H_2O \rightarrow PH_3 + NaH_2PO_2$

22. Show how the Laws of Equivalent and Multiple Proportions can be interpreted in terms of atoms.

23. 6·128 gm. of potassium chlorate ($KClO_3$) when strongly heated gave 3·728 gm. of potassium chloride (KCl). Assuming the atomic weights $Cl = 35·46$ and $O = 16·00$ calculate the accurate atomic weight of potassium.

24. A metal M is trivalent and its sulphate contains 18 molecules of water of crystallization. 5 gm. of the crystalline sulphate of M yielded 0·765 gm. of the oxide.

Calculate the atomic weight of the metal. **(C.)**

CHAPTER XIII

THE CHEMICAL COMBINATION OF GASES AND THE MOLECULAR THEORY

The Relative Volumes of Gases which React Together

It has been shown in Chapter X how an experimental study of the weights of substances which combine together led to the development of the Atomic Theory (Chapter XI).

It was natural to expect that a similar investigation of the volumes of gases which combine with each other might lead to equally fruitful results. As early as 1784 Cavendish had shown that the volumes of hydrogen and oxygen which combine to form water are in the ratio of 2 to 1. Gay-Lussac in 1805 confirmed this result; and in 1806 Davy found the same ratio was true for analysis as for synthesis when he decomposed water by an electric current (see p. 84).

Gay-Lussac proceeded to investigate other gaseous reactions, and in 1808 summed up his results as follows:

Gay-Lussac's Law of Volumes

The volumes of gases which react, and the volumes of the products if gaseous, when measured under the same conditions of temperature and pressure are in the ratio of small whole numbers.

Experimental Examples of Gay-Lussac's Law. (For equations, see p. 200)

1. A. Expt. 68. The volume of CARBON DIOXIDE obtained when carbon is burned in OXYGEN is equal to the volume of OXYGEN used.

B. Expt. 69. Similarly, SULPHUR DIOXIDE contains its *own volume* of OXYGEN.

Apparatus: In reactions where it is only required to show *no change* in volume there is no need to *measure any volumes*.

In fig. 67, a small piece of carbon (or sulphur) is placed in the metal cup of a deflagrating spoon. A small length of thin iron

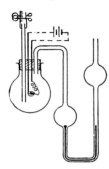

wire, wrapped round the carbon, is fired and melted by the current from accumulators. This sets fire to the carbon which burns in the oxygen with which the apparatus has previously been filled. After an initial movement due to expansion of the hot gas, the mercury returns to its original position.

2. Expt. 70. HYDROGEN SULPHIDE contains its *own volume* of HYDROGEN.

Fig. 68 shows a small length of glass tubing which contains a strip of copper or tin. The tube is drawn out at each end and a current of dry hydrogen sulphide is passed slowly through it. The ends of the tube are then sealed off by drawing out in a blowpipe flame. The tube is

FIG. 67.
Composition of
carbon dioxide.

warmed so that the metal combines with the sulphur, leaving hydrogen. On cooling to room temperature one end is broken off under

FIG. 68.   Composition of hydrogen
sulphide.

mercury. No mercury enters the tube and no gas comes out, showing that there has been no change in volume.

3. Expt. 71. *Two volumes* of HYDROGEN CHLORIDE contain *one volume* of HYDROGEN.

The eudiometer, fig. 69, with its right-hand limb graduated, contains dry hydrogen chloride (hydrochloric acid gas), whose volume at atmospheric pressure is measured after adjusting the mercury levels. Sodium amalgam (sodium metal dissolved in mercury) is allowed to drip slowly into the gas (after some mercury has been run out from the tap so as to reduce the pressure of the gas). A white deposit of sodium chloride is formed and hydrogen remains, but the reaction takes some time before it is complete. Mercury is poured into the left-hand side, and the volume of hydrogen is read at atmospheric pressure.

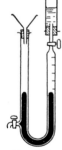

FIG. 69.
Composition
of hydrogen
chloride.

4. Expt. 72. *One volume* of HYDROGEN and *one volume* of CHLORINE give *two volumes* of HYDROGEN CHLORIDE.

The two bulbs, of equal volume, fig. 70, are filled with hydrogen and chlorine respectively. The centre tap is then opened.

After exposure for some days to a subdued light, and later to bright light, the tap

FIG. 70. Composition of hydrogen chloride.

From Siphon

Strong Ammonia

FIG. 71. Composition of ammonia gas.

at one end is opened under mercury—no change occurs.

It is then closed, and opened under water containing a little potassium iodide in solution. This fills both bulbs and the solution shows no brown colour due to iodine which would be set free if there were any free chlorine present. Hence hydrogen chloride (soluble in water) is the only product.

5. Expt. 73. In AMMONIA there are *three volumes* of HYDROGEN *to one volume* of NITROGEN.

A glass tube, fig. 71, divided into three equal volumes by rubber bands, is filled with chlorine.

A few c.c. of strong ammonia solution are allowed to drop into the tube, which is kept cool by stroking with cotton wool soaked in ether.

The hydrogen in the ammonia combines with the chlorine forming hydrogen chloride; this combines with excess of ammonia to form ammonium chloride, a solid which partly dissolves in the water of the ammonia solution.

Water, containing dilute sulphuric acid to dissolve any free ammonia, is allowed to siphon into the tube and fills two-thirds of the volume of the tube; the volume of residual gas, nitrogen, is thus seen to be one volume at atmospheric pressure.

Now we know from the previous experiment (no. 72) that every volume of chlorine combines with an equal volume of hydrogen. So the original 3 volumes of chlorine combined with 3 volumes of hydrogen (from the ammonia) leaving 1 volume of nitrogen.

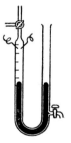

FIG. 72. Volume composition of water.

6. Expt. 74. *Two volumes* of HYDROGEN and *one volume* of OXYGEN form water. Oxygen is passed into a eudiometer, fig. 72,

7*

by means of a three-way tap, and its volume measured at atmospheric pressure. Hydrogen is then passed in and the additional volume measured, also at atmospheric pressure. The pressure is then slightly reduced, by running out 3 or 4 c.c. of mercury, to lessen the violence of the explosion. The mixture is sparked from an induction coil, a cork having been placed in the right-hand side to prevent the escape of mercury during the explosion. The residual volume of gas is measured at atmospheric pressure by adjusting the quantity of mercury in the right-hand side so that the levels in the two sides are the same (p. 130).

N.B.—The explosion may be dangerous if *all* the mixture reacts; but if equal volumes of the two gases are used, the extra oxygen will dilute the reactants, and can be tested afterwards by a glowing splint.

7. **Expt. 75.** *Two volumes* of HYDROGEN and *one volume* of OXYGEN form *two volumes* of STEAM.

Experiment 74 is repeated and, if the spark gap side of the eudiometer is jacketed so that it can be surrounded by the vapour from boiling amyl alcohol (b.p. 130° C.), the additional final volume

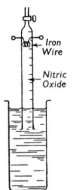

due to the fact that the water remains as steam can be measured.

8. Electrolysis (see expt. 39, p. 84) of acidified water gives *two volumes of* HYDROGEN to *one volume* of OXYGEN.

9. **Expt. 76.** NITROUS OXIDE contains *its own volume* of NITROGEN.

This can be shown by enclosing a certain volume of nitrous oxide over mercury in the apparatus (fig. 67) used to show the composition of carbon dioxide. The gas is decomposed by electrically heating a piece of iron wire in it. The oxygen combines with the iron, and the volume of nitrogen left is equal to that of the nitrous oxide originally used.

Fig. 73. Composition of nitric oxide.

10. **Expt. 77.** NITRIC OXIDE contains *half its own volume* of NITROGEN.

The simple apparatus of the previous experiment is not sufficient, because there is a change in volume; but the gas may be enclosed over water (if this is more convenient than the use of mercury) because it is almost insoluble.   The apparatus of fig. 73 is suitable, and the water-levels are adjusted after the nitric oxide is decomposed by the heated iron wire.

Explanation of Gay-Lussac's Law

When this law was discovered immediately after the publication of the Atomic Theory, an attempt was made by Dalton and Gay-Lussac to extend the latter to explain the new experimental law.   Since compounds were regarded as the result of joining simple whole numbers of atoms, and since in the case of gaseous reactions simple whole numbers of volumes are involved, Dalton and Gay-Lussac thought that these equal volumes of gases must contain equal numbers of atoms.

Applying this assumption to an example such as the combination of hydrogen and oxygen, the following result is obtained:

2 vols. of hydrogen$+1$ vol. of oxygen$\rightarrow$2 vols. of steam

$2n$ atoms of hydrogen$+n$ atoms of oxygen$\rightarrow$2n ''atoms'' of steam

$\therefore$ 2 atoms of hydrogen$+1$ atom of oxygen$\rightarrow$2 atoms of steam.

Now these two "compound atoms" of steam must be alike and must each contain some oxygen and therefore at least one atom.   Thus at least two separate atoms of oxygen must have come from the one atom of oxygen, and yet the fundamental assumption about the atom is that it is indivisible.

Hence *either* the Atomic Theory *or* Gay-Lussac's Law *or* the assumption about equal volumes containing equal numbers of atoms must be wrong.   The latter is the most suspect, and the solution of the difficulty was provided by Avogadro in 1811.

Avogadro suggested that the *molecule* of a substance is the smallest particle of a substance which is capable of an independent existence (see PLATE 13).   Now, as the ''compound atoms'' (i.e. molecules) of compounds must by their very nature contain more than one atom (e.g. H_2O, three atoms), it was not outrageous to suggest that the molecules of elements also might contain more than one atom (e.g. O_2, two atoms). (It must be remembered that although the atom of an element may not normally exist separately—see p. 164—it remains the smallest particle of an element which can take part in a chemical change.)

[*Photo by courtesy of Drs. K. Smith, Markham, and G. R. Crowe, Cambridge*

PLATE 13.   INDIVIDUAL MOLECULES OF HAEMOGLOBIN

These molecules are just large enough to be photographed using the electron microscope; their molecular formula is probably

$C_{758}H_{1203}O_{218}N_{135}S_3Fe$, with molecular weight 15,829

Magnification 70,000 diameters.

Avogadro then put forward his famous hypothesis, based on this conception of a new particle.

Avogadro's Hypothesis

Equal volumes of all gases, if measured under similar conditions of temperature and pressure, contain equal numbers of molecules.

The explanation of the combination of hydrogen and oxygen discussed above now becomes quite simple if the smallest particle of oxygen which can exist free, i.e. the molecule, is regarded as composed of two atoms of oxygen. As a result of the chemical change each of these two atoms joins up with two hydrogen atoms to form a molecule of water thus (fig. 74):

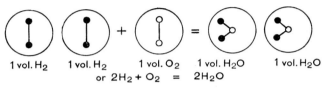

1 vol. H_2 1 vol. H_2 1 vol. O_2 1 vol. H_2O 1 vol. H_2O

or $2H_2 + O_2 = 2H_2O$

FIG. 74.   Avogadro's Hypothesis—water.

It is important to realize that Avogadro's Hypothesis only applies to gaseous substances, because the volume of a substance in its liquid or solid state is quite negligible compared with that in its gaseous state (e.g. 1 c.c. of steam condenses to 0·0006 c.c. of water). Therefore the formula of solid sulphur cannot be determined from expt. 69 (p. 187) where it was burnt in a given volume of oxygen to form an equal volume of sulphur dioxide. This is consistent with either of the following equations, whatever the value of x:

$$\underset{\text{"zero volume"}}{S} + \underset{\text{1 volume}}{O_2} = \underset{\text{1 volume}}{SO_2}$$

$$\underset{\text{"zero volume"}}{S_x} + \underset{x \text{ volumes}}{xO_2} = \underset{x \text{ volumes}}{xSO_2}$$

As the value of x cannot be found for substances in the solid state, the simplest (i.e. "empirical") formulae are usually written for them (e.g. S).

The surprising thing is that Avogadro's Hypothesis was not generally accepted for over forty years, the reason being that people, overawed by Dalton's authority, did not grasp clearly the distinction between an atom and a molecule; the application of it by Cannizzaro in 1858 to find the atomic weight of carbon (p. 204) at last convinced people of its truth.

Deductions from Avogadro's Hypothesis

1. *The Molecule of Hydrogen contains at least* TWO *atoms.* Experiment shows that, if measured under similar conditions of temperature and pressure:

    1 vol. of hydrogen+1 vol. of chlorine gives 2 vols. of hydrogen chloride

∴ by Avogadro,

    n mols. of hydrogen+*n* mols. of chlorine give 2*n* mols. of hydrogen chloride

    1 mol. of hydrogen+1 mol. of chlorine gives 2 mols. of hydrogen chloride.

Now each molecule of hydrogen chloride must contain some hydrogen, or it would not be hydrogen chloride, and hence at

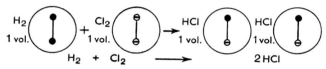

Fig. 75.   Avogadro's Hypothesis—hydrogen chloride.

least one atom of hydrogen.   The two molecules of hydrogen chloride must therefore contain at least two atoms of hydrogen, and these must be derived from the one molecule of hydrogen on the left-hand side of the equation.

The molecular formula for hydrogen is therefore written as H_2, since:

(*a*) in studying other volume reactions in which hydrogen takes part there is no reason to imagine that the molecule of hydrogen contains *more* than two atoms, and

(*b*) when the Kinetic Theory of Gases was developed, at a later date, a direct method was found for finding the number of atoms per molecule of gas (the "atomicity"), by measuring the ratio of the two specific heats of the gas (p. 203).   This also gave the result H_2.

The reaction between hydrogen and chlorine can therefore be represented thus (fig. 75):

2. *The Molecular Weight of a Gas is equal to* TWICE *its Vapour Density.*

The **vapour density** (or "relative density") of a gas is defined

as: $$\frac{\textbf{Wt. of any volume of the gas}}{\textbf{Wt. of equal volume of hydrogen at the same temperature and pressure}}$$

(N.B.—The same units must, of course, be used.)

The **molecular weight** of a gas is defined as:

$$\frac{\textbf{Wt. of 1 molecule of the gas}}{\textbf{Wt. of 1 atom of hydrogen}}$$

By Avogadro's Hypothesis:

$$\frac{\text{Wt. of any volume of gas}}{\text{Wt. of equal volume of hydrogen}}$$

$$=\frac{\text{Wt. of } n \text{ mols. of gas}}{\text{Wt. of } n \text{ mols. of hydrogen}}$$

$$=\frac{\text{Wt. of 1 mol. of gas}}{\text{Wt. of 1 mol. of hydrogen}}$$

$$=\frac{\text{Wt. of 1 mol. of gas}}{\text{Wt. of 1 atom of hydrogen}} \times \frac{\text{Wt. of 1 atom of hydrogen}}{\text{Wt. of 1 mol. of hydrogen}}$$

$$=\text{Molecular weight of gas} \times \tfrac{1}{2}$$

If the atomic weight of hydrogen is taken as 1 gm., then the molecular weight of any gas (in grams) is called its gram-molecular weight, or its G.M.W.

If $O=16$ is taken as the standard to which atomic weights refer, then the atomic weight of hydrogen is 1·008.

The molecular weight of any gas is then 2·016 times its vapour density (as defined above).

3. *The Molecular Weight, in grams, of any gas occupies* 22·4 *litres at N.T.P.* As the molecular weights (in grams) of all gases contain equal numbers of molecules—by definition—it follows from Avogadro's Hypothesis that they will all occupy the same volume at N.T.P.; this is called the gram-molecular volume (G.M.V.) Therefore, if we calculate this volume for one gas, say hydrogen, we have the value for any gas.

By density measurements (expt. 78A, below), 0·09 gm. of hydrogen occupy 1 litre at N.T.P.

∴ 2·016 gm. of hydrogen occupy $\dfrac{2 \cdot 016}{0 \cdot 09} =$ **22·4 litres at N.T.P.**

Using the hydrogen standard for atomic weights, this result would become:

$$\frac{2 \cdot 00}{0 \cdot 09} = 22 \cdot 2 \text{ litres.}$$

(If the accurate value for the density of hydrogen is used, viz. 0·0898 . . . neither of the above results is altered sufficiently to affect the first place of decimals.)

These values, 22·2 and 22·4 litres, are often used inconsistently and indiscriminately, much to the bewilderment of the student.

In solving numerical examples it is advisable to adopt the following rules:

(1) If the fact that "1000 c.c. of hydrogen weigh 0·09 gm." is given then the G.M.V. should be taken as $\dfrac{2 \times 1000}{\cdot 09} = 22 \cdot 2$ litres, for H=1 is normally used even though the other atomic weights given may be on the oxygen standard.

(2) When no precise information is given then G.M.V.=22·4 litres should be used.

The commonest gases contain only the following six elements, whose atomic weights must be remembered:

H=1,   C=12,   N=14,   O=16,   S=32,   Cl=35·5.

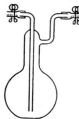

These weights can be used to work out molecular weights ("M.W.") if molecular formulae are known, e.g. HCl=1+35·5=36·5. As the *average* molecular weight of the gases in air is 28·8, this shows that hydrogen chloride is 36·5/28·8=1¼ times as heavy as air.

Determination of Molecular Weights from Density Measurements

Expt. 78A.   Finding the Molecular Weight of Sulphur Dioxide.

Fig. 76.
Density flask.

(*a*) A density flask (fig. 76) is weighed full of air. (*b*) It is then connected to a supply of dry sulphur dioxide (in a fume cupboard); the gas is passed in through the longer tube (because it is heavier than air and so fills the top last) for several minutes to remove all air; the clips are closed simultaneously so that the gas is at atmospheric pressure, and the flask and its contents are again weighed. (*c*) The room temperature and atmospheric pressure are then read. (*d*) If the volume of the flask is not already known, it is found by filling with water and then either weighing it or pouring the water into a measuring cylinder.

Volume of flask = 542 c.c.   *Room temperature* = 15° C.

Atmospheric pressure = 740 mm.

∴ volume of gas in flask reduced to N.T.P.

$$= 542 \times \frac{273}{288} \times \frac{740}{760} = \ 500 \text{ c.c.}$$

∴ Wt. of air in flask (1·29 gm. per litre at N.T.P.) =   0·645 gm.

Wt. of flask full of air .   .   .   . = 95·450 gm.

∴ Wt. of empty flask   .   .   .   . = 94·805 gm.

Wt. of flask full of sulphur dioxide .   .   . = 96·235 gm.

∴ Wt. of 500 c.c. of sulphur dioxide at N.T.P. . = 1·430 gm.

∴ Wt. of 22·4 litres of sulphur dioxide at N.T.P.

i.e. its (GRAM-)MOLECULAR WEIGHT $= \dfrac{1 \cdot 430 \times 22 \cdot 4}{0 \cdot 500} = \textbf{64·1 gm.}$

N.B.—An experimental error of 0·005 gm. in each weighing would give 1·44 gm. of sulphur dioxide, i.e. a G.M.W. of *64·5 gm.*

The best experimental result is actually *65.2 gm.*, because sulphur dioxide is too easily compressed (p. 358) and so does not obey the Gas Laws exactly.   Fairly accurate results are obtained for other gases such as carbon dioxide and hydrogen chloride.

In very accurate work, two thin, evacuated globes are balanced on opposite pans of a balance. One is then filled with the given gas at atmospheric temperature and pressure, and the difference weighed. Its volume is found by filling it with water as above.   The use of two similar globes eliminates errors due to changes in buoyancy.

A method for finding the molecular weights of volatile liquids is given at the end of the chapter (expt. 78B, p. 205).

Determination of Molecular Formulae of Gases

In general, the molecular formula of a simple gaseous compound may be deduced from the results of two experiments: (*a*) the composition of the gas by volume, and (*b*) the molecular weight.

Sulphur Dioxide

(*a*) Expt. 69 (p. 187) showed that:

1 volume of sulphur dioxide contains 1 volume of oxygen

∴ 1 molecule ,,   ,,   ,,   ,,   1 molecule ,,

∴ molecular formula is S_xO_2, and mol. wt. $=32x+2\times16$.

(*b*) Expt. 78A (p. 196) showed that the molecular weight is 64

∴ $32x+32=64$ ∴ $x=1$

∴ *Molecular formula is* SO_2.

In this particular example it should be noted that the result for one experiment, viz. that the molecular weight is 64, is sufficient to fix the formula. The molecule of the gas if it contains any sulphur at all must contain at least one atom, i.e. 32 gm. in 64 gm. If it contains two atoms (2×32) then there is no more weight left to represent oxygen. Hence the remainder is all oxygen and equivalent to 32, or 2 atomic weights of oxygen.

Such short cuts are possible in the case of several of the common gases.

Ammonia

(*a*) Expt. 73 (p. 189) showed that ammonia contains 3 volumes of hydrogen to every 1 volume of nitrogen. This means that 6 atoms of hydrogen combine with 2 atoms of nitrogen, i.e. 3 atoms with 1 atom, and so the empirical formula is NH_3 and the molecular formula is $(NH_3)_x$.

(*b*) The vapour density of the gas is found to be 8·5, and so the molecular weight (twice the vapour density, see p. 195) $=17$. As $N=14$, $H=1$, so x must be 1.

∴ *Molecular formula is* NH_3.

It can also be shown by experiment (p. 206) that 2 volumes of ammonia gas are decomposed by sparking to give 1 volume of nitrogen and 3 volumes of hydrogen. The only equation to fit these facts is $2NH_3=N_2+3H_2$, which establishes the molecular formula without even determining the vapour density.

It might be thought that as the molecular weight is found to be 17 and the gas can be made from nitrogen and hydrogen only, one could say that the molecular formula is $N_xH_y=17$, and that as $N=14$ so x cannot be greater than 1, and therefore $y=3$.

This argument, however, is dangerous, because a small experimental error in the vapour density measurement might give 8·0 or 9·0, i.e. $y=2$ or $y=4$, which are incorrect.

Nitrous Oxide and Nitric Oxide

(*a*) One volume of nitrous oxide is found (expt. 76, p. 190) to leave 1 volume of nitrogen when iron is heated in it to remove the oxygen.   Hence by Avogadro's Hypothesis:

One molecule of nitrous oxide contains 1 molecule of nitrogen$=2$ atoms of nitrogen.

The formula is therefore N_2O_x.

(*b*) But the molecular weight$=2\times$ vapour density$=2\times22$ $=44$

$\therefore N_2O_x=44$ $\therefore (2\times14)+16x=44$ $\therefore x=1.$

Similarly, it can be shown that nitric oxide is NO.

Hydrogen Sulphide

(*a*) An experiment has been previously described (no. 70, p. 188) to prove that hydrogen sulphide contains its own volume of hydrogen.

Hence the molecular formula is H_2S_x.

(*b*) Now vapour density$=17$. $\therefore$ molecular weight$=34$. $\therefore H_2S_x=34$ $\therefore x=1.$

As in the case of ammonia, one might be tempted to argue that since the molecular weight is 34, and since one atom only of sulphur is represented by 32, then there must be two atoms of hydrogen.   This argument would only be valid if the experimental value for the vapour density was reliable to within 1% (see p. 197).

Ozone

An interesting example of the use of volume relationships to establish the molecular formula of a gas is found in Soret's method for ozone (see p. 387), in which it is not even necessary to obtain pure ozone.

Writing Equations for Reactions involving Gases

The formulae of compounds have been deduced above, and those of elements follow either from a knowledge of their densities (p. 197) or from arguments similar to those used for hydrogen (p. 194).   Equations for examples 1–10 (pp. 187–191) may be written by putting the number of volumes of gas equal to the number of molecules (using Avogadro's Hypothesis).   In the equations given below, gases are shown in black type:

1. (a) $C+O_2$ $=CO_2$
   (b) $S+O_2$ $=SO_2$
2. H_2S+2Cu $=Cu_2S+H_2$
3. $2HCl+2Na$ $=2NaCl+H_2$
4. H_2+Cl_2 $=2HCl$
5. $3Cl_2+8NH_4OH=N_2+6NH_4Cl+8H_2O$
6. $2H_2+O_2$ $=2H_2O$
7. $2H_2+O_2$ $=2H_2O$
8. $2H_2O$ $=2H_2+O_2$
9. $4N_2O+3Fe$ $=Fe_3O_4+4N_2$
10. $4NO+3Fe$ $=Fe_3O_4+2N_2$

It is also possible, of course, to calculate from a known equation what volumes of gases are required to react together; this is done in the commercial synthesis of ammonia (p. 314), where the volume of hydrogen is continuously adjusted to be exactly three times that of the nitrogen ($N_2+3H_2=2NH_3$).

Molecular Formulae of Gaseous Hydrocarbons

The method may best be illustrated by a simple example:

10 c.c. of a gaseous hydrocarbon at $100°$ C. and 760 mm. gave on combustion with oxygen 20 c.c. of carbon dioxide and 20 c.c. of steam, both measured at $100°$ C. and 760 mm. Find the molecular formula of the hydrocarbon.

A hydrocarbon has the formula C_xH_y

Now 10 c.c. C_xH_y+oxygen gave 20 c.c. CO_2+20 c.c. H_2O

     1 c.c. ,,   ,,   ,, 2 c.c. ,, ,, 2 c.c. ,,
     1 mol. ,,   ,,   ,, 2 mols. ,, ,, 2 mols.
     1 mol. ,,   ,,   ,, $2CO_2$,, ,, $2H_2O$

∴   molecular formula must be C_2H_4 (ethylene).

In solving more difficult examples it is advisable to use the general equation for the combustion in oxygen of any hydrocarbon, C_xH_y. The C_x portion of this molecule will give xCO_2 and hence requires x molecules of oxygen. Similarly, the H_y portion will give $\frac{y}{2}H_2O$ and hence requires $\frac{y}{2}O$, i.e. $\frac{y}{4}O_2$.

The general equation is therefore:

$$C_xH_y+\left(x+\frac{y}{4}\right)O_2=xCO_2+\frac{y}{2}H_2O$$

Applying Avogadro's Hypothesis to this:

1 vol. C_xH_y requires $\left(x+\frac{y}{4}\right)$ vols. O_2, giving x vols. CO_2

and $\frac{y}{2}$ vols. H_2O (if steam) or negligible vol. (if water).

The contraction shown by this equation is volume of left-hand side minus volume of right-hand side,

or $\left(1+x+\frac{y}{4}\right)-\left(x+\frac{y}{2}\right)=\left(1-\frac{y}{4}\right)$ if water remains as steam,

or $\left(1+x+\frac{y}{4}\right)-\quad x\quad=\left(1+\frac{y}{4}\right)$ if steam condenses.

The student should clearly understand that it is unwise to try to solve problems of this type by assuming, as is often done, that the volume contraction shown by the equation when H_2O is water is equal to the volume of condensed steam.

This will only be true if the reaction is such that

contraction $1+\frac{y}{4}=\frac{y}{2}$ (vol. of steam which condenses),

i.e. when $y=4$

For example it is true for methane, CH_4, and for ethylene, C_2H_4, but not for ethane, C_2H_6, nor for acetylene, C_2H_2.

EXAMPLE. 15 c.c. of a gaseous hydrocarbon required 75 c.c. of oxygen for complete combustion and gave 45 c.c. of carbon dioxide. Calculate the molecular formula of the hydrocarbon.

15 c.c. C_xH_y required 75 c.c. O_2 and gave 45 c.c. CO_2
1 c.c. ,, required 5 c.c. ,, gave 3 c.c. ,,

Hence vol. of CO_2 from 1 vol. $C_xH_y=3$ vols. $=x$ (in above equation).

Similarly, vol. of O_2 required $=5$ vols. $=x+\frac{y}{4}$ (in above equation).

$$5=3+\frac{y}{4},\quad y=8$$

∴ Molecular formula is C_3H_8 (propane).

Molecular Formulae of other Volatile Compounds

In the case of more complicated compounds, such as occur in organic chemistry (Chapter XVIII), the general method is to:

(*a*) Determine the composition by weight and deduce the simplest or empirical formula as on p. 173. Results such as C_2H_6O for alcohol, CH for benzene, are obtained giving molecular formulae $(C_2H_6O)_x$ and $(CH)_y$ respectively.

(*b*) Measure the vapour density and hence calculate the molecular weight. This gives $x=1$ and $y=6$ in the above examples.

Simple methods for measuring vapour densities of such volatile liquids will be found in small print at the end of this chapter.

Molecular Weights and Diffusion

The diffusion of hydrogen, the diffusion of gases in general, and Graham's Law of Diffusion have been discussed in Chapter VII.

Since the molecular weight of a gas is equal to twice its vapour density, it follows from Graham's Law that the rates at which gases diffuse are inversely proportional to the square roots of their molecular weights. Hence if the rates of diffusion of two gases are compared and the molecular weight of one of them is known, then that of the other can be calculated.

EXAMPLE. A fixed volume of a certain gas requires 120 seconds to pass through a porous plug. An equal volume of oxygen, under the same conditions, requires 85 seconds. What is the molecular weight of the gas?

$$\frac{\sqrt{\text{Mol. wt. of gas}}}{\sqrt{\text{Mol. wt. of oxygen}}}$$

$$=\frac{\text{Vol. of oxygen diffusing in given time}}{\text{Vol. of gas diffusing in same time}}$$

$$=\frac{\text{Time taken for given volume of gas to diffuse}}{\text{Time taken for equal volume of oxygen to diffuse}}$$

$$=\frac{120}{85} \qquad \therefore \text{mol. wt. of gas}=\left(\frac{120}{85}\right)^2 \times 32 = \mathbf{63 \cdot 8} \ (SO_2)$$

Atomic Weights from Molecular Weights

(a) *Gaseous Elements.* The molecular weight of a gaseous element can be readily determined by measuring its vapour density and then multiplying by two.

In order to obtain the atomic weight of such an element it only remains to determine the "atomicity" (number of atoms in a molecule) of the element. Evidence for this is often obtained from a study of the volume relationships of the gas (see p. 194). Further evidence is often obtained from a knowledge of the ratio of the two specific heats of the gas. Various physical methods are available for finding this ratio, such as the determination of the velocity of sound in the gas, which is easier than actually observing both specific heats separately.

It is found experimentally in the case of gases whose atomicity is known, and it can also be deduced theoretically, that:

$$\frac{\text{Specific Heat at constant pressure}}{\text{Specific Heat at constant volume}}$$

$$= \frac{5}{3} = 1 \cdot 67 \text{ for monatomic gases}$$

$$= \frac{7}{5} = 1 \cdot 4 \text{ for diatomic gases}$$

$$= \frac{9}{7} = 1 \cdot 29 \text{ for triatomic gases.}$$

EXAMPLE: The vapour density of the inert gas argon is found to be 19·97. Its molecular weight is therefore 39·94.

A determination of the velocity of sound in this gas gives a value for the ratio of its specific heats of about 1·67. Hence it is monatomic, and:

$$\text{Atomic weight} = \frac{\text{Molecular weight}}{\text{Atomicity}} = 39 \cdot 94.$$

(b) *Elements which form a number of Volatile Compounds* ("**Cannizzaro's Method**"). Two sets of measurements are needed:

1. Vapour density measurements for a number of volatile compounds of the element (expt. 78A, p. 196, or expt. 78B, p. 205); from these the molecular weights can be calculated.

2. The weight of element present in the molecular weight of each compound; for a carbon compound, this is usually found by heating a weighed amount of it with copper oxide and then weighing the resultant carbon dioxide.

Now in the molecular weight of a compound there must be present one, two, or some small whole number of atoms of the element. If a sufficiently large number of compounds are examined, the chances are that at least one compound will be found which contains only one atom of the element.

Cannizzaro therefore took as his definition:

The Atomic Weight of an element is the smallest weight of that element ever found in the molecular weight of any of its compounds. (This agrees with the definitions given on p. 164 for an atom and for a molecule, on p. 164 for an atomic weight, and on p. 195 for a molecular weight; the reasons for this must be clearly understood.)

EXAMPLE: To find the atomic weight of carbon, which actually forms thousands of volatile compounds.

COMPOUND	VAPOUR DENSITY OF COMPOUND	MOLECULAR WEIGHT OF COMPOUND	WEIGHT OF ELEMENT PER 100 GM. COMPOUND	WEIGHT OF ELEMENT PER 1 MOL. COMPOUND
Carbon dioxide	22	44	27·3	12
Carbon monoxide	14	28	42·8	12
Acetylene	13	26	92·3	24
Ethylene	14	28	86·5	24
Methane	8	16	75·0	12
Ether	37	74	64·9	48
Benzene	39	78	92·3	72
Chloroform	59·75	119·5	10·04	12

The smallest weight of carbon shown in the last column is 12, and therefore the approximate atomic weight of carbon is 12.

(c) *Elements which form very few or no Volatile Compounds.* In such cases molecular weights are of no use, and so Dulong and Petit's Law may be used (see pp. 166–167).

It must be emphasized that results obtained by the above

methods are only approximate. Vapours do not obey the gas laws exactly, and so Avogadro's Hypothesis is not exactly true. *Accurate atomic weights* are exact multiples of the equivalents, and these are obtained by the accurate analyses of pure compounds (see p. 180).

Expt. 78B. Vapour Density of a Volatile Liquid.

Dumas's Method. A bulb with narrow stem, or a drawn-out boiling tube, is weighed. By heating this in a beaker of water and then cooling it whilst its end is dipped into some of the given liquid, a small quantity of the latter is drawn in to fill about an inch of the tube.

It is then placed in a beaker of boiling water or in a liquid whose boiling-point is well above that of the given liquid (fig. 77).

The liquid boils away and after a time the boiling tube is just full of vapour at atmospheric pressure and at the temperature of the heating

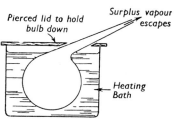

FIG. 77. Dumas's method for molecular weights.

bath. It is then sealed off with a blowpipe, and carefully dried and weighed.

The volume of vapour (which has now condensed to liquid) is obtained by breaking off the sealed tip of the tube under water and weighing or measuring the volume of water which enters the tube.

For example:

In an experiment with chloroform the following results were obtained:

Wt. of boiling tube (full of air) . . . = 48·48 gm.
Wt. ,, ,, ,, +chloroform vapour . = 48·81 gm.
Wt. ,, ,, ,, +water . . . = 173·48 gm.
Temperature of heating bath = 100° C.
Room temperature and pressure = 13° C. and 755 mm.
Wt. of water which fills the tube = 125 gm.

N.B.—Relative to this, the weight of air which fills the tube may be neglected.

Hence volume of the tube. . = 125 c.c.

This is originally full of air at 13° C. and 755 mm. pressure and later is full of chloroform vapour at 100° C. and 755 mm.

Volume of air at N.T.P. . . $= 125 \times \dfrac{273 \times 755}{286 \times 760} = 118 \cdot 5$ c.c.

Volume of chloroform vapour at

N.T.P. . . . . $= 125 \times \dfrac{273 \times 755}{373 \times 760} = 90 \cdot 9$ c.c.

Now $118 \cdot 5$ c.c. of air at N.T.P. weigh $\dfrac{118 \cdot 5 \times 1 \cdot 29}{1000}$ gm. $= 0 \cdot 153$ gm.

$\therefore$ Wt. of empty tube $= 48 \cdot 48 - 0 \cdot 153 = 48 \cdot 327$ gm.
and Wt. of chloroform $= 48 \cdot 81 - 48 \cdot 327 = 0 \cdot 483$ gm.

Hence *gram-molecular weight of chloroform* = weight of $22 \cdot 4$ litres

at N.T.P. $= \dfrac{0 \cdot 483 \times 22400}{90 \cdot 9} = \mathbf{119}$ **gm.**

The vapour density $= \dfrac{1}{2} \times$ molecular weight $= \dfrac{119}{2} = 59 \cdot 5$.

In Victor Meyer's method the vapour is made to displace an equal volume of air, which is measured at room temperature over water.

Suggestions for Practical Work

Expt. 78A for various gases. Dumas's experiment (expt. 78B) for chloroform or acetone or ether.

QUESTIONS ON CHAPTER XIII

1. State Gay-Lussac's law of volumes and mention (in bare outline only) *two* simple experiments which could be carried out to illustrate this law.

If 10 c.c. of carbon monoxide were exploded with 10 c.c. of oxygen, what volume of carbon dioxide would be produced and what volume of oxygen would remain? (C.)

2. State Gay-Lussac's law of volumes and illustrate it (*a*) by describing the best experiment you know for determining the volume composition of hydrogen chloride, (*b*) by means of the following data: 10 c.c. of dry ammonia were sparked over mercury in a eudiometer until the volume of gas became 20 c.c. and ceased to increase. To this $7 \cdot 5$ c.c. of oxygen were added and, after sparking the mixture, 5 c.c. of nitrogen remained. All the gases were measured at the same laboratory temperature and pressure. (L.)

3. A mixture contains 30 c.c. of hydrogen and 20 c.c. of chlorine in a graduated tube and is left for a considerable time in diffused daylight.

The tube is then opened under mercury and later under water. Explain what happens.

4. 20 c.c. of hydrogen, 10 c.c. of carbon monoxide, and 20 c.c. of oxygen are exploded in a eudiometer. Determine the *volume* and *composition* of the resulting gaseous mixture (*a*) if the experiment is conducted at room temperature, and (*b*) if the temperature is kept constant, but higher than 100° C., throughout the experiment. (L.)

5. State Avogadro's Hypothesis.

Show, without experimental details, how it can be deduced that (*a*) the molecule of hydrogen contains at least two atoms, (*b*) the molecular weight of a gas is twice its vapour density. (C.)

6. Define *vapour density* and *molecular weight*. Indicate how the relationship between them has been established.

A substance was found to contain 24·24% of carbon, 4·04% of hydrogen, and 71·72% of chlorine. Calculate (*a*) the simplest formula of the substance and (*b*) the molecular formula, it being known that the vapour density of the substance was approximately 50 times that of hydrogen. ($C=12$; $Cl=35·5$.) (L.)

7. It was at one time thought that equal volumes of gases under the same conditions of temperature and pressure contained equal numbers of atoms. Describe one experiment the results of which show that this is incorrect. How was the statement modified to fit the experimental evidence? Show the value of this corrected statement to chemists. (Navy.)

8. A density flask weighs 85·47 gm. when full of air and 86·37 gm. when full of sulphur dioxide, the temperature being 17° C. and the pressure 750 mm. The volume of the flask is found to be 609 c.c. If 1 litre of air at N.T.P. weighs 1·29 gm., what value does this experiment give for the molecular weight of sulphur dioxide?

9. In an experiment (with Victor Meyer's apparatus) the small tube weighed 2·144 gm. when empty and 2·260 gm. when partly filled with a certain liquid. The liquid when volatilized displaced 47·5 c.c. of air over water at 15° C. and 757 mm. The pressure of aqueous vapour at this temperature is 13 mm. Calculate the molecular weight of the substance.

10. At a temperature of 185° C., 0·215 gm. of a compound vaporized under a pressure of 332 mm. to give 113 c.c. of vapour. Calculate the molecular weight of the compound.

11. Give a brief account of the reasoning which leads to the view that (*a*) a molecule of hydrogen contains two atoms, *or* (*b*) a molecule of carbon dioxide contains one atom of carbon. (C.)

12. A mixture of 100 c.c. of hydrogen and 40 c.c. of oxygen was exploded in a eudiometer. After explosion the temperature was raised to 110° C. and the corrected volume of gases left was 100 c.c. On cooling to room temperature the corrected volume became 20 c.c. This gas was hydrogen.

(*All* the above volumes are reduced to S.T.P.)

Calculate the composition by volume of (*a*) the hot gases after explosion, (*b*) the same after cooling.

State what this experiment tells you about the molecule of oxygen.

Sketch the apparatus in which the experiment could be carried out. (O.)

13. The gas sulphur dioxide contains sulphur and oxygen only and has a density of 2·86 gm. per litre (reduced to N.T.P.). Show that these facts are sufficient to establish the formula SO_2.

14. A certain gaseous oxide of nitrogen contains its own volume of nitrogen. The density of the gas is 1·98 gm. per litre. What is its molecular formula?

15. When dry ammonia gas was passed through a tube containing red-hot copper oxide, the copper oxide lost 2·4 gm. in weight and 1120 c.c. of nitrogen (at N.T.P.) were obtained. Hence calculate (*a*) the percentage weights of hydrogen and of nitrogen in ammonia, (*b*) the empirical formula of ammonia. (O.)

16. 20 c.c. of carbon monoxide were mixed with 20 c.c. of oxygen and the mixture exploded. The volume of the products of explosion was 30 c.c. After treatment with sodium hydroxide the volume became 10 c.c., and this residue was completely absorbed by alkaline pyrogallol. (All volumes are given as at S.T.P.) Assuming the formula of carbon dioxide, show, from the above data, what must be the formula of carbon monoxide. (O.)

17. 15 c.c. of a gaseous hydrocarbon are sparked with 35 c.c. of oxygen and give 20 c.c. of gas of which 15 c.c. is absorbed by potash. What is the formula of the hydrocarbon?

18. 20 c.c. of a gaseous compound of hydrogen and carbon required 70 c.c. of oxygen for complete combustion. 40 c.c. of carbon dioxide were produced. What is the formula of the hydrocarbon? (D.)

19. A mixture of 10 c.c. of air and 20 c.c. of hydrogen was exploded in a eudiometer. After the gases had been allowed to cool to the initial room temperature and pressure, the volume of the residual gas was found to be 23·7 c.c. From these data calculate the percentage of oxygen by volume in the air. (L.)

20. Find the proportion by volume in which hydrogen and carbon dioxide should be mixed to yield a gas with the same density as carbon monoxide. (N.)

21. If all volumes are measured at N.T.P., state what will be the final volume of the gaseous product or products when (a) a mixture of 20 c.c. of hydrogen with 20 c.c. of oxygen is exploded, (b) a small piece of sulphur is burned in 50 c.c. of oxygen, (c) 80 c.c. of dry ammonia are completely decomposed by the passage of electric sparks. (L.)

22. Three litres of a mixture of nitrous and nitric oxides were passed over red-hot copper and 2·2 litres of nitrogen collected. Calculate the composition of the mixture. (O. and C.)

23. It was found that 8·8 c.c. of a mixture of methane (CH_4) and ethane (C_2H_6) required 20 c.c. of oxygen for complete combustion. What was the composition of the original mixture?

24. An element X forms a hydride, a chloride, and an oxide having vapour densities 17, 67·5, and 32 respectively. These compounds contain 94·1%, 47·4%, and 50·0% respectively of the element X.

Determine a probable value for the atomic weight of X.

25. To determine the atomic weight of an element X five of its volatile compounds were analysed. At the same time the vapour density of these compounds was determined, with the following results:

| % of X | 43·7 | 22·5 | 24·6 | 91·2 | 93·9 |
| Vapour density | 142 | 68·7 | 63 | 17 | 33 |

Calculate a probable value for the atomic weight of X. (A.)

26. The chloride of a metal has a molecular weight of 350 and contains 40·6% of chlorine by weight. (a) How many atoms of chlorine are there in a molecule of the chloride? (Atomic weight: Cl, 35·5). (b) What is the maximum value for the atomic weight of the metal? (L.)

27. Calculate the volume of oxygen at 17° C. and 720 mm. obtainable by heating to a high temperature 1 gm. of pure $KClO_3$. (O. and C.)

28. Calculate the volume of dry carbon dioxide measured at 12° C. and 750 mm. pressure required to convert 10 gm. of caustic soda into sodium carbonate.

29. Five gm. of water are subjected to the following reactions: (a) decomposed into its elements; (b) decomposed by sodium; (c) completely decomposed by heated magnesium. Calculate the volume of gas (reduced to 0° and 760 mm.) produced in each case. (C.)

30. Calculate (a) the volume of dry hydrogen, measured at 17° C. and 720 mm. pressure, required to reduce 26·33 gm. of cupric oxide to metal, (b) the weights of copper and of water obtained. (D.)

31. Until the middle of the last century the formula of water was written HO. Why was this formula put forward and why is it no longer accepted?

2·07 gm. of an element gave on oxidation 5·75 gm. of the oxide. The vapour density of the chloride is 40. Calculate (a) the equivalent, (b) the atomic weight, (c) the valency of the element. (Navy.)

32. You are told that a metallic element forms two oxides the molecular weights of which are 72 and 160 respectively and two chlorides of molecular weight 127 and 162·5 respectively. Are these figures consistent among themselves and what is the atomic weight of the element? (B.)

N.B.—Other examples of volumes of gases released during chemical reactions will be found on p. 266 nos. 8, 9; p. 341 nos. 6, 9; p. 392 nos. 2, 3; p. 416 nos. 13, 14.

CHAPTER XIV

ELECTROLYSIS AND THE ELECTROCHEMICAL SERIES

Electrolytes and Non-Electrolytes

We have already seen that a current of electricity can cause a chemical reaction to take place, e.g. the decomposition of water by electrolysis (p. 84), provided that some substance is present, e.g. an acid, alkali, or salt, which will carry the current. Such a substance is known as an **electrolyte**; this may be defined as a compound which, when molten or when dissolved in a suitable solvent (usually water), will conduct an electric current. **Non-electrolytes**, such as sugar, alcohol, glycerine, etc., will often dissolve in water, but do not conduct an electric current.

In the language of modern electronic theory, electrolytes are "electrovalent compounds" (p. 182), and non-electrolytes are "covalent compounds" (p. 182).

Metals, though they conduct electricity when either solid or molten, are not considered as electrolytes because they are *elements*; no chemical reaction can therefore occur in them because they cannot be split up further. The current is carried in them (or in mixtures of metals) by electrons moving in a direction *opposite* to the conventional direction of the current, i.e. the negatively charged electrons go from − to +.

Electrolysis

The decomposition of an electrolyte by an electric current is called *electrolysis*. The resulting chemical changes are observed only at the places where the current enters or leaves the electrolyte; the wire or plate connected to the positive terminal is called the ANODE, where the current enters the liquid; the one connected to the negative terminal is called the CATHODE (or "kathode") where the current leaves the liquid. (N.B.— Direct current from a battery must be used, not alternating current, which is the normal house supply.) (Fig. 78.)

Hydrogen or metals are normally set free at the cathode ($-^{ve}$) and are therefore said to be ELECTROPOSITIVE, because opposite electrical charges attract one another. Oxygen and

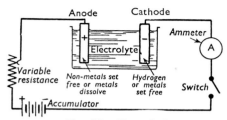

FIG. 78. Electrolysis.

other non-metals or acid radicals are set free or appear at the anode ($+^{ve}$) and so are called ELECTRONEGATIVE.

The Laws of Electrolysis

These were discovered by Michael Faraday in 1830, and are often called "Faraday's Laws."

1. The amount of decomposition is directly proportional to the quantity of electricity which has passed through an electrolyte. (Quantity = Current × Time.)

This provides the most accurate method of measuring an electric current, because it is found that 1 ampere flowing for 1 second will deposit exactly 0·001118 gm. of silver from a solution of silver nitrate. This weight is known as the *electrochemical equivalent* of silver. The quantity of electricity is measured in coulombs, and is equal to the current in amperes × the time in seconds.

The quantity of electricity bought by consumers from the first Electric Supply Company, in New York in 1882, was measured by electrolytic meters.

2. When different compounds are decomposed by the same quantity of electricity, equivalent quantities of the various products are obtained.

E.g. 1 coulomb of electricity will set free 0·001118 gm. of silver or 0·000329 gm. of copper.

$$\frac{107 \cdot 880}{0 \cdot 001118} = 96,540 \text{ coulombs}$$ will therefore set free $107 \cdot 880$ gm. of silver (the gram equivalent) or $96,540 \times 0 \cdot 000329 = 31 \cdot 8$ gm. of copper (which is the gram equivalent of copper).

These two laws may be summarized mathematically as follows: If w=the weight (in gm.) of substance set free, e=its chemical gram equivalent, c=current (in amps.), t=time (in seconds), then

$$w = \frac{e \times c \times t}{96,540}$$

An electrolytic cell used for measuring the quantity of electricity which has passed is known as a *voltameter*, e.g. a copper voltameter or a water voltameter.

The Ionic Theory

This theory has been developed in order to explain the above facts of electrolysis.

Electrolytes are considered to consist of "ions" (electrically charged atoms or radicals) which bear a charge equal to their valency, and which carry the current by moving through the liquid. When these ions reach the "electrodes" (anode or cathode) chemical changes will occur there, as a result of ions losing their electrical charges or of other ions being formed.

For example, if $2 \times 96,540$ coulombs of electricity (2 amp. for 96,540 sec.) are passed through a solution of copper chloride ($CuCl_2$) in water, $63 \cdot 6$ gm. of copper will be deposited on the cathode ($-$) and $71 \cdot 1$ gm. of chlorine gas will be set free at the anode ($+$). This is explained as follows (fig. 79): chlorine atoms which have each gained one electron and so gained a negative charge to become chlorine *ions* (Cl^-, see p. 181) move to the anode ($^+$) when the current is switched on; there they give up one electron each and become chlorine atoms, which combine together to give molecules of chlorine gas. Copper atoms (valency 2) which have each lost 2 electrons and so

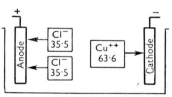

Fig. 79. Ionic theory.

acquired a double positive charge to become copper *ions* (Cu^{++}) move to the cathode ($-$), where they gain electrons and so become copper atoms which are deposited; as each copper ion carries a double charge, the amount of electricity which discharges 2 atomic weights ($=2$ equivalents) of chlorine will only discharge 1 atomic weight ($=2$ equivalents) of copper.

The above explanation shows (*a*) why the chemical changes are only seen at the electrodes, where the ions are discharged, and (*b*) why the amount of decomposition is proportional to the chemical *equivalent* rather than to the atomic weight.

The Properties of Ions

There is a very large amount of evidence in support of this theory, though most of it is beyond the scope of this book. One simple point may, however, be mentioned: all common solutions of copper salts, if sufficiently dilute, have the same blue colour because this is due to the ion Cu^{++}; the negative ions, NO_3^-, Cl^-, SO_4^{--} are colourless. If a current is passed through copper chloride solution until all the salt has been decomposed, the solution will no longer be blue and a current will no longer flow, because the only ions present will be a minute number of H^+ and OH^- ions from the water.

One early objection to the ionic theory was that if copper chloride contained chlorine ions, these should be expected to smell of chlorine, and similarly that the sodium ions (Na^+) of sodium chloride should be expected to react with water just like sodium metal. This is not so, because ions have totally different properties from the uncharged atoms, and in fact usually have structures similar to the inert gases (see p. 181).

Salts may be defined as "*substances, other than acids and bases* (see below) *which are completely split up into ions,*" e.g. Na^+Cl^-, $Ca^{++}NO_3^-NO_3^-$, $2Al^{+++}$ $3SO_4^{--}$, etc., which explains why (when in solution) all chlorides show similar reactions, and all calcium salts show similar reactions, etc. (see pp. 71, 401, 481). So-called "strong acids," such as hydrochloric, sulphuric, and nitric, are also completely ionized in solution, e.g. H^+Cl^-, as are strong alkalis such as the hydroxides of sodium and potassium, e.g. Na^+OH^-. Water, carbonic acid, and ammonium hydroxide, on the other hand, are only very slightly ionized:

$$H_2O \rightleftharpoons H^+ + OH^-$$
$$H_2O + CO_2 \rightleftharpoons H_2CO_3 \rightleftharpoons 2H^+ + CO_3^{--}$$
$$H_2O + NH_3 \rightleftharpoons NH_4^+ + OH^-$$

these "weak electrolytes" are therefore poor conductors of electricity (cf. hydrogen sulphide, p. 350 and sulphurous acid, p. 359).

Acids may be defined, on this theory, as "substances which give rise to hydrogen ions" (on this definition, water is an extremely weak acid). Similarly, bases may be defined as "substances which combine with hydrogen ions."

Examples of Electrolysis

In the table below the results of a number of cases of electrolysis are summarized.   The principles governing the nature

ELECTROLYTE	NATURE OF ANODE*	PRODUCT AT CATHODE $(-)$	PRODUCT AT ANODE $(+)$	RESULTING LIQUID
1. Conc. HCl soln.	C	H_2	Cl_2	More dilute
2. $CuCl_2$ soln.	C	Cu	Cl_2	More dilute
3. $CuCl_2$ soln.	Copper	Cu	Cu dissolves $\rightarrow Cu^{++}$	The same
4. $CuSO_4$ soln.	Copper	Cu	Cu dissolves $\rightarrow Cu^{++}$	The same
5. $CuSO_4$ soln.	C or Pt	Cu	O_2	H_2SO_4 at anode
6. Dil. H_2SO_4 soln.	C or Pt	H_2	O_2	More concentrated
7. *Molten* NaCl	C	Na	Cl_2	The same
8. Conc. NaCl soln.	C	H_2	Cl_2	NaOH at cathode
9. Dil. NaCl soln.	C or Pt	H_2	O_2	More concentrated
10. *Molten* NaOH	C or Pt	Na	$O_2 + H_2O$	More dilute, then $2Na + 2H_2O = 2NaOH + H_2$
11. NaOH soln.	C or Pt	H_2	O_2	More concentrated
12. Na_2SO_4 soln.	C or Pt	H_2	O_2	NaOH at cathode H_2SO_4 at anode

* The nature of the cathode is normally less important (but see p. 406).

of the products will then be discussed, and some important individual cases explained in detail by means of the ionic theory.

At the Cathode

(*a*) A reactive metal like sodium is set free only in the absence of water (nos. 7, 10; *not* nos. 8, 9, 11, 12), or at a mercury cathode (p. 406).

(*b*) Hydrogen is set free as gas from solutions of acids (nos. 1, 6) or of sodium compounds (nos. 8, 9, 11, 12).

(*c*) An unreactive metal like copper is set free in preference to hydrogen (nos. 2, 3, 4; and no. 5 even when the solution contains mostly H_2SO_4).

At the Anode

(*a*) Chlorine is set free only at an unreactive anode (i.e. carbon, nos. 1, 2, 7, 8).

(*b*) Reactive anodes dissolve to set free ions in the solution (nos. 3, 4). All metals do this in chloride solutions; many (but not platinum) in sulphate solutions (nos. 5, 6, 12).

(*c*) Oxygen is given off from solutions of oxysalts or oxyacids (nos. 5, 6, 12 at inert electrodes), or from hydroxides (nos. 10, 11), or from very dilute solutions of chlorides (no. 9).

Explanation of the above Examples of Electrolysis

(*a*) *Electrolysis of copper chloride solution* (*example* 2): see p. 213.

(*b*) **Electrolysis of molten ("fused") sodium chloride** (*example* 7).

This contains only sodium ions (Na^+), which go to the cathode ($-$) when the current is passing, and chlorine ions (Cl^-), which go to the anode ($+$).

At the Cathode (usually iron): The charges on the Na^+ ions are neutralized by electrons from the cathode, $Na^+ + e^- = Na$, thus forming metallic sodium, Na, which melts, floats to the surface, and is run off into moulds.

At the Anode (usually carbon, i.e. graphite): The charges on the Cl^- ions are neutralized by giving up electrons to the anode, $Cl^- = Cl + e^-$; the Cl atoms then combine in pairs to form Cl_2 molecules, which come off as a gas above the electrode.

The above process is used in the manufacture of sodium metal, though the high melting-point of sodium chloride (800° C.) often necessitates the use of sodium hydroxide (NaOH, m.p. 300° C., example 10) instead (see p. 451).

Magnesium metal is prepared similarly from $MgCl_2$ on an equally large scale (see pp. 453–5).

(c) Electrolysis of dilute sulphuric acid (*example* 6)

This contains H^+ ions and SO_4^{--} ions from the sulphuric acid, and also some H^+ ions and OH^- ions from the water, which is ionized to a very slight but measurable extent.

At the Cathode (platinum or carbon): The charges on the H^+ ions are neutralized by electrons from the cathode, $H^+ + e^- = H$; these H atoms combine in pairs to form H_2 molecules, which come off as a gas.

At the Anode (platinum or carbon): Although almost all the current is carried by the SO_4^{--} ions, these have a much higher "electrode potential" (see below, p. 221) than the OH^- ions. The charges on the OH^- ions are therefore neutralized by giving up electrons to the anode, $OH^- = OH + e^-$; the OH radicals react together to form oxygen gas, which bubbles off, and water: $4OH = O_2 + 2H_2O$.

The equilibrium between water and its ions, $H_2O \rightleftharpoons H^+OH^-$, is upset by the discharge of the ions, so that more water becomes ionized, and more H^+ and OH^- ions are formed as fast as others are discharged.*

At first sight it is perhaps difficult to visualize a convincing picture of this phenomenon.

The addition of the sulphuric acid to water results in a considerable

---

* On an older and no longer accepted theory, the sulphate ions were said to be discharged and then to react with the water, re-forming sulphuric acid, which then ionized to sulphate ions:

$$SO_4^{--} = SO_4 + 2e^-$$
$$SO_4 + H_2O = H_2SO_4 + O$$
$$2O = O_2 \nearrow$$
$$H_2SO_4 = 2H^+ + SO_4^{--}$$

increase in the conductivity of the electrolyte, i.e. a larger current passes for a given applied external e.m.f.   This is due to the much greater number of ions available, compared with the few ions provided by the slightly ionized water.

The passage of increased current through the external circuit does not occur unless and until increased numbers of ions are discharged at the electrodes.   Why should the arrival of, say, a large number of sulphate ions at the anode, though stopping there and not being discharged, cause an increase in the discharge of hydroxyl (OH⁻) ions?   The answer must be as follows:

A discharge of a negative ion involves the loss of an electron to the anode.   The production of a "strong atmosphere" of ions round the anode must stimulate the release of electrons to it, and owing to their lower electrode potential it is the hydroxyl ions which are first neutralized and discharged.   This immediately disturbs the equilibrium between water and its ions, more water is ionized, the freshly formed hydroxyl ions are discharged, and so on.

The result is that although there are very few hydroxyl ions present at any moment, they are in fact being discharged just as rapidly as if the sulphate ions themselves were being discharged.

The nett result is that only water is decomposed ("the electrolysis of water," p. 84), and the solution of sulphuric acid therefore becomes more concentrated.   This reaction occurs if an accumulator is overcharged; the acid must then be diluted to the required strength with distilled water.

Similar results are obtained with sodium hydroxide solution (example 11), because the hydrogen ions are discharged in preference to the sodium ions *; and in very dilute solutions of sodium chloride (example 9) neither Na^+ nor Cl^- ions are discharged, but only H^+ and OH^- from the water, giving H_2 and O_2; similarly with Na_2SO_4 (example 12).

(d) Electrolysis of copper sulphate solution (example 4)

This contains Cu^{++} and SO_4^{--} ions from the copper sulphate, and H^+ and OH^- from the water.

At the Cathode (pure copper): Cu^{++} ions have a lower electrode potential (p. 221) than H^+, and are therefore discharged, and copper is deposited in a thin film of pure metal

* On the older theory, the sodium ions were said to be discharged, forming sodium atoms, which then reacted with the water to form sodium hydroxide, which then ionized, re-forming sodium ions:

$$Na^+ + e^- = Na$$
$$Na + H_2O = NaOH + H$$
$$2H = H_2 \nearrow$$
$$NaOH = Na^+ + OH^-$$

on the electrode, which is thereby "plated": $Cu^{++} + 2e^- = Cu$. As copper is deposited in preference to most other metals, such as Fe, Zn, etc., this method is used to obtain the very pure copper required as an electrical conductor. (PLATE 14.)

At the Anode (*copper requiring to be purified*): Metals (except silver, gold, and platinum) have a greater tendency to form

[*Photo by courtesy of the International Nickel Co. of Canada, Ltd.*

PLATE 14.   COPPER PURIFIED BY ELECTROLYSIS

The cathodes of pure pink copper are lifted out by the travelling crane. Copper is mostly used for conducting electricity, as in wiring houses for electric lights, and must be 99·99% pure.

ions, by leaving electrons behind on the anode, than to allow the discharge of either OH^- or SO_4^{--} ions (see electrode potentials, p. 222): $Cu = Cu^{++} + 2e^-$.   The copper (+impurities) therefore dissolves.*

* On the older theory, the sulphate ions were said to be discharged, the SO_4 radicals then attacked the copper, and not the water as before (p. 217)—a weak point in this theory—forming copper sulphate, which then ionized to re-form sulphate ions:

$$SO_4^{--} = SO_4 + 2e^-$$
$$SO_4 + Cu = CuSO_4$$
$$CuSO_4 = Cu^{++} + SO_4^{--}$$

The nett result is that the concentration of copper sulphate in the solution is maintained because almost as much copper dissolves off the anode as is deposited in a pure form on the cathode; the impurities accumulate in the solution.

(*e*) **Electrolysis of concentrated sodium chloride solution** (*example* 8).

This is discussed later (p. 405) in connection with the manufacture of chlorine and of sodium hydroxide.

Other Commercial Applications of Electrolysis

(*a*) *Preparation of metals, etc.* Besides sodium, magnesium, and copper (and hydrogen, oxygen, chlorine, and sodium hydroxide), already referred to, *aluminium* can only be manufactured by a process of electrolysis (see p. 457); much zinc is prepared in this way; and much lead and nickel are refined in a similar way to copper.

(*b*) *Electroplating.* This is the depositing of a thin layer of one metal on top of another, in order to increase its attractiveness (e.g. silver on copper), or its resistance to corrosion (e.g. rhodium on silver), or its hardness (e.g. chromium on nickel for gramophone record matrices), or its thickness (e.g. nickel on worn steel machinery).

The metal is deposited on the cathode from a solution of a suitable compound (*nickel* ammonium sulphate, potassium *silver* cyanide, *chromic* acid, etc.), and the strength of the solution is usually maintained by using an anode of the metal required (e.g. Ni, Ag).

The top layer of chromium plating may be extremely thin (e.g. about 0·00004 inch) if the article is first plated with nickel, then with a layer of copper, then nickel again, and finally chromium; if chromium is plated directly on to iron or steel it very soon flakes off.

Very many other metals can be deposited in a similar manner, one recent application being the tinning of "tin cans."

NOTE.—In advanced work, positive ions (which go to the cathode) are called *cations*, and negative ions (which go to the anode) are called *anions*.

THE ELECTROCHEMICAL SERIES

We have already seen that metals are "electropositive," giving positive ions (e.g. Na^+) which go to the cathode, whilst non-metals are "electronegative," giving negative ions (e.g. Cl^-) which go to the anode. This is due to the electronic structure (see p. 181) of the elements concerned, and is one of the fundamental differences between metals and non-metals (p. 45).

There are also differences in electropositiveness between different metals, as is shown when mixtures of ions are electrolysed; sodium is more electropositive than hydrogen (i.e. it shows a greater tendency to form positive ions), and so sodium ions cannot be discharged in the presence of hydrogen ions, i.e. in aqueous solution (except on a mercury cathode, see p. 407); on the other hand, copper is less electropositive than hydrogen, so that its ions are discharged even in acid solution.

The measure of this electropositiveness is called the electrode potential, and it is usually expressed relative to hydrogen as zero.

Electrode Potentials

When a metal is in contact with a solution of one of its salts there is a tendency for the metal to dissolve, and this is called its "solution pressure." At the same time there is an opposing tendency for ions of the dissolved metal to be deposited on the solid metal, and this is called its "ionic pressure."

In the case of copper in contact with, say, copper sulphate solution the ionic pressure is greater than the solution pressure. Hence a few copper ions come out of solution and deposit copper, giving a positive charge to the metal and leaving an equivalent negative charge in the solution: $Cu^{++} + 2e^- = Cu$. The potential difference ($+0.3$ volts) thus set up prevents further deposition of copper. Copper is thus said to have an electrode potential of $+0.3$ volts.

In the case of zinc in contact with, say, zinc sulphate solution, the solution pressure is greater than the ionic pressure, with the result that the zinc dissolves slightly, giving the solution a positive charge and leaving a negative charge on the metal: $Zn = Zn^{++} + 2e^-$. Zinc is thus said to have a negative electrode potential (of -0.8 volts).

It is at first sight confusing that the more an element exhibits a tendency to send positive ions into solution (i.e. the more *electropositive* it is said to

8*

be), the more highly charged *negatively* it will become (because the ions leave electrons behind on the metal) and so the more negative is its electrode potential.

Table of Electrode Potentials

K	-2.9	volts
Na	-2.7	,,
Ca	-2.5	,,
Mg	-1.7	,,
Al	-1.3	,,
Zn	-0.8	,,
Fe	-0.4	.
Sn	-0.1	,,
Pb	-0.1	,,
H	zero	
Cu	$+0.3$	,,
OH	$+0.4$	,,
I	$+0.5$	,,
Hg	$+0.8$	,,
Ag	$+0.8$	,,
Br	$+1.1$	,,
Cl	$+1.4$	,,
Au	$+1.4$	..
Pt>	$+1.4$	,,
SO_4 }	very high	
NO_3 }	very high	
F	$+2.8$ volts	

This order of Electrode Potentials is known as the *Electrochemical Series*, which corresponds closely with the relative chemical behaviour of the metals and their compounds (see table opposite).

If two rods of two different metals are dipped side by side into dilute sulphuric acid, the difference in voltage produced by this "simple voltaic cell" is equal to the difference between their electrode potentials, e.g. zinc and copper give 1·1 volts. (Metals which are farther apart, e.g. zinc and silver—for light-weight accumulators, give a greater voltage.) Bubbles of gas (hydrogen) appear on the least electropositive metal (copper).

A metal high up in the displacement series (very "electropositive") will displace a less electropositive one lower down, e.g. an iron penknife dipped into copper sulphate solution will become coated with copper (see expt. 64, p. 141), a process used for recovering valuable copper from residues by means of scrap iron (PLATE 10B, p. 142). Similarly, metals above hydrogen can displace hydrogen from acids (see table, p. 97), but copper cannot.

Nearly all corrosion is an electrochemical phenomenon, e.g. the rusting of tinplate (see fig. 153, p. 461), and the corrosion of aluminium roofs at the points of contact with lead washers round the nails which hold the roof in place. Similarly, in the preparation of hydrogen (p. 91), zinc is more readily attacked when in contact with less active metals such as lead or copper.

In electrolysis, at the cathode the least "electropositive" metal will be discharged, e.g. Au rather than Ag, Ag than Cu, Cu than H, H than Na. At the anode the change corresponding with the smallest electrode potential will occur, e.g. Cu dissolves, instead of OH giving oxygen; bromine is set free more readily than chlorine (p. 411); and fluorine cannot be prepared in aqueous solution (p. 425). (Hydrogen and oxygen are discharged less easily than would be expected because of a phenomenon known as "over-voltage," thus Cl is discharged, not OH, on p. 406.)

The Electrochemical Series will be used throughout the book as a guide to the behaviour of metals and their salts.

Notes on the following table

(*a*) Metals occur in nature (col. 12) in a stable form; those metals which form the least stable compounds occur "native," i.e. uncombined (Pt, Au;

TABLE—CHEMICAL PROPERTIES AND THE ELECTROCHEMICAL SERIES

	1 ACTION OF ACIDS	2 ACTION OF WATER	3 HYDROGEN ON OXIDE	4 HEAT OF COMBUSTION	5 ACTION OF AIR	6 CARBON ON OXIDE	7 HEAT ON NITRATE	8 CHARACTER OF HYDROXIDE	9 CHARACTER OF CARBONATE	10 CHARACTER OF CHLORIDE	11 CHARACTER OF SULPHIDE	12 MOST COMMON OCCURRENCE	13 USES OF METAL	14 DENSITY GM./C.C.
K				86			Nitrite formed		Easily soluble in water			Chloride		0·85
Na	React to give Hydrogen	React to give Hydrogen	Not Reduced	99		No Reduced		Easily soluble in water	Not easily decomposed by heat	Soluble in water, and naturally occurring	Not precipitated from solution	Chlorides and Carbonates	Chemical reagent	0·97
Ca				152	Burn readily to form oxides									1·5
Mg				146				Slightly soluble					Aircraft	1·7
Al		Reversible action		130				Insoluble in water and Decomposed by heat	Insoluble in water and Decomposed by heat		Precipitated in alkaline solution	Oxide	Construc-tional work or alloys	2·7
Zn				84			Oxide formed					Oxide or Sul-phide		7·1
Fe				64		Reduced				Hydrolysed by water (especially those of higher valency)				7·9
Sn		No action		69				Unstable or not formed	Unstable or not formed		Precipitated even in acid solution			7·3
Pb	Only attacked by oxidizing acids		Reduced	52	Form oxides when heated	Oxides decompose to metal by heat alone	De-compose to metal			Lower chlorides and iodides insoluble in water		Sul-phides	Coinage or Decoration	11·4
Cu				35										8·9
Hg				22	No action									13·6
Ag				7								Free metal		10·5
Au	Little or no attack			0										19·3
Pt				17										21·5

also Ag, Cu); those with insoluble sulphides (col. 11) occur as such (Ag, Hg, Cu, Pb, Sn, Fe, Zn); those with the most stable carbonates (col. 9) or chlorides (col. 10) occur as such (Mg, Ca, Na, K).

(*b*) Metals are extracted usually by heating the oxide with carbon (col. 6) if the heat of combustion (col. 4, in thousands of calories per 16 gm. of oxygen) is less than that of carbon to CO_2 (94). The "light metals" (see col. 14) must be obtained by electrolysis.

(*c*) Oxysalts of the "noble metals" decompose to the metal (cols. 7, 8, 9) because the oxide itself is unstable to heat (col. 6); those of sodium and potassium are soluble in water and difficult to decompose.

(*d*) Those metals which are little affected by air and water (cols. 5, 2) are used (col. 13) for decoration or for coinage (Au, Ag, Cu) ; those which are affected even by cold water (Ca, Na, K) are not used at all for constructional work.

(*e*) The dates of discovery of the metals (pp. 521-3) are roughly in the order of the series: Au, Ag, Cu, 5000 B.C.; Pb, Fe, 3000 B.C.; Zn, A.D. 1700; Al, Mg, Ca, Na, K, after A.D. 1800.

Finally, remember that although this table is a useful aid to the memory, it is not an infallible guide : for example, aluminium is much *less* attacked by air or water or acids than is iron, and its carbonate does not exist !

Suggestions for Practical Work

(*a*) Investigate the changes occurring when (1) copper sulphate solution and (2) dilute sulphuric acid are electrolysed, using *direct* current (2 or 4 volts) and the following pairs of electrodes (+ and — respectively): Cu, Cu; C, C; Cu, C; C, Cu. Note any colour changes, plating, dissolving of the electrode (difficult to see), and the relative quantities of gases given off.

(*b*) Electrolyse solutions of (1) sodium sulphate and (2) sodium chloride, using carbon electrodes and a cell roughly divided into two by a wedge of blotting-paper. Test the liquids in each half with litmus-paper or litmus solution.

(*c*) Find the difference in voltage produced by dipping rods of two different metals side by side into dilute sulphuric acid (p. 222).

QUESTIONS ON CHAPTER XIV

1. Define the terms ion, cathode, electrolyte.

Explain carefully what occurs when crystals of sodium sulphate are dissolved in water and an electric current passed between platinum electrodes through the solution. (C.)

2. An electric current was passed through two voltameters in series containing respectively copper sulphate solution and water acidified with sulphuric acid. After the current had passed for a certain time, 0·124 gm. of copper had been deposited on the cathode, and 47·0 c.c.

of hydrogen, measured at 15° C. and 74 cm. pressure, had been liberated.   Calculate the equivalent of copper.

3. Describe and explain what you would observe when an electric current is passed through an aqueous solution of copper sulphate, (*a*) using platinum electrodes, (*b*) using copper electrodes.

Indicate briefly how you would use the results of (*a*) in order to determine the equivalent weight of copper.   (O.)

4. State and explain what may be observed when an electric current is passed between platinum electrodes immersed in the following liquids: (*a*) dilute caustic soda, (*b*) concentrated hydrochloric acid, (*c*) a strong solution of common salt.   (L.)

5. Describe what happens when a concentrated aqueous solution of sodium chloride is electrolysed with the use of (i) carbon electrodes, (ii) a mercury cathode.   (Navy.)

Calculate the volume of chlorine measured at 15° C. and 750 mm. of mercury pressure that could be obtained by a current of 0·2 amp. flowing for 5 hours through an aqueous solution of sodium chloride.

6. Explain why a dilute aqueous solution of sulphuric acid is a good conductor of electricity, whereas pure water and pure sulphuric acid hardly conduct at all.   (O. and C.)

7. State Faraday's Laws of Electrolysis.   Describe what happens when copper sulphate solution is electrolysed between (*a*) platinum and (*b*) copper electrodes, and when sodium chloride solution is electrolysed between (*a*) platinum and (*b*) carbon electrodes.   (L.)

8. What do you understand by the Electrochemical Series? Show how the positions of the common elements in this series are related to their characteristic chemical properties.

9. What do you understand by the statement that one metal is more electropositive than another?

Describe *three* methods by which you would demonstrate that zinc is more electropositive than lead.   (O.)

10. Give an account of any *one* industrial process in which electrolysis is used, stating the nature of the products and the purposes for which each is used.   (O.)

11. If a chromium-plated copper towel-rail is installed in the bathroom of a house with a hot-water system of galvanized iron pipes, there is usually trouble after a few years. What trouble would you expect, and can you explain why?

CHAPTER XV

THE FACTORS AFFECTING CHEMICAL CHANGE

It has been explained previously (see p. 177) that a chemical equation gives valuable information as to the weights (and volumes if gaseous) of the substances which take part in a reaction.

There is, however, important information which a chemical equation, as ordinarily written, does not give. For example:

(1) It does not show whether heat is evolved or absorbed during the reaction.

(2) It does not indicate the ease nor the rate with which the reaction proceeds.

(3) It does not state the physical conditions necessary to produce a desired result.

And yet this knowledge is often of vital importance both in the laboratory and in industrial processes.

For a complete treatment of this subject the student should, at a later stage, consult text-books on Physical Chemistry; but a simple outline of the principles involved should not be beyond him even now.

Reversible Reactions

In elementary practical work the student will have met some experiments, e.g. the combination of iron filings and powdered sulphur (expt. 24, p. 51), in which a good deal of heat is evolved and a rapid reaction occurs. In others, e.g. the removal of water of crystallization from a salt (expt. 41, p. 86; expt. 42, p. 87) and the replacement of copper by iron in copper sulphate solution (p. 141), some time must elapse before the reaction is complete.

There are, however, many reactions in chemistry which are

not only slow but also reversible: examples are the reaction of mercury with oxygen and the reaction of iron with steam:

$$2Hg + O_2 \nearrow \rightleftharpoons 2HgO \qquad \text{(expt. 11, p. 20)}$$
$$3Fe + 4H_2O \nearrow \rightleftharpoons Fe_3O_4 + 4H_2 \nearrow \quad \text{(expt. 34, p. 81)}$$

Thus, in general, the change $A + B \rightarrow C + D$ may occur under certain conditions, but the reverse change, $C + D \rightarrow A + B$, may also occur if the conditions of the experiment are changed.

Such a reversible reaction if left to itself will usually reach an equilibrium position in which the forward reaction is proceeding at the same rate as the backward reaction. In equations for reversible reactions, therefore, the " $=$ " sign is usually replaced by two arrows, thus

$$A + B \rightleftharpoons C + D$$

The equilibrium may be compared with that of a man walking down an escalator which is travelling up. Both man and escalator are moving, but his position in space will remain fixed if his speed downwards is equal to the speed of the stairway upwards. Such a state of equilibrium is called "kinetic equilibrium."

(It will be noticed that the existence of reversible reactions slightly complicates one of the elementary distinctions between physical and chemical changes on p. 12.)

Another example is the conversion of limestone (calcium carbonate) into quicklime (calcium oxide) and carbon dioxide (see p. 267):

$$CaCO_3 \rightleftharpoons CaO + CO_2 \nearrow$$

If the calcium carbonate is strongly heated and the carbon dioxide allowed to escape, the decomposition is complete and calcium oxide alone remains. But if the heating is carried out in a closed vessel, an equilibrium is reached and both solids remain. And if carbon dioxide is supplied under pressure, then the reaction goes to completion in the reverse direction.

Le Chatelier's Principle

Before dealing separately with the various factors which determine the behaviour of reactions, it will be helpful to examine a general principle which often predicts the effects of these factors. This is known as the Principle of Le Chatelier, and it states that:

The equilibrium position will move in such a way as to oppose the effect of any external change applied.

Thus in the reversible reaction between iron and steam already referred to, if an attempt is made to increase the concentration of steam by passing more and more steam over the iron, then the equilibrium position moves so as to oppose this increase in steam, i.e. it moves from left to right because the iron combines with the steam to give more and more hydrogen.

The reactions in a "Permutit" water-softener (p. 277) and the "causticizing of soda" (expt. 99, p. 283) are also reversible.

The student of Physics will have met several other applications of this general principle, which may be called "the cussedness of Nature," in connection with the phenomena of induced currents.

The Effect of Concentration

This effect was worked out by Guldberg and Waage in 1864 and is summarized in the **Law of Mass Action**, which states that

The rate at which a chemical action proceeds is proportional to the molecular concentrations of the reacting substances.

It is important to realize that it is not the total weights of substances which are effective, but the numbers of molecules in a given space. The greater this number the more chances there are of one molecule meeting another, and the frequency of these meetings will determine the rate of their combination or reaction.

If the reaction is reversible, then as the products are formed and the concentrations of the original substances are diminished, the rate of the reverse reaction will increase until it equals that of the forward reaction, and then an equilibrium is reached. This can be disturbed, as stated in the reaction iron/steam/iron oxide/hydrogen, by altering the concentration of one of the substances.

The Effect of Pressure

With gaseous substances an increase in pressure will cause a decrease in volume (Boyle's Law, p. 122), and so the molecules will be compressed into a smaller space and their rate of reaction will be thereby speeded up.   If the reaction is reversible and the products are also gaseous, then increase of pressure will similarly increase the rate of the backward reaction. Whether the equilibrium position is moved from left to right or vice versa will obviously depend on which of the two rates is the more affected, and Le Chatelier's Principle will help to decide the matter.

Thus if the change from left to right is accompanied by a contraction in volume, then an increase in applied pressure will move the equilibrium from left to right, for in that way the reacting mixture reduces its pressure.

EXAMPLE (*a*).   In the very important industrial process—the Haber Process—used for making ammonia from its elements (see p. 313) the equation for the reaction is

$$N_2 + 3H_2 \rightleftharpoons 2NH_3$$

Thus 4 volumes of the gaseous elements (see Avogadro's Theory, p. 195) give 2 volumes of product, i.e. there is a contraction in volume from left to right.   Therefore if an increase of pressure is applied, the equilibrium position will be moved so as to increase the *yield* of ammonia.   In practice in the various modifications of the process, pressures from 200 to 1000 atmospheres have been used.

EXAMPLE (*b*).   In the well-known reversible reaction used for combining the nitrogen and oxygen in air to give nitric oxide (see p. 336)

$$N_2 + O_2 \rightleftharpoons 2NO$$

there is no volume change, since two volumes of mixture give two volumes of compound, and therefore a change of pressure has *no* effect on the yield of nitric oxide.

The Effect of Temperature

As with increase of pressure, so a rise in temperature will increase the *rate* of any reaction, because the molecules will move more quickly, and hence will have more frequent chances of reacting. (As a rough general rule, the rate of reaction is approximately doubled for every 10° C. rise in temperature.)

Here, again, the effect on the equilibrium position in a reversible reaction, and therefore on the yield of a particular product, will depend on whether the forward rate is speeded up more than the backward rate, or vice versa. The final effect can be predicted by applying Le Chatelier's principle.

If a reaction is *exothermic*, that is, if heat is evolved when it proceeds from left to right, then a rise of temperature will cause the equilibrium position to move so as to counteract this rise. It will therefore move from right to left, for in that direction heat is absorbed:

$$A+B \rightleftharpoons AB + \text{heat evolved (``exothermic reaction'')}.$$

Rise of temperature will here reduce the proportion of AB in the equilibrium mixture.

Conversely if a reaction is one which absorbs heat (i.e. is *endothermic*), then an applied rise of temperature will result in the equilibrium position moving from left to right, and so the yield of product will be increased:

$$C+D+\text{heat absorbed} \rightleftharpoons CD \text{ (``endothermic reaction'')}.$$

Rise of temperature will here *increase* the amount of CD in the equilibrium mixture.

Thus heating will speed up the RATE of all reactions, but if they are reversible and exothermic then the YIELD of the product will be diminished. Now the majority of reactions are exothermic, and in several industrial processes it is more economical to aim at obtaining a small yield quickly rather than a larger yield slowly, even though it *may* necessitate the cost of supplying heat.

It is just this type of problem whose solution is assisted by the discovery of a suitable catalyst (see below, p. 234), because a catalyst possesses the very convenient property of speeding up rates without affecting yields.

EXAMPLE (a).   In the Haber process referred to in discussing the effect of pressure, the equation can be written more completely as:

$$N_2 + 3H_2 \rightleftharpoons 2NH_3 + 24,000 \text{ calories.}$$

This means that 24,000 calories of heat (1 calorie is that amount required to raise the temperature of 1 gm. of water through 1° C.) are *evolved* when the quantities of substances represented in the equation react, i.e. when 34 gm., or $2 \times 22 \cdot 4$ litres at N.T.P., of ammonia are produced from its elements.

Since this reaction is exothermic, the yield of ammonia will be greater the lower the temperature.   However, at low temperatures the rate of obtaining the yield is too slow, and hence a temperature of about 500° C. is used, with a catalyst too of course.

EXAMPLE (b).   The synthesis of nitric oxide from its elements is an *endothermic* reaction:

$$N_2 + O_2 \rightleftharpoons 2NO - 43,000 \text{ calories}   \text{(see p. 336)}.$$

In this case, therefore, a high temperature will increase both the yield and the rate at which the product is obtained; when the process was in commercial operation, the highest possible temperature (3000°–3500° C.) was in fact used.

EXAMPLE (c).   The Contact process for the manufacture of sulphur trioxide and thence sulphuric acid (see p. 362) provides a problem similar to that of synthetic ammonia:

$$2SO_2 + O_2 \rightleftharpoons 2SO_3(\text{gas}) + 45,000 \text{ calories}$$

This reaction is exothermic, and therefore a compromise temperature of about 400° C. is used to give a reasonable yield at a convenient rate.   Again a catalyst is important, and the student will probably have seen a laboratory demonstration of the production of sulphur trioxide by passing sulphur dioxide and oxygen over heated platinized asbestos (expt. 138, p. 361).

As in the ammonia equation, there is a reduction in volume from left to right in the sulphur trioxide equation, and hence an increase in pressure would also help to raise the yield.   In practice good results are obtained without this, and pressures of $1\frac{1}{2}$ to 2 atmospheres are used, i.e. sufficient only to maintain the circulation of the gases.

A compound, such as ammonia or sulphur trioxide, which is formed in an exothermic reaction from its elements, is sometimes called an "exothermic compound." *Endo*thermic compounds include nitric oxide, and acetylene, ozone, and chlorine dioxide (which can be explosive).

The Importance of Heats of Reaction

It is clear from the above examples that a knowledge of heats of reaction is important in deciding what are the best physical conditions necessary for carrying out a chemical process efficiently.

Another important branch of this study of *Thermochemistry* deals with heats of combustion, especially in the case of the various solid, liquid, and gaseous substances which are used as fuels.

Such measurements are made by burning weighed quantities of the particular fuel in oxygen in a suitable container. The amount of heat is found by immersing the container in a known amount of water and observing the rise in temperature which is produced.

Coal gas is supplied to consumers at a price which depends on its heat of combustion, or "calorific value," and this value is expressed in units called "therms." One British Thermal Unit is the amount of heat required to raise the temperature of 1 lb. of water through 1° F., and a therm is 100,000 of these units, or 25,000,000 calories.

One therm is given by the *complete* combustion of approximately:

7 lb. of house coal or coke	but the *efficiency* of a fire
or 10 lb. of peat	in using this heat varies
or 14 lb. of wood	from 15–20% for the open
or 5 lb. of coal gas (200 cu. ft.)	domestic hearth, to over
or 5 lb. of petroleum	50% for an efficient gas
or 2 lb. of hydrogen (400 cu. ft.)	fire or a closed coal or
(or 30 units of electricity)	coke stove, or 100% for
	an electric radiator.

The Energy Value of Foods

In studying the energy value of food it has been found that its heat of combustion, measured as above, is the same as that given out during its combustion in the human body (p. 304). The approximate values, in calories per gram, are:

Beer	500	It has been calculated that a normal
Milk	700	human being, at rest, requires between
Potatoes	900	1,500,000 and 2,000,000 calories per day.
Beef	1700	In addition to this, he will require any-
Bread	2300	thing up to another 3,000,000 calories
Sugar	4000	depending on his occupation, i.e. on the
Chocolate	5500	amount of muscular energy which he has
Butter	8000	to expend.

These large figures are usually quoted in terms of "Big Calories," equivalent to 1000 ordinary calories: e.g. the average number of these Calories in the food consumed in Britain in 1956 was about 3000 per head per day = 3,000,000 ordinary calories.

It is interesting to note, in this connection, that brain work as such does not appear to require any calories. The growing boy, however, needs almost as much as the adult doing heavy manual labour, but this is because he is growing and not because he may be thinking.

The Effect of Catalysts

In the laboratory preparation of oxygen from potassium chlorate (expts. 18 and 19, p. 29) it was proved that manganese dioxide acts as a catalyst: i.e. it increases the rate of chemical reaction without itself being affected in quantity or in chemical composition.

Catalysts are often specific in their action, that is to say, a substance which catalyses one reaction will not necessarily catalyse another; and there are cases where different catalysts even give different products from the same initial materials. A substance such as finely divided platinum will, however, catalyse several different reactions.

It has been previously stated that in a reversible reaction the catalyst will speed up both the forward and backward rates, and will therefore not affect the yield of product, but only the rate at which the yield is obtained. Catalysts are therefore important only in exothermic reactions, where the alternative plan for increasing the rate, i.e. a rise of temperature, would diminish the yield.

The success of many modern industrial processes depends

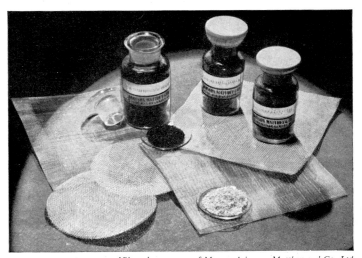

[*Photo by courtesy of Messrs. Johnson, Matthey and Co. Ltd.*

PLATE 15A.　PLATINUM CATALYST

200 ounces of the platinum-rhodium gauze shown in this picture will—during its useful working life—catalyse the production of about 20,000 tons of nitric acid from ammonia. The catalyst is arranged in multi-layer pads, containing 240 square feet of gauze.

on the discovery of suitable catalysts, and examples illustrating their use will be found in:

(*a*) The synthesis of ammonia from nitrogen and hydrogen by the Haber process: catalyst—finely divided iron, etc. (p. 314).

(*b*) The oxidation of ammonia to nitric acid (p. 320): catalyst—platinum gauze (PLATE 15A).

(c) The manufacture of sulphuric acid by the Contact Process (pp. 231, 362): catalyst—vanadium pentoxide V_2O_5 (PLATE 15B) or platinized asbestos.

[*Photo by courtesy of Monsanto Chemicals Ltd.*

PLATE 15B.   VANADIUM CATALYST

The vanadium pentoxide (V_2O_5) catalyst shown here will catalyse 10 times its own weight of finished sulphuric acid per day.   Its lifetime is about twenty years.

(d) The manufacture of sulphuric acid by the lead chamber process from sulphur dioxide, air, and steam (p. 364): catalyst —nitrogen dioxide.

(e) The manufacture of hydrogen from steam and carbon monoxide (p. 93): catalyst—finely divided iron.

(f) The reactions of hydrogen with various products (fig. 34, p. 101) to produce petrol from coal, margarine from whale oil, raw materials for plastics, etc.

Many catalysts are made inactive ("poisoned") by various impurities, such as dust, arsenic compounds, etc., and often elaborate precautions are needed to purify the raw materials (see p. 362).

"Negative catalysts" which slow down reactions may also be important, e.g. lead tetra-ethyl, which prevents compressed petrol vapour from combining with air ("knocking") until it is sparked.

Enzymes

A group of catalysts known as "enzymes," associated with living processes, are important in the study of Organic Chemistry.

These are more sensitive than the ordinary catalysts met with in Inorganic Chemistry, for their activity is easily destroyed by too high a temperature. Moreover, a particular enzyme will normally only catalyse one particular process.

Thus the well-known fermentation of the sugar glucose to give alcohol depends on the enzyme *zymase*, which is present in the living cells of the yeast plant (see p. 302):

$$\underset{\text{Glucose}}{C_6H_{12}O_6} = \underset{\text{Alcohol}}{2C_2H_6O} + \underset{\text{Carbon Dioxide}}{2CO_2 \nearrow}$$

When, however, milk turns sour, this is due to milk sugar being fermented to lactic acid by an enzyme present in bacteria in the milk. Yeast will not cause this fermentation:

$$C_6H_{12}O_6 = 2C_3H_6O_3$$

Starch is converted into malt sugar by the enzyme diastase, present in malt (obtained by allowing damp barley to sprout):

$$C_{600}H_{1000}O_{500} + 50H_2O = 50C_{12}H_{22}O_{11}$$

This is the first stage in the brewing industry before the malt sugar is fermented to glucose and thence to alcohol.

Another enzyme, very similar to diastase, called ptyalin, is present in saliva, where it catalyses the conversion of starch into more easily digestible malt sugar (see expt. 107, p. 305).

The precise action of these enzymes is not yet fully understood, but there is no doubt that they are of the utmost importance in many life processes.

It is also probable that the importance of **Vitamins** (p. 307) is due to their acting as catalysts in several vital bodily processes.

Suggestions for Practical Work

(*a*) Take some 2% hydrochloric acid (1 c.c. conc. + 15 c.c. water) and add it to test-tubes containing "hypo" solutions of different concentrations, e.g. 2%, 1%, 0·5%, 0·2%, 0·1%. Note the times taken for a visible reaction (p. 114) to occur.

(*b*) Repeat the above experiment with hypo and dilute acid solutions which have both been heated to 100° C.

(*c*) Expt. 19 (p. 29).

(*d*) Place gas-jars of carefully dried hydrogen sulphide and sulphur dioxide mouth to mouth (p. 353). No reaction should occur until one drop of water is introduced as a catalyst.

QUESTIONS ON CHAPTER XV

1. What is a reversible reaction? State briefly but exactly what you would do to find out whether the action of steam on red-hot iron is reversible. (O.)

2. Explain why the synthesis of ammonia is carried out under pressure but the synthesis of nitric oxide was not. State the general principle governing such reactions.

3. Deduce, from the principles explained in this chapter, the most suitable conditions for preparing hydrogen from steam by the reactions (p. 93):

$$C + H_2O \rightleftharpoons CO + H_2 - \text{heat};$$
$$CO + H_2O \rightleftharpoons CO_2 + H_2 + \text{heat}.$$

4. What are the chief characteristics of a *catalyst*? Outline *two* industrial processes in which a catalyst is employed, pointing out the advantages gained by the presence of the catalyst in each case. (C.)

5. Assuming that your diet provides 3000 Calories per day (actually it will be much more than this), calculate approximately

what percentages of this are provided by the six foodstuffs named on p. 233 in the amounts which you eat of them.

6. Calculate the relative cost, in pennies per calorie, of heating your sitting-room by (*a*) wood, (*b*) coal, (*c*) gas, (*d*) electricity.

N.B.—Other questions on the general principles discussed in this chapter will be found at the end of other chapters (XIX, no. 3; XXII, no. 9) and in nos. 19 and 36 of the miscellaneous questions on p. 512.

PART 3
THE NON-METALS

CHAPTER XVI

CARBON AND ITS OXIDES. FUELS

Carbon is an extremely important element because all living matter—human beings, other animals, and plants—is made up of its compounds. All fuel and power, with the exceptions of hydro-electricity and atomic energy, is also obtained from carbon or its compounds such as wood, peat, coal, petroleum, etc. And large numbers of artificial products such as dyes, drugs, explosives, and plastics are carbon compounds which have been prepared synthetically. The total number of carbon compounds known (about a million) is far more than those of *all* the other elements.

Carbon dioxide occurs in the atmosphere as the result of the respiration of living matter (expt. 13, p. 23) and the burning of fuels (expt. 12, p. 22) and is the indispensable source of food for plants (p. 36). Carbonates of various metals occur naturally and are discussed in Chapter XVII.

Carbon as an Element

Carbon occurs naturally as the element in several more or less pure forms, which are very different from one another. Diamond and graphite are fairly pure forms which are mined, and can also be obtained artificially. Various kinds of charcoal can be made by "charring" wood or other forms of animal or vegetable matter, i.e. heating it with insufficient air to burn it; and soot is yet another form of the same element. The most abundant form, coal, contains only about 85% of carbon, but coke which is obtained from it (p. 244) is purer.

Different forms of the same element are called *allotropes*, and the ability to exist in more than one form is known as *allotropy*. As it can easily be shown by experiment (p. 245) that diamond, graphite, and sugar charcoal consist of carbon only, the differences between them must be due to different arrangements of the carbon atoms; X-ray analysis proves that this is so (fig. 80A and fig. 80B opposite).

THE ALLOTROPIC FORMS OF CARBON

1. Diamond.   This form of carbon, in every way different from the others, is found naturally in Africa, India, Brazil; the bulk of the world's supply is now obtained from South Africa.   It is the hardest substance known, and diamonds can only be cut and polished by the use of smaller and less valuable diamonds.   Diamonds have a very high refractive index and, when cut so as to display many small faces, reflect light very brilliantly.   The typical shape of diamonds seen in a jeweller's window is not their natural crystal shape but one which displays to the greatest advantage their optical properties.   In addition to their value as gems, diamonds are used for cutting glass, and drilling pottery and hard rock.

Diamonds have been successfully produced artificially by crystallizing carbon from molten iron under great pressure, but the products are inferior in quality to the natural ones and of little value.

The great hardness and cutting power of the diamond is due to its peculiar crystal structure.   X-ray analysis has shown that the carbon atoms are joined together to form a continuous pyramidal structure, which has no weak points (fig. 80A).

2. Graphite.   This is the substance used in pencils.   It occurs naturally in many parts of the world, particularly Ceylon.   British deposits in Cumberland are now almost worked out.   The crystals of graphite are flat hexagons which are not joined to the hexagons in the planes above or below (fig. 80B).   They therefore, unlike diamond, easily slip over one another (fig. 80B) and so graphite is a useful lubricant, especially as it burns only at very high temperatures.   So high is its temperature of ignition in air that it is actually used for the manufacture of crucibles in which to melt metals.

The best known use of graphite is for making the "leads" of pencils.   Finely ground graphite is mixed with clay and squeezed through a small die, thus producing a thin rod which is afterwards baked and fixed into the wood. The proportion of clay to graphite determines the "hardness" of the pencil.

Large quantities of graphite are manufactured artificially near Niagara by the Acheson process, in which coke is heated to a very high temperature in electric furnaces. The enormous supplies of electric energy needed for this process make it economical only where cheap sources of electricity are

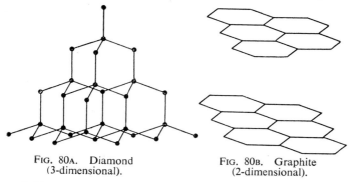

FIG. 80A. Diamond
(3-dimensional).

FIG. 80B. Graphite
(2-dimensional).

available; very pure graphite is obtained in this way. For use as a lubricant it is sometimes mixed with grease, and sometimes used dry, e.g. for the bearings of small electric motors.

Graphite (850 tons) is used in the Atomic Pile ("BEPO") at Harwell, because it absorbs neutrons and so moderates the artificial disintegration of uranium (40 tons), thus setting free Atomic Energy in a controlled manner for central heating.

Graphite, unlike diamond and nearly all other non-metals, is a reasonably good conductor of electricity. It is therefore used for electrodes (pp. 406, 449, 454, 457), and for powdering on to non-conducting objects which are to be electroplated.

3. Amorphous, i.e. Non-crystalline Carbon. Strictly speaking, these forms are composed of crystals also, but of less than microscopic size. They differ from one another in their method of preparation and their degree of purity.

(*a*) *Charcoal.* When wood is heated out of contact with air, so that it cannot burn, certain volatile products are driven off and charcoal remains. A laboratory experiment (no. 91, p. 258) to illustrate these changes is described later in the chapter. Before the time of coal, charcoal was a common fuel and was prepared in large quantities by allowing great heaps of wood to burn slowly in a very limited supply of air. This was done by covering the heap with soil or turf and admitting only enough air to keep the mass smouldering. The method may be imitated in the laboratory by heating wood covered with sand. There is no need in this case to admit any air, since the

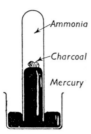

FIG. 81. Charcoal absorbs gases.

necessary heat is supplied by a bunsen under the tray on which the wood is heated. Charcoal is a black, porous solid which marks paper. Its most outstanding property is its ability to absorb gases (including air).

Expt. 79. If a small piece of *freshly-heated* charcoal is pushed into a tube containing ammonia gas collected over mercury (fig. 81) it floats on the mercury, and slowly absorbs the gas. The mercury rises as the gas is absorbed, until it nearly reaches the top of the tube.

This property is employed in gas-masks, the canisters of which contain a highly absorbent kind of charcoal to absorb poison gases, such as chlorine.

Charcoal is very unreactive; and if wooden stakes are charred before being driven into the ground, they last much longer   Wooden supports used by the Romans during the occupation of Britain are occasionally found and probably owe their preservation to this property.

(*b*) *Coke.* When coal is heated in the absence of air, as described for wood, coke is left behind after all the volatile products have been driven off. This process is so important for the manufacture of both coal gas and coke that it is described in detail later in this chapter (p. 259). Coke is used in very large quantities in slow-combustion furnaces for the central heating of schools, offices, shops, etc.; in the extraction of metals from their ores (p. 246), and in making various gaseous fuels (see p. 256).

(c) *Animal Charcoal.* When crushed bones are heated in absence of air, animal charcoal remains. This is finely divided carbon mixed with much calcium phosphate. Carbon in this form is used to take the *colour* from solutions; sugar solution, for instance, is boiled with animal charcoal to decolorize it before crystallizing out the white sugar.

Expt. 80. If diluted ink or litmus solution is boiled with a little animal charcoal and then filtered, the filtrate will be found to be almost colourless. Similarly, certain colourless substances such as quinine sulphate are also absorbed and can no longer be tasted.

(d) *Soot.* Lampblack is the very fine soot formed when oils or turpentine are burned in an insufficient supply of air. It is used for the manufacture of printers' ink, black shoe polish, and other black colouring matters; it is also incorporated in rubber tyres (to the extent of about 30% by weight) to reduce wear on the tyres (see p. 525).

Soot from domestic chimneys and factories is a less fine form of the same kind of carbon. Since almost all of it will burn, its production represents a needless waste of fuel. In addition it is the curse of towns and industrial areas (PLATE 16B), where it hangs as a pall in the sky, shutting out sunlight, blackening buildings, and acting as the chief cause of winter fogs (see p. 261).

(e) *Sugar Charcoal.* If glucose (or ordinary sugar) is heated strongly in the absence of air, water is driven off and a very pure form of charcoal remains:

$$C_6H_{12}O_6 = 6C + 6H_2O$$

The densities of the three main allotropes are very different: diamond 3·5, graphite 2·5, charcoal (air-free) about 1·5 gm. per c.c.

Chemical Properties of Carbon

(a) *All pure allotropes* of carbon consist of the same chemical element and therefore *have the same equivalent weight.* This may be proved by burning each of them (diamond, graphite,

S.C.T.—9

sugar charcoal) separately in oxygen (see expt. 61, p. 139)
When the potash bulbs show no further increase in weight, it
will be found that 1 gm. of each allotrope has produced 3·66 gm.
of carbon dioxide, i.e. the equivalent—see p. 139—of carbon
in each case is 3.

(b) *Carbon is a reducing agent.*   Carbon not only combines
with free oxygen but will take oxygen from other compounds.

Expt. 81.   Heat lead oxide (litharge) on a charcoal block by
means of a mouth blowpipe   Silvery beads of metallic lead are
formed and will mark paper.

$$2PbO + C = 2Pb + CO_2 \nearrow$$

Expt. 82.   Mix powdered charcoal with black copper oxide and
put into a test-tube fitted with a delivery tube.   Heat, and pass the
gas into lime-water to test for carbon dioxide (see p. 249).   The
lime-water turns cloudy, and possibly traces of pink copper may
be seen in the mixture.

$$2CuO + C = 2Cu + CO_2 \nearrow$$

This type of reaction is used on a large scale in the extraction
of metals such as zinc, iron, tin, and lead from their ores
(see pp. 460, 465, 471, 473).

CARBON DIOXIDE, CO₂

The processes which add carbon dioxide to the atmosphere
or remove it from it are summarized in the following diagram
of the "Carbon Dioxide Cycle" (fig. 82).

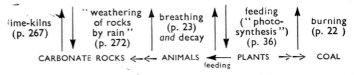

CARBON DIOXIDE

FIG. 82.   "The carbon dioxide cycle."

The vital importance of carbon dioxide to all forms of life
has been emphasized already (p. 36).

Laboratory Preparation of Carbon Dioxide

Expt. 83. Dilute hydrochloric acid is poured on to marble chips (calcium carbonate) or any other carbonate in a flask (see fig. 83).

$$\underset{\substack{\text{Calcium} \\ \text{Carbonate}}}{CaCO_3} + \underset{\substack{\text{Hydrogen} \\ \text{Chloride}}}{2HCl} = \underset{\substack{\text{Calcium} \\ \text{Chloride}}}{CaCl_2} + \underset{\substack{\text{Carbonic} \\ \text{acid}}}{H_2CO_3} \underset{\substack{\text{i.e. Hydrogen} \\ \text{Carbonate}}}{}$$

The carbonic acid decomposes at once, without heating, and carbon dioxide is given off with effervescence:

$$H_2CO_3 = H_2O + CO_2 \nearrow$$

The gas may be collected either by displacing air upward—because it is heavier than air (see Chapter XIII: Avogadro, p. 196), or over water, but in this case the water will dissolve about its own volume of carbon dioxide (p. 114). The calcium chloride remains in solution in the flask.

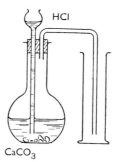

HCl

CaCO₃

Fig. 83. Laboratory preparation of carbon dioxide.

For the preparation of larger quantities of the gas, Kipp's apparatus (p. 90) is normally used. Marble chips are cheap, and convenient because they are not soluble in water and are large enough not to fall through into the bottom compartment. Sulphuric acid should not be used, because it forms an insoluble layer of calcium sulphate on the outside of the marble, and so prevents the reaction continuing after a little time.

If required pure and dry, the carbon dioxide should be passed through a dilute solution of sodium bicarbonate to remove any hydrochloric acid carried over as spray:

$$HCl + NaHCO_3 = NaCl + H_2O + CO_2 \nearrow$$

it may then be dried by passing through concentrated sulphuric acid.

Physical Properties of Carbon Dioxide

Carbon dioxide is a colourless heavy gas (molecular weight = 44; air having an *average* M.W. of 28·8) without smell. It dissolves in water (about 1 volume in 1 volume at room temperature and pressure) to form a solution with a pleasantly acid taste; it is therefore used as "soda water" and mineral waters, which are solutions of carbon dioxide under pressure in water, sometimes with colouring or flavouring materials added.

Carbon dioxide dissolved in the water provides sea-plants with food for photosynthesis, and so makes possible life in the sea.

The high **density** of the gas is shown in the following experiments (fig. 84):

Expt. 84. (*a*) Bubbles blown with air in soap solution will float very easily if shaken into a large vessel of carbon dioxide;

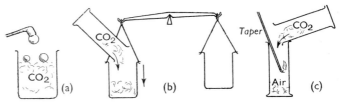

FIG. 84.   The high density of carbon dioxide.

(*b*) If a counterpoised beaker has carbon dioxide poured into it, it slowly sinks; (*c*) If carbon dioxide is poured on to a taper burning in air in a gas-jar, the taper is quickly extinguished. The gas is evidently heavy enough to be poured from one vessel to another.

Chemical Properties of Carbon Dioxide

1. The gas *will not support combustion* and a lighted taper or spill is extinguished when pushed into the gas. This property is turned to advantage in fire-extinguishers. One type of extinguisher is virtually a carbon dioxide generator in which the acid and the carbonate are prevented from reacting until the bottle containing the acid is broken. The stream of carbon dioxide excludes the air from the fire, and so smothers it, unless it has become too widespread. Fig. 85 (p. 250) illustrates in diagrammatic form the construction of such an extinguisher.

Expt. 85. Burning magnesium is hot enough to decompose the gas, combine with the oxygen liberated, and leave carbon. A strip of magnesium ribbon lighted in the bunsen and lowered into a jar of the gas, splutters as though burning with difficulty, but continues to burn. When it has burned out there will be found black specks of carbon on the sides of the jar and the familiar white ash of magnesium oxide on the bottom. This ash turns damp red litmus-paper blue; if a little dilute acid is added, it quickly dissolves, leaving the carbon.

$$\text{Magnesium} + \text{Carbon Dioxide} = \text{Magnesium Oxide} + \text{Carbon}$$
$$2Mg \qquad\qquad CO_2 \qquad\qquad 2MgO \qquad\qquad C$$

This experiment shows the presence of both oxygen and carbon in the gas, but it does not prove that these are the only two elements present.

2. *Action on Water*

Expt. 86. The solution of carbon dioxide in water is found to colour blue litmus wine-red showing it to be a weak acid, carbonic acid. (p. 47.)

$$\text{Carbon Dioxide} + \text{Water} = \text{Carbonic acid}$$
$$CO_2 \qquad\qquad H_2O \qquad\qquad H_2CO_3$$

(In its reaction with alkalis such as lime-water and caustic soda, it is best to regard this acid as being first formed with the water of the solution, and then reacting with the base to form a salt and water. This practice is followed in the equations given in the following paragraphs.)

When the carbonic acid solution containing litmus is boiled, the red colour quickly disappears as the gas is boiled out, thus indicating that the acid is unstable as well as weak. Hence, in reactions of acids with carbonates when carbonic acid is formed as the result of double decomposition, it at once decomposes and a brisk effervescence of carbon dioxide is observed (see expt. 83, p. 247).

3. *Reactions with Lime-Water*

Expt. 87. (*a*) If carbon dioxide is bubbled into lime-water a white precipitate of chalk is formed and the clear lime-water becomes cloudy. If this precipitate is filtered off and a little dilute acid added to it, an immediate effervescence of carbon dioxide is produced, showing that it is a carbonate.

Calcium Hydroxide	+	Hydrogen Carbonate	=	Calcium Carbonate	+	Hydrogen Hydroxide (water)
$Ca(OH)_2$		H_2CO_3		$CaCO_3 \downarrow$		$2H_2O$

This reaction is the test by which carbon dioxide is identified, as no other gas gives a white precipitate with lime-water.

(*b*) When more of the gas is bubbled through the cloudy lime-water the precipitate of chalk disappears and a colourless solution remains. The insoluble chalk has combined with the excess carbon dioxide to form a soluble substance. This new compound is called calcium bicarbonate.

Calcium Carbonate	+	Hydrogen Carbonate	=	Calcium Hydrogen Carbonate (Calcium Bicarbonate)
$CaCO_3$		H_2CO_3		$CaCO_3.H_2CO_3$, i.e. $Ca(HCO_3)_2$

This new compound only exists in solution at room temperature; attempts to isolate it in the solid state result in decomposing it to form calcium carbonate with evolution of carbon dioxide:

$$Ca(HCO_3)_2 = CaCO_3 + H_2O + CO_2 \nearrow$$

These reactions have an important bearing on the question of the hardness of water (see Chapter XVII, p. 272).

Carbonic acid is thus seen to form two sets of salts, carbonates and bicarbonates. Both sodium compounds can be isolated as crystalline solids (see expt. 32, p. 72) and therefore carbonic acid is said to be a "dibasic acid" (p. 71). Sodium or potassium hydroxides remove carbon dioxide (see expt. 61, p. 139, and expt. 89, p. 253) by reacting to form the carbonates.

The properties of the carbonates are discussed in the next chapter (pp. 279–86).

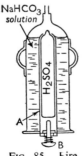

NaHCO₃ solution

H₂SO₄

A

B

Fig. 85. Fire extinguisher.

Uses of Carbon Dioxide

1. *Fire Extinguishers* (see Chemical Properties, p. 248). In fig. 85, which illustrates one type of fire extinguisher, the inner metal case A contains a glass bottle of sulphuric acid. When the plunger B is struck on the ground the bottle is broken and the acid reacts with

the solution of sodium bicarbonate with which the rest of the extinguisher is filled. Carbon dioxide is produced under pressure and is ejected, as a froth with the liquid, at the nozzle. This jet has considerable carrying power, reaching 10 or 12 yards.

$$2NaHCO_3 + H_2SO_4 = Na_2SO_4 + 2H_2O + 2CO_2 \nearrow$$

In a different type known as "foam extinguishers" the carbon dioxide and liquid frothing out are made to give a much more permanent foam by the addition of a substance called saponin. The liquid in these extinguishers is a solution of aluminium sulphate, which reacts with sodium bicarbonate to yield sodium sulphate, aluminium hydroxide, and carbon dioxide.

$$Al_2(SO_4)_3 + 6NaHCO_3 = 2Al(OH)_3 + 3Na_2SO_4 + 6CO_2 \nearrow$$

(One might expect aluminium carbonate to be formed, but this is too unstable to exist.)

The layer of foam "blankets" the fire (the aluminium hydroxide being a jelly-like solid), thus preventing access of air to it. The method is especially valuable in dealing with oil or petrol fires, where water is of little use because the burning oil floats on it. Cylinders containing carbon dioxide liquefied under pressure are very useful extinguishers because they make no mess.

"Pyrene" extinguishers contain carbon tetrachloride, CCl_4, a low-boiling liquid, which gives a vapour three and a half times as heavy as carbon dioxide (b.p. 77° C., M.W. 154).

2. "Fizzy Drinks" (see Physical Properties, p. 248)

3. Solid Carbon Dioxide for Refrigeration. Ice-cream containers are frequently cooled by putting in them pieces of solid carbon dioxide. On standing in warm air this white solid "sublimes," i.e. turns directly from solid to gas without first melting. For this reason it is often called "dry ice." The gas is comparatively easy to liquefy, and at lower temperatures to turn to a solid. When mixed with ether, a freezing mixture giving a temperature of −78° C. is obtained, which is often valuable for laboratory experiments. Recent

experiments on adding "dry ice" to rain-clouds are illustrated in PLATE 16A.

Commercial Preparation of Carbon Dioxide

The carbon dioxide required for these or other uses is obtained as a "by-product" from the preparation of nitrogen

[Photo by courtesy of "Nature" and the C.S.I.R.O.

PLATE 16A.   SOLID CARBON DIOXIDE MAY HELP IT TO RAIN

The tall cloud like a thundercloud was made artificially.   The intense cold of solid CO_2 ($-78°$ C.) dropped from the aeroplane caused the moisture in the air to form ice crystals.   The ice then turned to rain.

(p. 33) or alcohol (p. 302) or quicklime (p. 267).   Its cost is therefore extremely small.

CARBON MONOXIDE, CO

1. *Preparation from Carbon Dioxide*

Expt. 88.   Carbon dioxide, generated by the action of dilute hydrochloric acid on marble, is passed through a long iron tube packed with wood charcoal, made red hot in a furnace, as shown in fig. 86. Some carbon dioxide may pass through the tube unchanged, and so a wash-bottle and a trough of caustic soda are put in to absorb this. The gas which emerges is inflammable, and poisonous; it is without action on lime-water and litmus, but, after burning in air, the gas produced turns lime-water milky and litmus wine-red. The gas can only be a compound of carbon and oxygen from the

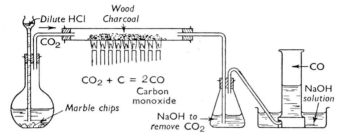

FIG. 86. Preparation of carbon monoxide—1.

manner of its preparation, and it must contain less oxygen than carbon dioxide since on burning (i.e. combining with more oxygen) it yields carbon dioxide.

$$2CO + O_2 = 2CO_2$$

carbon monoxide   oxygen   carbon dioxide
(2 vols.)   (1 vol.)   (2 vols.)

It is called carbon monoxide, and its formula can be shown to be CO by application of the methods outlined in Chapter XIII (p. 197).

2. Preparation from Oxalic Acid

Expt. 89. A more convenient way for the preparation of this gas in the laboratory is to heat together oxalic acid crystals and concentrated sulphuric acid (fig. 87). The action of the sulphuric acid in this experiment is to dehydrate (remove water from) the oxalic acid; the product of the reaction is a mixture of equal volumes of carbon monoxide and carbon dioxide, as shown in the equation below:

$$H_2C_2O_4.2H_2O - 3H_2O = CO + CO_2$$

The carbon dioxide is dissolved in the flask of caustic soda solution and the carbon monoxide collected over caustic soda solution as in the last experiment.

9*

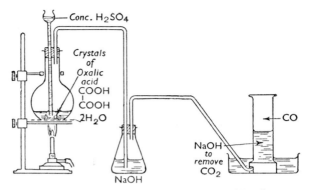

FIG. 87.   Preparation of carbon monoxide—2.

3. *Preparation from Formic Acid*

By action of concentrated sulphuric acid on formic acid or formates, carbon monoxide is obtained alone.

$$H_2CO_2 - H_2O = CO$$

Occurrence of Carbon Monoxide in Everyday Life

Whenever carbon or its compounds are burned—intentionally or otherwise—with an insufficient supply of air or oxygen for complete combustion, some carbon monoxide is formed.

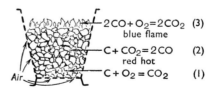

FIG. 88.   Coke brazier.

(This reaction is used in the preparation of gaseous fuels, see below.) As this gas is extremely poisonous it is very important that its presence should be realized.

In a coal or coke fire (fig. 88) carbon dioxide is first formed when the air entering under the fire meets the coal (1). But in passing through the fire some carbon dioxide is reduced by red-hot carbon to carbon monoxide (2); this burns at the surface of the fire with bright blue flames (3). There is little danger from the gas in this case as it meets excess of air and is certain to be burned. Slow-combustion stoves do, however, need to have an efficient chimney.

In the engine of a motor-car or motor-bicycle, the petrol which is exploded with air to provide the motive power is never mixed with enough air to burn it away completely to carbon dioxide and water. In consequence, the exhaust fumes contain about 10% of carbon monoxide. For this reason a car engine should not be run in an enclosed place such as a garage. It will be observed that since carbon monoxide is inflammable, its presence in the exhaust gases of an engine represents a waste of power and fuel. Streets with much motor traffic have been shown to contain as much as 50 parts of carbon monoxide per million parts of air, and in places like the Mersey Tunnel the concentration would be much higher if special steps were not taken to prevent it.

After explosions in coal-mines caused by methane (p. 291), carbon monoxide (called "after-damp" by the miners) remains, because there is insufficient air for complete combustion. This is extremely dangerous, and rescue parties have to be equipped with oxygen-breathing apparatus.

The Properties of Carbon Monoxide

1. *Poisonous nature.* When breathed, carbon monoxide unites with the haemoglobin of the blood (p. 24) to form a bright pink compound called carboxy-haemoglobin. This prevents oxygen from uniting with it, and so the affected person immediately suffers from oxygen-starvation. A concentration of 0.1% is fatal if breathed for half an hour, and unpleasant effects result from breathing for some time even as little as 10 parts per million.

As the gas has no smell, it gives no warning of its presence. The poisonous nature of coal gas is due to the carbon monoxide in it (p. 260).

2. *Inflammability.* Carbon monoxide burns with a pale blue flame to form carbon dioxide. (It therefore affects lime-water after burning, but not before, see expt. 88, p. 253.)

$$2CO + O_2 = 2CO_2$$

It is also an important inflammable constituent of the three gaseous fuels (producer gas, water gas, and coal gas) described below.

3. *Reducing power.* Carbon monoxide will also combine with the oxygen in compounds:

(*a*) with steam and a catalyst, it gives hydrogen;

$$CO + H_2O = CO_2 + H_2 \text{ (see p. 93)}$$

(*b*) with iron oxide, it gives iron;

$$3CO + Fe_2O_3 = 3CO_2 + 2Fe$$
(see the Blast Furnace, p. 465).

Expt. 90. If carbon monoxide is passed over heated copper oxide or lead oxide, the metal is produced exactly as when hydrogen is used (expt. 63, p. 141):

$$CO + PbO = CO_2 + Pb$$

4. *Solubility.* Carbon monoxide is very much less soluble than carbon dioxide in ordinary water (p. 114), and as it is not acidic it does not dissolve in alkalis. It is, however, easily absorbed by a solution of cuprous chloride (CuCl) in either concentrated hydrochloric acid or concentrated ammonia. Such solutions are useful in estimating the proportion of carbon monoxide in gaseous fuels (see below) such as coal gas, or in purifying the hydrogen required for the manufacture of ammonia (pp. 92–93).

GASEOUS FUELS

For many industrial and domestic purposes a gaseous fuel is much more convenient than a solid fuel; its combustion is much easier to control by varying the quantities of the gas burned and of the air mixed with it.

(*a*) **Producer Gas.** By passing a stream of air over red-hot coke, carbon dioxide is first formed as in a coal fire, and this is then reduced to carbon monoxide by the rest of the coke. The issuing gas is then a mixture of nitrogen and carbon monoxide.   As the following equation shows, approximately one-third of the mixture is inflammable:

$$O_2(+4N_2)+2C=2CO+4N_2$$

It is unnecessary to supply heat to the coke during the process because the reaction is exothermic (p. 230), i.e. it gives out heat.

Producer gas is used for heating the retorts in which coal is converted into coal gas (p. 259), and for heating lime-kilns (p. 267) and steel furnaces (p. 468), and glass furnaces (p. 435).

The production of this gas may be imitated in the laboratory by blowing air through the apparatus illustrated in fig. 86 (p. 253) for the preparation of carbon monoxide.   The gas which collects will be found to be readily inflammable.

(b) **Water Gas.**   When steam is passed over red-hot coke a mixture of carbon monoxide and hydrogen in approximately equal volumes is produced, and is known as water gas:

$$C+H_2O=CO+H_2$$

This is an even more useful fuel than producer gas, because both its constituents are inflammable.

This reaction, however, is endothermic (p. 230), i.e. it absorbs heat, and the temperature rapidly falls unless heat is supplied.   It is therefore customary to make water gas and producer gas alternately in the same apparatus.   While air is being passed over the red-hot coke it is heated up and glows brightly, then when air is replaced by steam the temperature falls; the duration of the two processes is controlled so that it is not necessary to heat the coke.   A mixture of the gases, made by portable generators on trailers, was used to drive buses during the 1939 war because of the petrol shortage.

Water gas is widely used as a source of hydrogen (see p. 93), as a fuel to mix with coal gas (see p. 260), and in the *Mond Nickel Process*.   In this, water gas is passed over nickel oxide (mixed with impurities), and the hydrogen in it reduces the nickel oxide to nickel:

$$NiO+H_2=Ni+H_2O$$

This then combines with the carbon monoxide to form a volatile compound, nickel carbonyl,

$$Ni + 4CO = Ni(CO)_4 \nearrow$$

which goes off as a gas leaving the impurities behind. This compound is easily decomposed by heat to give pure nickel, and carbon monoxide which can be used again.

Producer gas and water gas can be produced more cheaply than coal gas, but have less heating value and are therefore not so suitable to supply for domestic use. They are used for firing ovens in which pottery is to be heated and for furnaces in which steel is made or melted.

(c) Coal Gas.

Expt. 91. If small pieces of coal are heated strongly in the apparatus shown in fig. 89 an inflammable gas will collect over water in the gas-jar, a tarry liquid with a watery layer above it in the flask, and coke will remain in the test-tube. The gas will probably be dis-

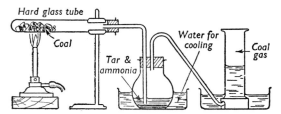

Fig. 89. Laboratory preparation of coal gas.

coloured and far from the purity expected of commercial coal gas, but the apparatus illustrates the essential principles of coal-gas manufacture. In the test-tube all the volatile constituents are driven off from the coal, leaving only coke. The liquids in the flask represent those volatile products which are easily condensed, and may be shown to consist of two main constituents, namely coal tar and an aqueous solution of ammonia. The residual gas is a mixture of hydrogen, methane and carbon monoxide, with smaller quantities of hydrogen sulphide and other gases.

Similar changes occur when wood is used, the solid being charcoal, but the watery liquid is acid (acetic acid), and there is no hydrogen sulphide in the gas obtained.

Commercial Production of Coal Gas

The coal is heated to a temperature of about 1000° C. by means of producer gas in large vertical retorts, without any air being allowed to enter. It falls through the retorts under the action of gravity, and the coke (p. 244) formed is removed from the bottom (fig. 90).

The volatile products come off and pass to a water main, where some of the tar condenses. Further cooling in large air- and water-cooled condensers removes the rest of the tar, which collects in the tar-well under water.

The next process is to remove the ammonia by washing the gas very thoroughly in "scrubbers." In these, water dissolves out the ammonia.

The hydrogen sulphide must now be removed by passing the gas over "bog iron ore," ferric oxide. This is spread on wire-mesh trays enclosed in large iron boxes. The sulphur of the

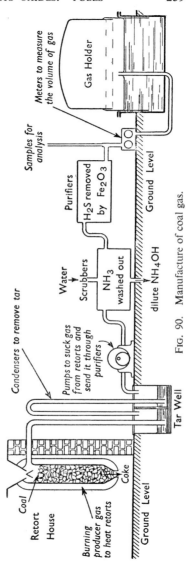

Fig. 90. Manufacture of coal gas.

hydrogen sulphide is replaced by oxygen from the iron oxide, which in turn becomes iron sulphide:

$$Fe_2O_3 + 3H_2S = Fe_2S_3 + 3H_2O$$

When the oxide is exhausted ("spent"), a current of air is passed through to convert the iron sulphide into free sulphur and regenerated iron oxide:

$$2Fe_2S_3 + 3O_2 = 2Fe_2O_3 + 6S$$

This is now fit to use again. When the proportion of sulphur reaches 50–60% the "spent oxide" is sold for the manufacture of *sulphuric acid* (p. 355), although less than half the amount available in this country is so used (PLATE 21, p. 344).

The purified coal gas contains a certain amount of benzene (p. 295) and naphthalene, which it is profitable to extract; this is done by "scrubbing" with oil, which dissolves them. The gas is then measured by meters, collected over water in the familiar large gas-holders, and sent in large pipes ("mains") to the consumers as required.

The Nature of Coal Gas

Coal gas is a mixture of variable composition containing about 50% hydrogen (H_2) *by volume*, 30% methane (CH_4), 10% carbon monoxide (CO); these gases burn readily in air to give carbon dioxide and water and a good deal of heat.

Gases such as ethylene, C_2H_4 (p. 292), containing a higher percentage of carbon, are also present to the extent of about 5%. These give a certain amount of soot which when white hot gives out light (p. 297).

Finally there is present in coal gas about 5% of impurities such as carbon dioxide and nitrogen.

If not all the coke made is required for sale, some of it is converted into water gas (p. 257), which is then mixed with the coal gas.

By-products of Coal Gas

1. *Ammonia*. From the "ammoniacal liquor," as the aqueous solution of ammonia is called, the ammonia gas may be distilled off and converted into ammonium sulphate by

dissolving it in dilute sulphuric acid. This compound finds widespread use as a fertilizer (p. 301).

2. *Sulphuric acid.* The hydrogen sulphide in the crude gas is converted to "spent oxide," and thence (p. 356) into sulphuric acid.

3. *Tar.* On distillation and purification, coal tar yields a very large number of extremely important derivatives. Among these are benzene, toluene, naphthalene, anthracene, phenol

[*Photo by courtesy of the News Chronicle*

PLATE 16B. SMOKE AND ITS PREVENTION—STOKE-ON-TRENT
Stoke-on-Trent (population 270,000) in the Potteries has smoke issuing from every chimney, domestic and industrial (p. 262).

("carbolic acid"), creosote. From these substances in turn are obtained many other essential substances, for the manufacture of drugs, dyestuffs, plastics, and explosives.

As *Punch* once remarked:

> Oil and ointment, and wax and wine,
> And the lovely colours called aniline,
> You can make anything, from a salve to a star,
> (If only you know how) from black Coal Tar.

So valuable are these by-products of coal, that it is very short-sighted to permit their loss as the result of burning raw coal. When this aspect of the problem of domestic coal fires is considered as well as that of the smoke-laden atmosphere of our towns (see PLATES 16B and 16C), it is difficult to escape the conclusion that the comfortable and romantic appearance of the coal fire is a very poor excuse for continuing a wasteful and unhealthy practice.

Even from the point of view of heating alone, the official Simon Report on Domestic Fuel Policy, published in 1946,

[*Photo by Kenneth Hutton*

PLATE 16C.   SMOKE AND ITS PREVENTION—STOCKHOLM

Stockholm (population 700,000), where the only smoke seen is from ships in the harbour.   All main railways and factories are electrified.

says: "Our coal is used for domestic heating with a degree of inefficiency which is not, so far as we can ascertain, even approached in any other country in the world." And Sir Henry Tizard, in his 1948 Presidential Address to the British Association, stated that if we apply the knowledge we already possess about methods of economizing coal, the benefits to this country during the next twenty years will be greater than those resulting from the production of atomic power.

The Use and Misuse of Coal is illustrated in fig. 91.

THE USE AND MISUSE OF COAL

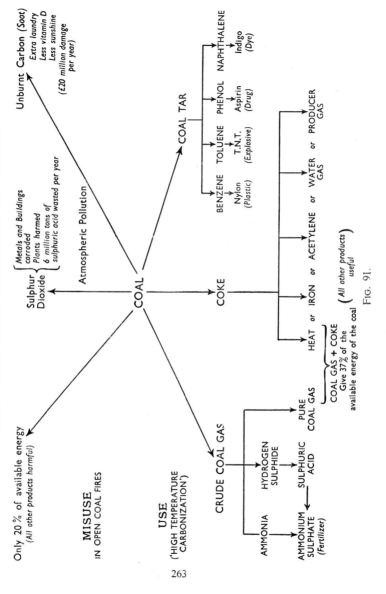

MISUSE
IN OPEN COAL FIRES

Only 20% of available energy
(All other products harmful)

Sulphur Dioxide { Metals and Buildings corroded
Plants harmed
6 million tons of sulphuric acid wasted per year }

Atmospheric Pollution

Unburnt Carbon (*Soot*)
*Extra laundry
Less vitamin D
Less sunshine
(£20 million damage per year)*

COAL TAR

BENZENE   TOLUENE   PHENOL   NAPHTHALENE
Nylon   T.N.T.   Aspirin   Indigo
(Plastic) *(Explosive)* *(Drug)* *(Dye)*

COAL

USE
('HIGH TEMPERATURE CARBONIZATION')

CRUDE COAL GAS

AMMONIA   HYDROGEN SULPHIDE   PURE COAL GAS

AMMONIUM SULPHATE   SULPHURIC ACID
(Fertilizer)

HEAT *or* COKE   IRON *or* ACETYLENE *or* WATER *or* PRODUCER GAS
                                                         GAS

COAL GAS + COKE
Give 37% of the available energy of the coal

(All other products useful)

263

Fig. 91.

Other Uses of Coal

(a) *Low-temperature Carbonization.* This modern process carries out the "destructive distillation" of coal at a lower temperature (500° C.) than is used in the ordinary gas-works plant.

A smaller quantity of gas is obtained, though of higher heating value per cubic foot. The solid residue, "Coalite," is smokeless, like coke, but contains more volatile matter and so burns more readily in air. The tar gives a liquid fuel like petrol, though not the same products as the coal tar obtained by high-temperature carbonization.

(b) *Hydrogenation of Coal.* This has been in operation in this country during the last fifteen years. Coal, or more usually creosote, is treated with hydrogen at high pressures and temperatures in the presence of catalysts to convert it into oil. Although the cost is high, it may be of importance if, as seems likely, the world's oil supplies are exhausted before the coal supplies.

(c) *Generation of Electricity.* In spite of the extreme importance and convenience of electricity, it must be remembered that at best only 30% of the energy of the coal is made available, and no chemicals are produced as by-products.

The Nature of Coal and other Solid Fuels

Coal is formed by the gradual decay of the cellulose (p. 301) and other constituents of vegetation, as shown in the table below; the amount of heat (in calories per gram) produced by burning increases as the percentage of carbon increases.

	% C	% H	% O	cal./gm.
(Cellulose)	44	6	50	4150
Wood (pine)	50	6	43	5000
Peat	55	6	37	5500
Lignite	73	5	21	6500
Coal	85	5	9	8200
Anthracite	93	3	3	8700

Actually all these substances contain also moisture (especially peat), sulphur (usually about 1%), nitrogen, and ash (averaging about 10% if the coal has been cleaned, but of course more in coke). Ash is largely silicates of aluminium and iron.

Liquid Fuels

The most important of these are petroleum products (p. 289). Alcohol (p. 302) is especially useful in tropical countries, where coal and petroleum are absent but carbohydrate crops grow rapidly.

Suggestions for Practical Work

Expts. 80–83, 84c, 85–87, 32 (p. 72).

Expt. 91, testing coal gas for CO_2 before and after burning, also for H_2S (see p. 351). Heat liquid with sodium hydroxide and test for ammonia with wet red litmus paper. Burn two pieces of filter paper after soaking *one* of them in tar.

Repeat the experiment using small pieces of wood instead of coal, and compare the products.

QUESTIONS ON CHAPTER XVI

1. Charcoal, graphite, and diamond are considered to be different forms of the same element. What phenomenon is indicated by this, and how would you prove experimentally that this is the case? (W.)

2. Compare the properties of diamond, graphite, and charcoal, and show how their uses depend on these properties.

3. How could you prepare in the laboratory a small quantity of wood charcoal? Describe an experiment to demonstrate the absorptive properties of charcoal for *either* ammonia *or* chlorine. Mention an important use of this property of charcoal. (L.)

4. Explain, with examples, the meaning of the statement that carbon is a reducing agent.

5. Describe the laboratory preparation of carbon dioxide. Discuss the results of passing this gas into lime-water.

6. (*a*) Describe a form of slow-combustion stove and explain its advantages. What are the chemical changes involved?

(*b*) Draw up a scheme or diagram to show the carbon cycle in nature (no account is required). (C. Gen. Sc.)

7. It is stated that when oxalic acid is heated with concentrated sulphuric acid, equal volumes of carbon monoxide and carbon dioxide are evolved. Describe, with sketches, how you would obtain each of these gases in a state of reasonable purity.

Briefly indicate how you would determine the percentage by volume of each gas in the mixture.   (O.)

8. Write an equation to show the chemical reaction that takes place when carbon dioxide is passed over red-hot carbon.

Describe the properties of the resulting gas.

What will be the final volume when 10 c.c. of this gas are mixed with 30 c.c. of air and the mixture sparked?   (O. and C.)

9. Describe the method you would use for the preparation of *pure* carbon monoxide.   Show in tabular form how the properties of this gas compare with those of carbon dioxide.

How would you prove that the formula of carbon monoxide is CO, knowing that the formula of carbon dioxide is CO_2?   (D.)

10. What reactions take place when (*a*) carbon dioxide, (*b*) air, (*c*) steam, are passed separately through a long tube containing charcoal heated to bright redness?

Give a sketch of the apparatus.

In the case of (*c*), how would you establish that the reaction proceeds as you state?   (C.)

11. What are (*a*) producer gas (air gas), (*b*) water gas, and how are they prepared?

Mention the uses of these gases.

How would you determine the percentage of carbon dioxide in a mixture of this gas and carbon monoxide?   (C.)

12. Give a short account of the manufacture and purification of coal gas.

Of what two gases does coal gas chiefly consist?   What gases are often added to it, and why?   (O.)

13. What are the *chief* constituents of coal gas?   Indicate methods of obtaining (not necessarily from coal gas itself) any *two* of these gases in a pure, dry state.

How would you show what are the chief products of the combustion of coal gas in air?   (W.)

14. Give an account of the importance of the gas industry. What substances does it produce, and how are they used?   What advantages would result from a greater use of gas?

CHAPTER XVII

LIMESTONE AND OTHER CARBONATES
HARDNESS OF WATER

Carbon occurs to a considerable extent in compounds such as carbonates which form rocks in the earth's crust. Carbonates of copper, lead, iron, zinc, and magnesium are all important minerals, but by far the commonest is that of calcium, which occurs in many different forms, limestone being one.

Chalk, Limestone, and Marble

Many living creatures produce a layer of calcium carbonate as a form of protection. Egg-shells and sea-shells and coral are formed in this way. In the course of time the shells from dead marine animals (molluscs) formed the soft rock *chalk*, which still contains "fossils," i.e. the remains of these animals which existed millions of years ago. In places where other rocks covered the chalk and subjected it to pressure, it was converted into the harder rock *limestone*; the combined effect of heat and pressure produced *marble*; and the clear, crystalline form known as *Iceland spar* was deposited from solutions of calcium bicarbonate *Pearls* are produced similarly.

All these are varieties of the same chemical substance, calcium carbonate, and will react in the same way with hydrochloric acid to give carbon dioxide and calcium chloride (expt. 83, p. 247). The harder forms are used as building material, e.g. Portland stone for St. Paul's Cathedral; but they are of course liable to attack by the acids produced in smoke pollution (fig. 91, pp. 263, 343).

Action of Heat on Limestone. Manufacture of Quicklime

When limestone is strongly heated in lime-kilns, *quicklime* is formed:

$$CaCO_3 = CaO + CO_2 \nearrow \quad \text{(see p. 227).}$$

Calcium Carbonate   Calcium Oxide   Carbon Dioxide

Fig. 92 illustrates a very simple type of kiln, in which coke and limestone are put in at the top, and the burning coke heats the limestone to about 1000° C., decomposing it to quicklime, which is removed at the bottom. The kilns are designed for continuous working on a large scale (for the sake of cheapness), and modern kilns use producer gas (p. 256) as fuel to avoid contamination by ash.

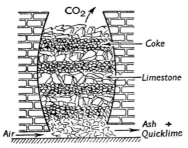

FIG. 92. Lime-kiln.

Expt. 92. Hold a piece of marble with tongs and heat it strongly in a bunsen flame just above the tip of the bright blue flame (see p. 298). After 5 or 6 minutes, allow it to cool and put it on a watch-glass. The product differs from calcium carbonate in its reactions (a) with water (see below) and (b) with acids; if it has been heated strongly enough—a muffle furnace is best for this—it will dissolve in dilute hydrochloric acid without giving off any carbon dioxide:

$$CaO + 2HCl = CaCl_2 + H_2O$$

Calcium Oxide — Hydrogen Chloride — Calcium Chloride — Hydrogen Oxide

This reaction is the simple neutralization of an acid by a basic oxide to make a salt (calcium chloride) and water (p. 64).

Reaction of Quicklime with Water. Production of Slaked Lime

Expt. 93. A little freshly made quicklime is placed on a watch-glass, and water allowed to drip on to it (fig. 93). Much heat is given out, producing steam, and the mass cracks, crumbling

FIG. 93. Action of water on quicklime.

at length to a powder of slaked lime (calcium hydroxide) which is still dry.

$$CaO + H_2O = Ca(OH)_2 \quad \text{(see p. 64).}$$

Quicklime — Water — Slaked Lime

The addition of more water produces a mixture of wet lime and water ("milk of lime"), which when filtered gives a clear, dilute solution of calcium hydroxide ("lime-water"), which can be tested with carbon dioxide (expt. 13, p. 23).

Use of Slaked Lime as Mortar

Building mortar consists of slaked lime, stirred to a paste with water and with three or four times as much sand thoroughly mixed in. The mortar first dries, and later combines with carbon dioxide from the air to form calcium carbonate; this hardening process may take centuries:

$$Ca(OH)_2 + CO_2 = CaCO_3 + H_2O$$

Cow-hair is added to make the mixture bind; the sand also helps to do this, and it makes the mixture porous so that the carbon dioxide can penetrate it.

Expt. 94. Mortar, made as above in an evaporating basin gradually hardens during several weeks when exposed to the air. It should be tested with hydrochloric acid from time to time to see if the formation of carbonate can be detected. Some old mortar should be treated similarly, the gas evolved being passed into lime-water.

The Weathering of Mortar

In the last chapter it was shown that lime-water which goes cloudy when carbon dioxide is first passed into it afterwards becomes clear because of the formation of the soluble bicarbonate:

$$CaCO_3 + H_2CO_3 = Ca(HCO_3)_2 \text{ (soluble) (see expt. 87, p. 250)}.$$

A similar change affects the outer layers of mortar in time, and the calcium carbonate begins to be washed out by the rain (containing carbonic acid) as it is changed to calcium bicarbonate. This is especially noticeable on the south-west side of a building, facing the prevailing wind. The gaps between the bricks must then be filled by "pointing" with new mortar or cement.

Cement

A mixture of limestone or chalk with clay (aluminium silicate=aluminium oxide combined with silicon dioxide) is heated with powdered coal or coke in huge rotating cylinders. The product, cement (calcium silicate+calcium aluminate) is cooled and powdered.

$$2CaCO_3 + SiO_2 + Al_2O_3 = CaSiO_3 + CaAl_2O_4 + 2CO_2 \nearrow$$

Limestone   Clay   Cement

It is used mixed with sand and water in the same way as mortar, but differs from it in that it will set even under water, because it requires no carbon dioxide for its setting. (The setting of cement is a complicated reaction with the water.) It is also harder and more permanent, because it does not weather. Nine tons of it are used in building a house.

Concrete

This is cement mixed with gravel or rubble (broken bricks, stones, etc.) and is therefore much cheaper. When spread over a framework of steel it is greatly strengthened and is known as *reinforced concrete*. The devastation of British land and scenery by gravel quarrying (for concrete-making), especially in the Thames Valley, is an urgent problem.

Other Uses of Limestone and its derivatives

A number of these are shown in fig. 94, "Compounds of Calcium," most of which are described in this chapter. The following should be noted:

1. Finely ground limestone (p. vii) is very widely used as a fertilizing agent, for neutralizing excess acids in the soil (p. 313). Mixed with linseed oil (p. 284) it makes *putty*.

2. Limestone is very important in providing the calcium oxide to combine with silicon dioxide in the blast furnace for the production of iron (see equation above, and p. 467).

3. Quicklime has so great an affinity for water (p. 268) that it is used for drying ammonia gas (p. 315) and alcohol (p. 302).

4. Milk of lime is used to soften hard water (see later in this chapter, p. 276); as lime-wash for farm outbuildings, etc., because it is a destroyer of insect-pests; and in the extraction of magnesium from sea-water (p. 453), because it is the cheapest alkali.

COMPOUNDS OF CALCIUM

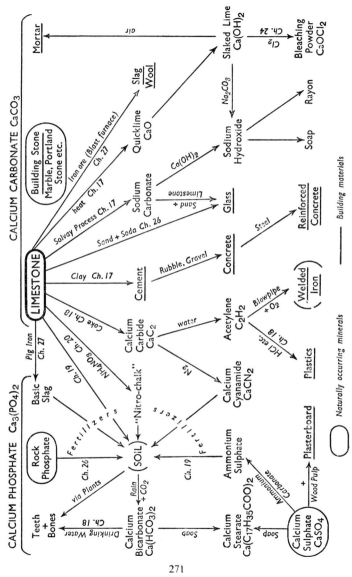

FIG. 94.

Britain possesses vast reserves of limestone and chalk; 30 million tons per year are produced from 48 different counties in England and Wales.

HARD WATER

Water which will not readily give a lather with soap is described as "hard water." In natural waters this is due to the presence of dissolved *calcium and magnesium salts*. These are divided into two classes:

(*a*) the *bicarbonates*, which are decomposed on boiling (p. 250), and are therefore said to produce *temporary hardness*;

(*b*) the *sulphates and chlorides*, which are unaffected by boiling; water containing these is said to be *permanently hard*.

Natural hard water usually contains both types of compounds, and so

Total Hardness = Temporary Hardness + Permanent Hardness.

Fig. 95 shows the approximate hardness of water supplied to different districts of the British Isles. (The water in most parts of Scotland and Ireland is soft.)

The Sources of Hardness in Water

(*a*) *Temporary hardness.* Rain-water contains small quantities of dissolved carbon dioxide from the air through which it has fallen. This very dilute carbonic acid solution flowing over the limestone or chalk reacts with it to form the soluble bicarbonate (see p. 250):

$$CaCO_3 + H_2CO_3 = Ca(HCO_3)_2, \text{ i.e. the acid salt } CaCO_3.H_2CO_3$$

Thus whenever rain-water comes into contact with calcium carbonate in the ground, a dilute solution of calcium bicarbonate will be formed. The corresponding magnesium salt is similarly formed from magnesium carbonate.

(*b*) *Permanent hardness.* Calcium sulphate occurs naturally as gypsum, $CaSO_4.2H_2O$, which dissolves directly in the water in which it is slightly soluble. The chloride and the two corresponding magnesium salts behave similarly.

The amounts of these dissolved substances are very small, totalling less than 0.1%. In popular speech they are often described quite inaccurately as chalk or lime.

Disadvantages of Hard Water

(a) *Waste of Soap.* Soap is a mixture of the sodium salts of the so-called fatty acids, i.e. sodium stearate, palmitate, and oleate (see p. 306). It dissolves in water, and forms a lather to which its cleansing properties are due. But when it is added to a solution of any calcium or magnesium salt, double decomposition occurs, and the insoluble calcium salt of the fatty acid is formed.

$$\begin{matrix} \text{Sodium} \\ \text{Stearate} \\ \text{(soap)} \end{matrix} + \begin{matrix} \text{Calcium} \\ \text{salt} \end{matrix} = \begin{matrix} \text{Calcium} \\ \text{Stearate} \downarrow \\ \text{(scum)} \end{matrix} + \begin{matrix} \text{Sodium} \\ \text{salt} \end{matrix}$$

The curdy precipitate of calcium stearate forms a scum on the top of the water, and continues to be formed until all the calcium compound in the water has been removed, i.e. until the water has been "softened" by the soap. Much soap is thus wasted, amounting in London for example to over four-fifths of the total used. In laundry work further trouble is caused by the fact that it is difficult to rinse out the "calcium soap" (as the scum is sometimes called), and if any of it is left in the fabrics to be cleaned, they are eventually both dis-coloured and damaged by rubbing with the hard, solid particles.

(b) *Boiler Scale and Kettle Fur.* As already mentioned, the bicarbonates of calcium and magnesium are decomposed by boiling. The following action occurs:

$$\underset{\text{Calcium Bicarbonate}}{Ca(HCO_3)_2} = \underset{\text{Calcium Carbonate}}{CaCO_3 \downarrow} + \underset{\text{Carbon Dioxide}}{CO_2 \nearrow} + \underset{\text{Water}}{H_2O}$$

The insoluble calcium carbonate is deposited in kettles as "fur" and in boilers as "boiler scale." The deposit is soft when first formed, but slowly hardens. The effect in boilers is particularly troublesome, and so water for such use is now usually "softened" (see below) before use, at least to the extent of removing the temporary hardness. In many industrial

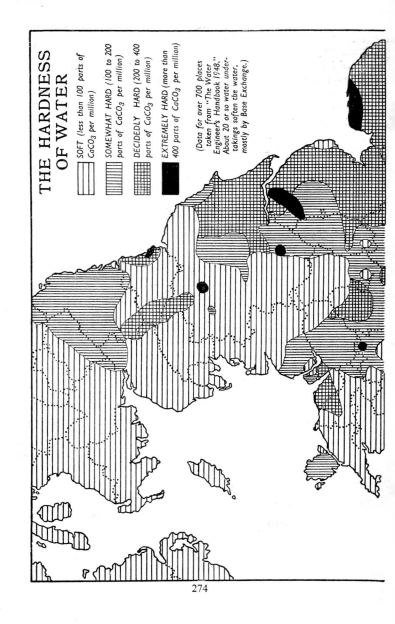

THE HARDNESS
OF WATER

SOFT (less than 100 parts of
CaCO₃ per million)

SOMEWHAT HARD (100 to 200
parts of CaCO₃ per million)

DECIDEDLY HARD (200 to 400
parts of CaCO₃ per million)

EXTREMELY HARD (more than
400 parts of CaCO₃ per million)

(Data for over 700 places
taken from "The Water
Engineer's Handbook 1948."
About 20 or so water under-
takings soften the water,
mostly by Base Exchange.)

274

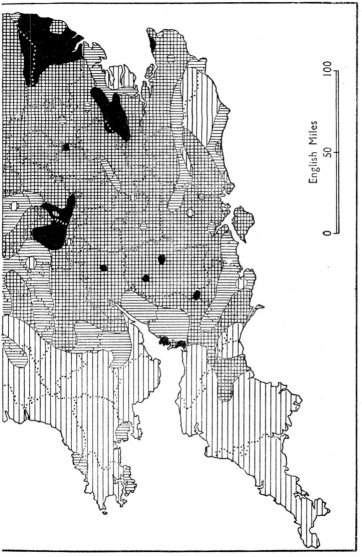

English Miles

0   50   100

FIG. 95.

plants it is customary to condense the exhaust steam, and to use the water again so that the cost of softening is small. If scale is allowed to form it has to be removed periodically, as its low conductivity for heat results in considerable loss of efficiency, and might in time lead to actual danger. The same reaction may cause the blockage of domestic hot-water pipes and boilers (PLATE 6B, p. 78). Scale in kettles can usually be removed by treating with a dilute acid, e.g. acetic acid (see p. 303), which has no appreciable action on the metal.

Advantages of Hard Water

(a) Soluble calcium salts are of considerable value to the human system by helping to form strong bones and teeth (mostly calcium phosphate, see p. 306). There is some evidence to show that people in hard-water districts (see fig. 95) suffer less from dental decay than those where the water is soft, although it seems probable that traces of fluorides (see pp. 307, 426) are even more important.

(b) Very soft water (in the presence of carbon dioxide) will slowly dissolve lead (see p. 81), and if it is to be conveyed in lead pipes for drinking purposes it must first be artificially hardened to avoid the risk of lead poisoning.

Methods of Softening Hard Water

1. *Boiling* (only temporary hardness removed). All the calcium bicarbonate (responsible for the temporary hardness) is converted by boiling into the insoluble carbonate and so removed. This is an expensive method, and also is incomplete because the permanent hardness remains.

2. *Addition of Slaked Lime* (only temporary hardness removed). This will react with the carbonic acid present in the calcium bicarbonate, to form calcium carbonate as a precipitate. (In the laboratory, lime-water may be used to show this.)

$$CaCO_3.H_2CO_3 + Ca(OH)_2 = 2CaCO_3 \downarrow + 2H_2O$$

This method is cheap and is used by many water supply authorities, e.g. Canterbury, Southampton. The calculated amount of lime must be used, or else some will dissolve in the water and introduce an additional cause of hardness.

The action of ammonium hydroxide (p. 322) is similar.

3. *Addition of Washing Soda. Removes both types of hardness.* Washing soda (sodium carbonate) reacts with any calcium or magnesium salts in solution, to form precipitates of the carbonates, and leaves sodium salts in solution:

$$CaSO_4 + Na_2CO_3 = CaCO_3 \downarrow + Na_2SO_4$$

| Calcium | Sodium | Calcium | Sodium |
| Sulphate | Carbonate | Carbonate | Sulphate |

$$Ca(HCO_3)_2 + Na_2CO_3 = CaCO_3 \downarrow + 2Na(HCO_3)$$

| Calcium | Sodium | Calcium | Sodium |
| Bicarbonate | Carbonate | Carbonate | Bicarbonate |

Since soaps are compounds of sodium, the presence of other compounds of sodium in the water does not affect them.

Bath salts are usually coloured and perfumed crystals of washing soda.

4. *The Base Exchange ("Permutit") Process. Removes both types of hardness.* This is used both by households and by some water supply authorities, e.g. Henley, Cambridge. The chemical reagent used is normally sodium aluminium silicate ("Permutit"), either in some naturally occurring form or specially manufactured (fig. 96A).

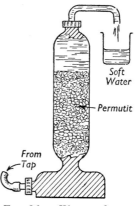

FIG. 96A.   Water softener.

When the hard water flows through this substance, the following reactions occur:

CaSO_4		Sodium		Na_2SO_4		Calcium
or	+	Aluminium	=	or	+	Aluminium
Ca(HCO_3)_2		Silicate		2NaHCO_3		Silicate
(in water)		(in softener)		(dissolves)		(remains in softener)

After some time the contents of the softener are entirely

converted to the calcium compound, and so it is no longer effective. To regenerate it, strong salt solution is run slowly through the softener to re-form the original sodium compound:

$$2NaCl \quad + \quad \begin{matrix} \text{Calcium} \\ \text{Aluminium} \\ \text{Silicate} \end{matrix} \quad = \quad \underset{\substack{\text{(washed away to} \\ \text{drain)}}}{CaCl_2} \quad + \quad \begin{matrix} \text{Sodium} \\ \text{Aluminium} \\ \text{Silicate} \\ \text{(remains in softener)} \end{matrix}$$

This reversible reaction is a good example of the Law of Mass Action (p. 228); when calcium salts are in excess, the softener is used up; when sodium salts are in excess, the softener is regenerated.

Expt. 95. The first three processes described above may be used on tap-water or—if the water is naturally soft—on a solution of calcium bicarbonate, which may easily be prepared by squirting soda-water from a siphon into lime-water until the precipitate redissolves. Portions of the resulting "softened waters" should be kept for the next experiment.

To Compare the Hardness of Different Types of Water

Expt. 96. The simplest laboratory method is to compare the quantities of soap solution required to give a permanent lather with equal volumes of the waters to be tested.

To prepare the soap solution, slice about 15 gm. of flakes from a tablet of pure soap (Castile), and dissolve this in 200 c.c. of methylated spirit, making the solution up to 1 litre with distilled water. (If it is desired to *measure* the hardnesses—not merely to compare them—1 c.c. of soap solution should represent 1 degree of hardness on the official scale, i.e. 1 part of $Ca(HCO_3)_2$ per 43,000 parts of water, which when decomposed would produce 1 grain of $CaCO_3$ —about $\frac{1}{16}$ gram—per gallon.)

The following types of water should be tested: distilled, tap-water, rain-water, and water softened by each of the four methods described. 25 c.c. of the water is put in a conical flask or reagent bottle, and the soap solution added in small quantities from a burette After each addition the bottle is corked and well shaken. When a lather is obtained which entirely covers the surface of the water and which persists for a minute, the number of c.c. used is measured.

The value for distilled water (which is almost completely soft) must be subtracted from the other readings to give the relative hardness of each. The amount of permanent hardness is obtained from the figure for water which has been boiled and filtered.

Stalactites and Stalagmites

As already explained, rain-water flowing over limestone reacts with the rock to form calcium bicarbonate which dissolves into the water. Whenever such water evaporates, a precipitate of calcium carbonate is formed. In limestone caves, like those found in Cheddar Gorge and Dovedale, hard water of this kind drips from the roof and to a slight extent loses CO_2, gradually forming a growth of the precipitated calcium carbonate like an icicle. Similarly, a corresponding upward growth starts from the

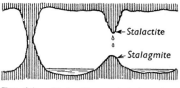

Fig. 96B. Stalactites and stalagmites.

floor of the cave (fig. 96B and PLATE 17). The downward growths are called *stalactites* and the upward ones *stalagmites*. In some cases the two meet to form irregular columns. The rate of growth is very slow and it is estimated that many thousands of years have been necessary to produce the remarkable examples to be seen in the caves at Cheddar.

CARBONATES

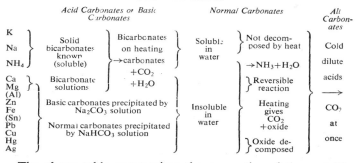

The above table summarizes the properties of the metallic carbonates and bicarbonates. (Those of aluminium and tin are not known, see p. 251.)

[*Photo by courtesy of Professor Dr. Jovan Hadzi, of the
Spelaeological Society of Ljubljana*

PLATE 17.   STALACTITES AND STALAGMITES (p. 279)

Deposits of calcium carbonate from the dripping of hard water in
the cave of Krivnajama, Yugoslavia.

Potassium Carbonate, K_2CO_3, is found in small quantities in wood ash, because potassium compounds are necessary to all plants (see p. 302). In early times it was the only alkaline substance available for making soap or glass, and is still used to make shaving soap and hard glass (p. 435).

Sodium Carbonate, Na_2CO_3, is an exceedingly important industrial chemical, of which the world production is about 4 million tons per year, used largely for making soap (p. 306) and glass (p. 435). The crystal-line form, $Na_2CO_3.10H_2O$ (see p. 86), is known as "washing soda."

Manufacture of Sodium Carbo-nate by the Solvay ("Ammonia Soda") Process

The raw materials for this process are salt and limestone (both very cheap) and ammonia gas (which is recovered and used again). Carbon dioxide, obtained by heating limestone,

$$CaCO_3 = CaO + CO_2 \nearrow$$

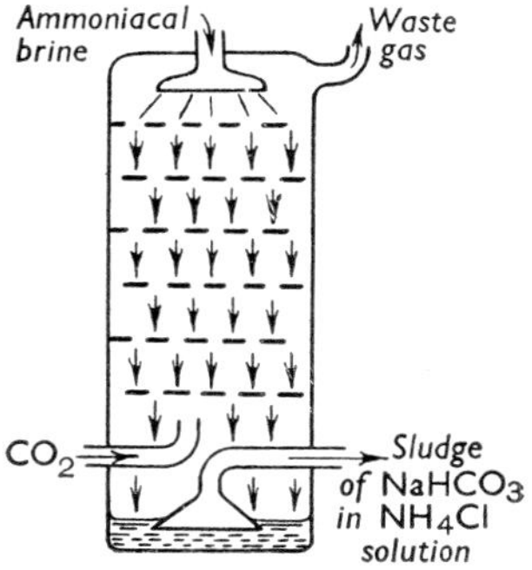

FIG. 97. Manufacture of sodium carbonate ("Solvay Process").

is passed up a tower (fig. 97), down which is trickling brine (a strong solution of salt in water) saturated with ammonia gas. The perforated partitions in the tower break up the descending stream of ammoniacal brine and ensure that it makes thorough contact with the ascending gas. The reaction between them produces sodium bicarbonate:

$$NH_4OH + HHCO_3 = NH_4HCO_3 + HOH$$

Ammonium Hydroxide   Hydrogen Bicarbonate   Ammonium Bicarbonate   Hydrogen Hydroxide

$$NH_4HCO_3 + NaCl = NH_4Cl + NaHCO_3 \downarrow$$

Ammonium Bicarbonate   Sodium Chloride   Ammonium Chloride   Sodium Bicarbonate

as the sodium bicarbonate is only slightly (10%) soluble in water, it separates out as a white sludge at the bottom of the tower; the other product is ammonium chloride.

The sodium bicarbonate is filtered from the ammonium chloride solution, dried, and heated to form anhydrous sodium carbonate, "soda ash." The carbon dioxide evolved in this reaction is used again in the tower.

$$2NaHCO_3 = Na_2CO_3 + H_2O + CO_2 \nearrow$$

If crystalline washing soda is required, as for domestic purposes, the anhydrous compound is crystallized from solution in water. The crystals which form have ten molecules of water of crystallization

$$Na_2CO_3 + 10H_2O = Na_2CO_3.10H_2O.$$

To recover the ammonia from the ammonium chloride, this is heated with quicklime; the latter was produced in the reaction used to generate the carbon dioxide from the limestone:

$$CaO + 2NH_4Cl = CaCl_2 + H_2O + 2NH_3 \nearrow$$

| Calcium Oxide | Ammonium Chloride | Calcium Chloride | Water | Ammonia |

The only waste product of this very economical process is calcium chloride.

Properties of Sodium Carbonate

On standing in air, crystals of washing soda effloresce (p. 87), losing 9 of their 10 molecules of water of crystallization, and becoming covered with a layer of white powder, $Na_2CO_3.H_2O$.

Expt. 97. The action of heat.
Washing soda crystals lose all their water of crystallization on heating, but do *not* evolve carbon dioxide (test with lime-water), unlike the carbonates of the "heavy metals," i.e. all others except potassium.

Expt. 98. The action of acids.
With all acids, dilute or concentrated, cold or hot, sodium carbonate—like all other carbonates, bicarbonates, and basic carbonates—immediately liberates carbon dioxide (p. 11). For this reason it is the best substance to use for neutralizing acid which has been spilt anywhere, because any suspicious liquid will betray itself by fizzing:

$$Na_2CO_3 + 2HCl = 2NaCl + H_2O + CO_2 \nearrow$$

Expt. 99. Conversion to sodium hydroxide.

Sodium carbonate solution is boiled in a beaker with an excess of slaked lime, until a test portion after filtering no longer gives an effervescence of carbon dioxide when dilute acid is added:

$$Na_2CO_3 + Ca(OH)_2 = CaCO_3 \downarrow + 2NaOH$$

The precipitated calcium carbonate is filtered off, and a solution of sodium hydroxide remains. This reaction is reversible unless a large excess of slaked lime is used (see " Law of Mass Action," p. 228). Formerly all the caustic soda of industry was obtained by this method, but now a large part is made by the electrolysis of sodium chloride solution (see p. 405).

Expt. 100. Precipitation of metallic carbonates.

A little sodium carbonate solution is added to a solution of copper sulphate—or other metallic salt. A light-blue precipitate of basic copper carbonate (see p. 73) is formed; this may be filtered off, and on heating it turns black, due to the decomposition to black copper oxide:

$$Na_2CO_3 + CuSO_4 = Na_2SO_4 + CuCO_3 \downarrow$$

| Sodium Carbonate | Copper Sulphate | Sodium Sulphate | Copper Carbonate |

$$Na_2CO_3 + H_2O + CuSO_4 = Na_2SO_4 + Cu(OH)_2 \downarrow + CO_2 \nearrow$$

$$Cu(OH)_2 . CuCO_3 = 2CuO + H_2O + CO_2 \nearrow$$

In solution in water sodium carbonate is alkaline to litmus and other indicators, and may be titrated against acids as if it were an alkali (see p. 501).

The principal domestic use of washing soda is for softening hard water, by precipitating any calcium or magnesium salts in the water as carbonates. It also assists in "washing up" by making fats and grease soluble, and therefore easier to remove.

Industrially the anhydrous form is usually used, since this avoids the cost of transport of the large proportion (nearly two-thirds) of water in the crystals.

Ammonium Carbonate, $(NH_4)_2CO_3$, is used in smelling-salts, because it decomposes slightly, even at room temperature, into carbon dioxide, water, and ammonia which has a stimulating action:

$$(NH_4)_2CO_3 = 2NH_3 \nearrow + H_2O + CO_2 \nearrow$$

Magnesium Carbonate, $MgCO_3$, is chemically extremely similar to calcium carbonate, which has already been described. It is an abundant mineral (see p. 444) and is used as a source of magnesium metal (p. 453). Like the carbonates of less electropositive metals, it must be prepared by precipitation with sodium *bi*carbonate:

$$MgSO_4 + 2NaHCO_3 = MgCO_3 \downarrow + Na_2SO_4 + H_2O + CO_2 \nearrow$$

(If sodium carbonate is used, a mixture of hydroxide and carbonate, i.e. a basic carbonate—compare expt. 100—is precipitated.)

The carbonates of zinc, iron, lead, and copper, MCO_3, are very similar to the above, but do *not* (except iron) form soluble bicarbonates. They occur naturally, but are less important ores than the sulphides or oxides.

Basic Lead Carbonate, $Pb(OH)_2.2PbCO_3$, has approximately the composition of "white lead," the solid substance in ordinary white paint. On the commercial scale "white lead" is prepared by exposing the metal to the action of air and warm acetic acid vapour, which corrode it, together with carbon dioxide, which converts the basic acetate into the basic carbonate:

$$2Pb + 2H\bar{A} + O_2 = Pb(OH)_2.Pb\bar{A}_2 \text{ (where } \bar{A} = \text{acetate)}$$

It makes an extremely useful paint because of its excellent covering power, but its use causes painters to suffer from lead poisoning, and it blackens in air containing hydrogen sulphide because of the formation of black lead sulphide (p. 351). *Paint* consists essentially of a finely ground pigment ("white lead," or other substances, e.g. the oxide of the abundant metal, titanium) mixed with linseed oil, which oxidizes on exposure to the air, forming a continuous solid film.

Expt. 101A. Prepare these metallic carbonates as described in expt. 100. Show that carbon dioxide is given off when they are heated or are treated with dilute acids (nitric is best, as all nitrates are soluble) Prepare crystalline specimens of the salts resulting from these reactions (see expt. 27B, p. 69).

BICARBONATES

Sodium Bicarbonate, NaHCO₃, is manufactured by the Solvay process (p. 281), and is prepared in the laboratory as in expt. 32 (p. 72).

Properties and Uses

(*a*) *Action of Heat.* Like all other bicarbonates, this is decomposed by heat, forming the carbonate. This is used on both the commercial and laboratory scale for the preparation of pure anhydrous sodium carbonate (pp. 72, 178, 282, and 502).

(*b*) *Action of Acids.* Like all other bicarbonates, carbonates and basic carbonates, this is decomposed by all acids, e.g.

$$NaHCO_3 + HCl = NaCl + CO_2 \nearrow + H_2O$$

giving carbon dioxide at once. The following uses result:

(1) As *baking powder*, which consists of a mixture of sodium bicarbonate with a weak and harmless acid such as tartaric; when wet and warm, this sets free carbon dioxide throughout the mass of dough (as in cake making), thus puffing it up and making it "light."

(2) In "*Health salts*" which are very similar. As the acid used (citric or tartaric) is a solid, no fizzing occurs until the mixture is dissolved in water.

(3) *For indigestion*, which is often caused by excess acid in the stomach; this excess acid is neutralized by taking sodium bicarbonate. which is itself harmless.

(4) In fire extinguishers (see pp. 250–1).

Suggestions for Practical Work

Experiments 92–101A inclusive; also the reactions of sodium bicarbonate, including tests on the residue left after heating, and comparing its action on magnesium sulphate solution with that of sodium carbonate; also expt. 101B (below).

Expt. 101B. Find the loss in weight per gram when chalk is (*a*) heated in a muffle furnace for 20 minutes. (*b*) treated with
10*

hydrochloric acid in the apparatus shown in fig. 98. The volume of carbon dioxide may also be measured by using the apparatus of expt. 59 (p. 134) if a layer of paraffin or other oil is floated on top of the water to prevent the carbon dioxide dissolving.

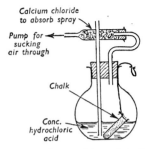

Calcium chloride
to absorb spray

Pump for
sucking
air through

Chalk

Conc.
hydrochloric
acid

FIG. 98. Composition of chalk.

QUESTIONS ON CHAPTER XVII

1. Describe the qualitative and quantitative experiments you would make to show that limestone and chalk are modifications of the same compound. (L. Gen. Sc.)

2. Give the names and formulae of some common minerals containing the metal calcium.

Starting with calcium carbonate, indicate how to prepare from it quicklime. calcium chloride, and calcium carbide.

What are the chief constituents of ordinary mortar?

Give reasons for the setting of mortar. (W.)

3. Explain the chemical changes involved in the following processes: (*a*) the slaking of lime; (*b*) the setting of mortar; (*c*) the addition of washing soda to hard water.

What reasons have you for believing that the slaking of lime is a chemical change? (O.)

4. How would you determine *either* the weight *or* the volume of carbon dioxide contained in 100 gm. of calcium carbonate? (O.)

5. Why are the deposits of limestone and chalk in this country of such great chemical importance? Describe how they are used for five different purposes.

6. State and explain what happens when carbon dioxide is passed for a long time through lime-water.

State and explain what happens when soap solution is shaken up with the final product (*a*) before it has been boiled, (*b*) after it has been boiled.   (N.)

7. Why is it necessary to use distilled water in chemical experiments?

State and explain what occurs when (*a*) sodium carbonate, (*b*) lime-water, (*c*) soap, are added separately to ordinary tap-water. (O. and C.)

8. Explain how both temporary and permanently hard waters can be softened by sodium carbonate and why they cannot be softened by sodium bicarbonate.

What are the advantages or disadvantages of very soft water for (*a*) drinking, (*b*) raising steam?   (C.)

9. What substances cause "temporary" and "permanent" hardness in natural waters?   Describe small-scale methods which are used for softening water.

If you were given soap solution and water containing both permanent and temporary hardness, what would you do to find out the *relative* quantities of temporary and permanent hardness in the water?   (D.)

10. Describe *one* method by which sodium carbonate is manufactured on a large scale.

A strong solution of sodium carbonate is prepared and divided into three portions (*a*), (*b*), and (*c*):

(i) Through (*a*) excess of carbon dioxide is passed.

(ii) To (*b*) quicklime is added.

(iii) Strong hydrochloric acid is added to (*c*).

Describe and explain what happens in each of these three cases. (A.)

11. How is sodium bicarbonate prepared on a large scale?

How does it differ from sodium carbonate?   Mention some use to which the bicarbonate is put.   (O. and C.)

12. (*a*) Explain, giving the formulae, how sodium carbonate and sodium bicarbonate are related to each other.   (*b*) If you were given a specimen of each in the form of a fine powder, how would you determine which was the carbonate and which the bicarbonate? (*c*) How could you prepare a specimen of washing soda crystals from sodium bicarbonate?   (L. Gen. Sc.)

13. By what methods are metallic carbonates usually prepared? Give examples.

What is the action of heat on (a) normal carbonates, (b) bicarbonates?

14. How would you prepare magnesium carbonate from magnesium chloride?

Why is it used in stomach powders?

15. How is "white lead" obtained by the "Dutch" (acetic acid) process? Give an explanation of the reactions which occur. (C.)

16. Give an account of *two* natural processes in which atmospheric carbon dioxide plays a part. (O.)

17. One of the authors had 6 gallons of strong hydrochloric acid (36·5 gm. of HCl per 100 c.c.) and 24 gallons of water pumped into his domestic hot-water system, after the boiler itself had been scaled and the system drained. Some aniline had been added to the acid so as to make corrosion of the iron pipes negligible. After 24 hours, when all evolution of carbon dioxide had ceased, 30 gallons of liquid were drained out, containing 1·82 gm. of HCl per 100 c.c.

Assuming that 1 gallon = 4·5 litres and 1 kg. = 2·2 lb., calculate the weight (in lb.) of calcium carbonate which was dissolved from the pipes.

CHAPTER XVIII

ORGANIC CHEMISTRY

Carbon forms such an immense number of compounds (p. 241), that they are considered in a separate branch of chemistry, known as Organic Chemistry. This is of very great importance to everyday life, though much of it is outside examination syllabuses.

The reason for this great variety is that the carbon atom has the unique property of forming long chains or rings of atoms (see below), which allow the formation of complicated molecular structures of the compounds. These compounds will here be divided up into those occurring in (*a*) minerals, e.g. *hydrocarbons* obtainable mostly from petroleum; (*b*) vegetable sources, e.g. carbohydrates from *green plants*; (*c*) animals, e.g. proteins in the *human body*. The majority of organic compounds do not occur naturally, but have been made artificially ("*synthesized*"); those which have been built up from smaller compounds into *plastics* (which can at some stage be moulded into shape) will be specially emphasized.

HYDROCARBONS

Petroleum ("oil"), which is found naturally in many places, especially in the U.S.A., is a complex mixture of compounds, mostly hydrocarbons (see p. 200), which contain only carbon and hydrogen. The simplest one, methane, CH_4, is a gas; those with larger molecules are liquids, e.g. octane, C_8H_{18}, used in petrol; and those with still larger molecules are solids, e.g. $C_{20}H_{42}$, which occurs in vaseline. By "fractional distillation" (p. 302 and PLATE 18) petroleum is separated into fractions of different boiling-point, which are used as petrol, diesel oil, paraffin oil for lamps, lubricating oil, vaseline, and as paraffin wax (p. 299) for candles. The non-volatile residue, "pitch," is used for road-making, as is the similar substance left behind when coal-tar is distilled.

PLATE 18.   PETROLEUM REFINERY

Part of the Abadan refinery, Iran, the largest in the world; it can deal with 24 million tons of crude oil per year.   The tall towers are fractionating columns; at the top of these low-boiling vapours come off; higher-boiling vapours come off lower down.

The molecules of all these hydrocarbons are made up of chains of carbon atoms, thus:

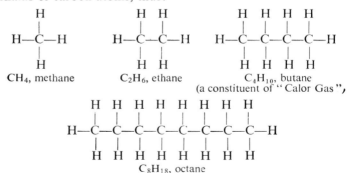

CH_4, methane C_2H_6, ethane C_4H_{10}, butane
(a constituent of "Calor Gas",

C_8H_{18}, octane

The general formula can be seen to be C_nH_{2n+2}; the valency of carbon is always 4, and the valency of hydrogen always 1.

Methane, CH_4

This occurs in the natural gas from oil-wells, and has already been met as a constituent of coal gas (p. 260). It is produced by the rotting of vegetation, and is the "marsh-gas" stirred up from the mud of a stagnant pond; large amounts of it could be—and in some places are—recovered at sewage works. The methane which is found in coal-mines, trapped in pockets in the coal seams, was probably produced in the same way. As it is a very inflammable gas, there is an ever-present danger of explosions, and it has caused many mining disasters. Miners call the gas "fire-damp" and exercise the greatest care to prevent its collecting in dangerous concentrations (p. 190) by ensuring adequate ventilation. After an explosion, a large amount of carbon monoxide is present (p. 255) and practically no oxygen, so that oxygen-breathing apparatus must be used by rescue teams (p. 31).

If methane is required in the laboratory, it may be prepared by heating anhydrous sodium acetate with solid sodium hydroxide:

$$CH_3\overline{|COONa+NaO|}H = Na_2CO_3+CH_4\nearrow$$

Properties of Methane

It is almost insoluble in water (compare petrol) and burns with a pale-blue flame:

$$CH_4+2O_2 = CO_2+2H_2O$$

Other hydrocarbons, however, require so much more oxygen that some carbon remains unburnt (as soot—see p. 298), e.g.

$$2C_8H_{18} + 25O_2 = 16CO_2 + 18H_2O$$
(2 volumes)   (25 volumes) i.e. 125 volumes of air required

Apart from this important use as fuel, and the reaction with chlorine (see p. 409), methane and similar hydrocarbons are very unreactive compounds; they are not attacked by concentrated acids or alkalis, and so are known as "paraffin" hydrocarbons (from the Latin *parum*=little, *affinis*=affinity).

Ethylene, C_2H_4

As the most valuable hydrocarbons are those which can be used in petrol, the more complex ones are decomposed by "cracking," i.e. heating to a high temperature with a catalyst $(AlCl_3)$ in the absence of air. The principle is seen most easily in a simpler example:

$$
\begin{array}{ccccc}
\text{H} \quad \text{H} \quad \text{H} & & \text{H} \quad \text{H} & & \text{H} \\
| \quad | \quad | & & | \quad | & & | \\
\text{H---C---C---C---H} & = & \text{C}=\text{C} & + & \text{H---C---H} \\
| \quad | \quad | & & | \quad | & & | \\
\text{H} \quad \text{H} \quad \text{H} & & \text{H} \quad \text{H} & & \text{H}
\end{array}
$$

C_3H_8, propane   = C_2H_4, ethylene + CH_4, methane.

Here one paraffin hydrocarbon (methane) has been formed, together with a rather different compound (ethylene), which has less hydrogen than a paraffin (C_2H_4 instead of C_2H_6), and is therefore called "unsaturated."

Ethylene is a gas which occurs to a small extent in coal gas (see p. 260), but methods for recovering it (by liquefaction) are not yet in operation on the commercial scale. It is obtained either by "cracking" petroleum or by dehydrating alcohol; in the laboratory this latter process is done by heating it with concentrated sulphuric acid, and the gas can be collected over water:

$$C_2H_6O - H_2O \left(\begin{array}{c} \text{absorbed by} \\ \text{conc. } H_2SO_4 \end{array} \right) = C_2H_4 \nearrow$$

Properties of Ethylene

The outstanding difference between ethylene and methane is that ethylene has too little hydrogen to satisfy the valencies of the carbon atoms, and can therefore add on other atoms:

$$
\begin{array}{ccc}
\text{H} \quad \text{H} & & \text{H} \quad \text{H} \\
| \quad | & & | \quad | \\
\text{C}=\text{C} & \text{behaves as} & \text{---C---C---} \\
| \quad | & & | \quad | \\
\text{H} \quad \text{H} & & \text{H} \quad \text{H}
\end{array}
$$

Four examples of this are specially important:

(*a*) Ethylene adds on to itself ("polymerizes") under pressures of over 1000 atmospheres to form an extremely large molecule, the *plastic* known as *polythene*:

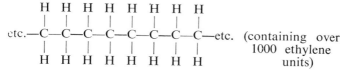

etc.—C—C—C—C—C—C—C—C—etc. (containing over 1000 ethylene units)

This is the best electrical insulator yet known, because—as a hydrocarbon—it is almost completely resistant to the action of moisture, which tends to form a conducting film over the surface of most other insulators; polythene is therefore used in radar, and for 100,000 volt submarine cables in Sweden.

Similar polymerization reactions are involved in the preparation of "synthetic rubber," and of the transparent glass-like plastics "perspex" and "polystyrene"; a common object made of perspex is the ink-container of a Biro pen.

(*b*) Ethylene (and similar unsaturated compounds) reacts with concentrated sulphuric acid (expt. 63, p. 140) to give

$$H—SO_4—C—C—H$$

ethyl hydrogen sulphate. This reaction is used in purifying the paraffin hydrocarbons of petroleum, because they do *not* react. Long-chain unsaturated compounds resulting from "cracking" (see above) are used to make "*soapless soaps*" (e.g. *D.10, Teepol, Quix, Fab, Wisk, Tide, etc.*), because the sodium salts, e.g. $C_{16}H_{33}SO_4^-Na^+$ are similar in constitution to soap (p. 306); these *detergents*, unlike soap, have soluble calcium salts, and so are not affected by hard water (p. 272).

(*c*) Ethylene (and similar unsaturated compounds, e.g. whale oil—see fig. 34, p. 101) will add on hydrogen in the presence of a nickel catalyst:

$$\underset{\substack{|\\H}}{\overset{\substack{H\quad H\\|\quad|}}{C}}=\overset{}{C} + H_2 = H-\underset{\substack{|\\H}}{\overset{\substack{H\\|}}{C}}-\underset{\substack{|\\H}}{\overset{\substack{H\\|}}{C}}-H \quad \text{ethane.}$$

(*d*) The addition of bromine to ethylene (p. 421).

Acetylene, C_2H_2

This is a very important gas, both because it is unsaturated like ethylene and therefore reactive and because it is made from coal. If coke (made from coal, p. 244) is heated with limestone to a very high temperature (2500° C., in an electric furnace where hydro-electric power is available), calcium oxide is first formed (p. 267). and this then reacts to give *calcium carbide*:

$$CaO + 3C = CaC_2 + CO \nearrow$$

Calcium carbide reacts rapidly with cold water to give acetylene:

$$CaC_2 + H_2O = CaO + C_2H_2 \nearrow$$

(the calcium oxide then forms the hydroxide). This reaction may be used equally well for the laboratory preparation.

Uses of Acetylene

It is used in oxy-acetylene welding (p. 31), because it is more convenient to make and transport than any other gaseous fuel.

Apart from this, it is important as the source of (*a*) *acetic acid* and (*b*) *poly-vinyl chloride*.

(*a*) $H-C{\equiv}C-H + H_2O = H-\overset{\substack{H\\|}}{\underset{\substack{|\\H}}{C}}-C{\overset{H}{\underset{O}{\diagup}}}$ acetaldehyde

$$H-\overset{\substack{H\\|}}{\underset{\substack{|\\H}}{C}}-C{\overset{H}{\underset{O}{\diagup}}} + \underset{\text{from air}}{O} = H-\overset{\substack{H\\|}}{\underset{\substack{|\\H}}{C}}-C{\overset{O-H}{\underset{O}{\diagup}}} \quad \text{acetic acid;}$$

both reactions require catalysts.

Acetic acid has a large number of important uses, including the manufacture of the plastic "cellulose acetate" (see p. 301) for non-inflammable "safety film" and "Cellophane" wrapping. "Peardrop" sweets are flavoured with amyl acetate.

(b)   H—C≡C—H + HCl   = $\begin{matrix} H & H \\ | & | \\ C=C \\ | & | \\ H & Cl \end{matrix}$ vinyl chloride,

which, like ethylene, is still unsaturated and will therefore polymerize to poly-vinyl chloride, "P.V.C.":

$$\text{etc.—}\overset{\displaystyle H}{\underset{\displaystyle H}{C}}—\overset{\displaystyle H}{\underset{\displaystyle Cl}{C}}—\overset{\displaystyle H}{\underset{\displaystyle H}{C}}—\overset{\displaystyle H}{\underset{\displaystyle Cl}{C}}\text{—etc.,}$$

this is another plastic which is now very widely used as the coloured, rubber-like insulation on electric wires, and in coloured transparent waterproofs.

Benzene, C_6H_6

Several hydrocarbons, quite different in character from those already described, are obtained when coal tar (p. 261) is distilled. The simplest and best-known of these is benzene, a liquid, b.p. 80° C., the carbon atoms of which are joined in a ring (compare graphite, p. 243, fig. 80B).

Very large quantities of this are extracted for use as a constituent of some motor fuels, as a solvent, and for preparing derivatives such as aniline ($C_6H_5NH_2$), phenol ("carbolic acid," C_6H_5OH), and toluene ($C_6H_5.CH_3$) for the manufacture of drugs and dyes and plastics, most of which have very complicated structures.

Chlorine can add on to the double bonds of benzene (compare ethylene above) to form $C_6H_6Cl_6$, the insecticide "Gammexane."

Naphthalene, $C_{10}H_8$, is a solid used in firelighters and in moth-balls, and was part of the fuel used in the torches for the Olympic Games, 1948. Its structure is of a similar type. Owing to the large amount of carbon in these molecules occurring in coal tar, they give a luminous and very sooty flame when coal is burnt in an ordinary open fire (compare PLATES 16B and 16C, p. 261). The dyestuff used on the cover of this book (see p. vi) was made from naphthalene.

FLAME

A flame consists simply of very hot gas which is "incandescent," i.e. giving out light. Just as a heated solid may eventually become white hot, so gases become luminous when hot enough; in this state they are said to be flames. Any substance which gives a flame is commonly said to "burn," and so the flame of hydrogen combining with chlorine (p. 409) is said to be "hydrogen burning in chlorine."

Similarly, "a supporter of combustion" is the term used for a substance which combines with the flaming gas, e.g. "air supports the combustion of coal gas"; but a jet of air can equally well be made to give a flame in an atmosphere of coal gas, and so also "air burns in coal gas."

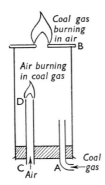

FIG. 99. Relative combustion.

Expt. 102. Coal gas is passed into the wide glass tube of fig. 99 at A. The top of the wide tube is closed by holding a piece of asbestos over the opening, shown at B, in the asbestos lid. The coal gas issues at C, and may be lighted after waiting a moment or two to permit the air in the apparatus to be displaced by coal gas. The hole in B is now uncovered and the gas lighted there. The flame at C will be drawn up into the wide glass tube and burn quietly at D. This flame is now air burning in an atmosphere of coal gas.

The Structure of Four Typical Flames

1. *Burning hydrogen.* This pale blue flame is seen to consist of two distinct zones (fig. 100). The inner one (*a*) corresponds

to unburnt hydrogen making its way to that part of the flame where it can mix with air. The outer, blue flame, (b), is the zone where the reaction occurs.

$$2H_2 + O_2 = 2H_2O$$

Expt. 103. The three simple tests illustrated in fig. 101 show that the dark inner zone consists of cool, unburnt gas. In A, a fairly thick piece of paper has been depressed on to the flame for a moment, and the scorch mark shows that the flame is only hot round the edge. In B, a match is supported by a pin pushed through it just below the head, so that the match head is actually in

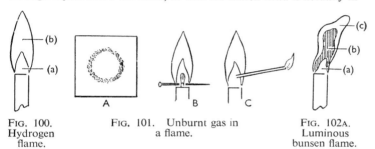

FIG. 100.
Hydrogen
flame.

FIG. 101. Unburnt gas in
a flame.

FIG. 102A.
Luminous
bunsen flame.

the flame. It will be found that the match does not ignite for some time. In C, unburnt gas is actually passing from the centre of the flame up the narrow tube and may be lighted at the top.

All flames contain this zone of unburnt gas, and its presence may be illustrated by similar experiments.

2. *Coal Gas burning at a bunsen-burner with the air shut off.* As shown in fig. 102A, there are three distinct zones in this flame:

(*a*) Unburnt gas.

(*b*) A luminous zone of incomplete combustion, yellow in colour probably because of the presence of particles of solid carbon in the flame. This flame is dirty, and deposits soot on vessels heated in it. If a light is shone through it on to a screen it casts a shadow, which suggests the presence of solid particles. (Similarly, if acetylene or benzene is burnt without extra air being supplied, a very luminous and very smoky flame is obtained.)

(c) The third (dark purple) zone corresponds to the final oxidation of carbon monoxide and hydrogen which were not completely oxidized in the inner flame because of lack of air.

Thus in this flame, as in all in which hydrocarbons burn, the actual oxidation occurs in two or more stages.

The following equations for the combustion of a typical hydrocarbon, methane, show clearly the way in which the amount of oxygen available decides which products are formed.

(1) Little air $\quad 2CH_4 + 2O_2 = \underset{\text{Soot}}{2C} + 4H_2O$

(2) More air $\quad 2CH_4 + 3O_2 = \underset{\substack{\text{Carbon} \\ \text{Monoxide}}}{2CO} + 4H_2O$

(3) Enough air $2CH_4 + 4O_2 = \underset{\substack{\text{Carbon} \\ \text{Dioxide}}}{2CO_2} + 4H_2O$

3. *Coal Gas burning at a bunsen-burner with full air supply.* Again there are three important zones (see fig. 102B), with the difference this time that the central zone of incomplete combustion is bright blue, and the flame is free from soot and is hotter than the last.

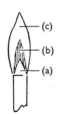

(a) Unburnt gas.

(b) Incomplete combustion, some carbon monoxide and hydrogen remaining to be burnt in the outer flame.

(c) The purple outer mantle in which the combustion becomes complete.

FIG. 102B. Non-luminous bunsen flame.

The absence of soot, which corresponds to more perfect combustion, makes this flame both hot and clean, and therefore the one chosen for heating purposes in both laboratory and home.

The burners of gas-fires and gas-cookers are like "Bunsens" with suitable-sized air-holes.

If the gas supply is reduced while the air-holes are wide open, *burning-back* occurs. The reason is that the flame is travelling *down* the bunsen tube at a greater rate than the gases are travelling up. Normally, the flame stays at the top because the rate at which the gas burns is less than the rate at which it arrives at the top of the tube. As the proportion of air to gas arriving up the tube increases, the rate of burning increases until it may become explosive. The gas burns at the jet after "striking back" because beyond that there is no air in the gas, and burning is therefore impossible.

4. *The candle flame.*

The burning gas in this case is the hydrocarbon vapour formed from paraffin wax (p. 289). The melted wax is drawn up the wick by capillary action and vaporizes at the top. Four zones of flame are to be observed (fig. 103):

(*a*) Unburnt gas.

(*b*) The yellow, luminous, inner zone where combustion of the hydrocarbons is incomplete; the solid particles of carbon in the flame give out light, and carbon monoxide is also present.

(*c*) The non-luminous outer mantle of complete combustion.

Fig. 103.
Candle
flame.

(*d*) A small blue zone at the base of the flame where a plentiful air supply makes the combustion much more nearly complete than in the yellow inner flame. If one blows gently at the candle, thus increasing the air supply, nearly all the flame is blue.

Incandescent Gas Mantles

The earliest gas lighting was very inefficient, depending on the yellow, luminous flame of coal gas when burnt without enough air; only the small amount of ethylene and benzene (p. 260) gave any light, as the hydrogen, methane and carbon monoxide which make up 90% of the coal gas all burn with pale-blue flames.

Modern gas lighting depends on the heating power (calorific value, p. 232) of the gas, and uses a "mantle" of thorium oxide, which gives out a bright light when heated strongly.

Ignition Temperature

A flame will not continue if its temperature is cooled below a certain point (the "ignition temperature"), because the chemical reaction will cease, e.g. blowing out a match.

Expt. 104. A familiar example of this is a bunsen-burner with a gauze above it; the metal of the gauze conducts the heat away, and the flame does not occur above the gauze; similarly if the gas is lit *above* the gauze, it does not easily burn below it.

This principle was applied in the first miner's safety lamp, invented by Davy before the use of electric lamps, to prevent explosions with methane (p. 291). Nowadays such lamps are used to *test* for the presence of gas; the methane comes through the gauze and makes the flame larger.

Liquids such as petrol, benzene, and carbon disulphide (p. 51) have very low ignition temperatures and so very easily catch fire. So has white ("yellow") phosphorus (p. 18).

GREEN PLANTS

These consist very largely of compounds of carbon, which are built up in the leaves by *photosynthesis* (described on p. 36) from the carbon dioxide of the air:

$$6CO_2 + 6H_2O + \text{energy} = C_6H_{12}O_6 + 6O_2$$

$$\underset{\substack{\text{from the} \\ \text{air}}}{6CO_2} + \underset{\substack{\text{from the} \\ \text{soil}}}{6H_2O} + \underset{\substack{\text{from the} \\ \text{sun}}}{\text{energy}} \underset{\substack{\text{chlorophyll} \\ \text{(green pigment)} \\ \text{as a catalyst}}}{=} \underset{\text{sugar}}{C_6H_{12}O_6} + \underset{\text{oxygen}}{6O_2}$$

These sugars, of which glucose is one, are members of the family of **carbohydrates**, i.e. substances containing carbon, together with hydrogen and oxygen in the same proportion as in water, with the general formula $C_x(H_2O)_y$. Sugars are transported in solution from the leaves, through the stem, to other parts of the plant, where they are built up into other compounds as food-reserves or as structural materials.

In certain plants, such as the sugar-cane or the sugar-beet, the food reserve is *sucrose*, $C_{12}H_{22}O_{11}$ (i.e. $2 C_6H_{12}O_6 - H_2O$), which is ordinary table sugar. Other plants build up *starch*, which has the approximate formula $C_{600}H_{1000}O_{500}$, usually written as $(C_6H_{10}O_5)_n$:

$$nC_6H_{12}O_6 - nH_2O = (C_6H_{10}O_5)_n$$

This starch is deposited in seeds (e.g. wheat) or roots (e.g. carrots) or tubers (e.g. potatoes), which are used for food by human beings (see pp. 233 and 304).

Expt. 105. Test for Starch.

If a drop of iodine solution (e.g. "tincture of iodine," p. 423) is put on to bread, raw potato, or rice, a deep blue-black colour is developed which is a test for starch. Other substances, e.g. sugar, do not respond to this test. The starch grains become clearly visible under the microscope.

Cellulose is an even larger molecule $(C_6H_{10}O_5)_n$, where n is about 1000, and forms long fibres which are the structural basis of the plant. It provides the rigid framework (stem, etc.) on which the leaves of the plant or tree are hung in order to carry out photosynthesis. Cellulose is digestible by the bacteria in the stomach of herbivorous animals (cow, horse, sheep, etc.), but not by man. Fairly pure forms of cellulose are filter-paper (from wood pulp) and especially cotton-wool. It is used as natural fibres, such as cotton, linen, hemp, ramie, etc., because of its strength, and also for making *plastic* fibres such as *rayon* (artificial silk), cellulose nitrate ("nitrocellulose," for celluloid and leathercloth), and cellulose acetate ("Celanese"). This book (see p. v) is largely made of cellulose.

Other elements besides carbon, hydrogen, and oxygen are necessary to the plant. These include nitrogen, phosphorus, potassium, calcium, magnesium, iron, and sulphur; of these N, P, and K are the most important. A ton of wheat removes from the soil about 50 lb. of combined nitrogen (equivalent to 230 lb. of $(NH_4)_2SO_4$), and 10 lb. each of combined phosphorus and potassium, so that these must be replaced in the form of *fertilizers* if the ground is not to become poorer (but see Chapter XIX, p. 313). The nitrogen and phosphorus are necessary for the formation of proteins (p. 304), especially in the seeds (e.g. peas and beans p. 311). The potassium is present throughout the plant, and its presence can be shown by burning, when the potassium compounds are converted to the oxide (K_2O), which combines with carbon dioxide to form potassium carbonate (K_2CO_3) in the ash ("pot-ash," p. 281).

Fermentation

Simpler chemicals such as *alcohol*, C_2H_6O, can be obtained when carbohydrates are broken down by fermentation (see enzymes, p. 236).

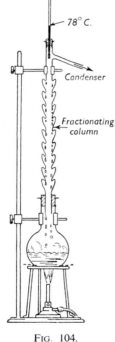

78° C.

Condenser

Fractionating column

Fig. 104.

Expt. 106. Preparation of Alcohol.

(Note: strictly speaking, the brewing of even 2 gm. of alcohol for educational purposes is illegal, but usually "The Law does not worry about trifles.") 50 c.c. of a 10% sugar solution are put in a 1 or 2-litre flask together with a few grams of brewer's yeast (baker's yeast is not so good). After a few hours the contents will begin to froth, and a test-tube of lime-water, connected to the flask by a delivery-tube, will show that carbon dioxide is being evolved.

$$C_6H_{12}O_6 \quad = \quad 2C_2H_6O \quad + \quad 2CO_2 \nearrow$$
(simple sugars, formed from cane-sugar)   (alcohol)

After three or four days the liquid is filtered and treated with quicklime to absorb the water. It is then very slowly distilled (expt. 33, p. 79), preferably with a *fractionating column* (fig. 104), which provides an "obstacle race" and allows only the vapour of lower-boiling liquid to escape. The first one or two c.c. of liquid collected (b.p. 78° C.) will be found to be inflammable, and to react violently when added to concentrated nitric acid; this is alcohol.

Similar processes are used on a large scale for the manufacture of alcoholic drinks. These contain approximately the following percentages of alcohol:

(*a*) *Fermented drinks:* beer, cyder, 2–6%; light wines, 8–10%.

(b)   "*Fortified*" *drinks* with extra alcohol added: port, sherry, 15–20%.

(c) *Distilled spirits:* gin, rum, brandy, whisky, 35–50%; vodka, snaps, aquavit, up to 70%.

There is a very large excise duty on alcohol, and so for industrial purposes *methylated spirit* is used; this contains 5% of the more poisonous *methyl* alcohol (see fig. 34, p. 101), which makes it undrinkable, and often also evil-tasting liquids (from coal tar) and a violet aniline dyestuff.

The main uses of alcohol are as a fuel (p. 265), as a solvent for varnishes, and as an "anti-freeze" for car radiators (see p. 80). Alcohol is also used in the preparation of ether (p. 368) and chloroform, and (coloured red) as a thermometric liquid because of its high coefficient of expansion and low freezing-point.

The poisonous dose of *pure* alcohol is less than 1 pint (570 c.c.) for an adult; 80 c.c. has killed a child. 50 c.c. of *methyl* alcohol is fatal.

Vinegar is a 5% solution of **acetic acid** prepared from alcohol by a further fermentation process:

$$C_2H_6O + O_2 = C_2H_4O_2 + H_2O$$

Alcohol   Air   Acetic acid

The flavour and colour of vinegar depend on the source (beer, wine, etc.) of the alcohol used.

Pure acetic acid was formerly made by the distillation of wood (p. 258), but now is manufactured from acetylene (p. 294). It forms white crystals, melting at 18° C. (room temperature), with a pungent smell, and forms salts called acetates (pp. 284, 291, 349). It is a weak acid (pp. 64, 215)

THE HUMAN BODY AND ITS FOOD

Proteins

"Flesh and blood," the characteristic features of the human (or higher animal) body, are both made up of compounds known as *proteins*. As the various cells of the human body are being continuously broken down and reformed, the food we eat must contain proteins to replace those which have "worn out". and—in children—to provide for growth.

The amount of protein required per day is about 3 oz.; of this, at present, roughly $\frac{1}{2}$ oz. is obtained from meat, 1 oz. from milk, cheese, and eggs, and the remainder from bread, other cereals, fruit and vegetables. Animal products are, in general, much richer in protein than vegetable products, but are also, of course, much more expensive and scarcer.

Proteins have the general formula—CO.NH.CHX.CO.NH. CHY—etc., where X, Y, are complex (with N, S, etc.). Before they can be built up into human tissue, the animal or vegetable proteins must first be broken down by digestion into the molecules of "amino-acids" of which they are made. As at least eight different amino-acids are known to be essential to human life, the importance of a varied diet is seen. Proteins are chains of at least 30 molecules in length; each molecule can be any one of 24 different amino-acids; the number of possible proteins is thus at least 24^{30} i.e. 1,000,000,000,000, 000,000,000,000,000,000,000,000,000,000. Some of these are: albumen in eggs, gelatin in bones, casein in milk, keratin in hair. Wool, silk and "Ardil" (from peanuts) are protein molecules of great length; the synthetic fibre "Nylon" is built up on a somewhat similar pattern, but is not a protein:— $(CH_2)_6NH.CO(CH_2)_4CO.NH.(CH_2)_6NH$— etc.

Expt. 107A. Test for Proteins.

Warm the substance with nitric acid; if it is a protein (e.g. human skin or the "skin" of boiled milk) it will turn yellow. On adding ammonia, the colour changes to orange.

Carbohydrates (see p. 300)

The energy needed by man to keep his body temperature (98·4° F.) above that of the surroundings, and for his muscular work (see pp. 24, 233), *could* be provided by the combustion of proteins, but this would be expensive. The cheapest energy-giving foods, such as bread and potatoes obtained from plants (p. 300), contain carbohydrates. The starch in these is then digested (i.e. broken down into simpler and more soluble molecules which can diffuse through into the blood stream), by the action of enzymes to form sugars. Unlike starch, the sugar *glucose*, $C_6H_{12}O_6$, requires no digestion; it is therefore very useful for invalids, and in the form of boiled sweets as a readily available source of energy for children or mountaineers. Sugars which are not immediately required are built up into *glycogen* ("animal starch"), which is stored round the liver and is easily broken down again to glucose.

Expt. 107B. Digestion of Starch.

Starch solution is put into two test-tubes which are standing in a beaker of water at body temperature (37° C.) Saliva is then added to one; both are left to "incubate" for 10 minutes, and are then cooled and tested with iodine (expt. 105, p. 301). The untreated starch still goes blue, but the other does not; this shows that starch has been digested (to a solution of malt sugar) by the enzymes in the saliva (see p. 479).

Expt. 107C. Test for Carbohydrates.

All carbohydrates except cellulose, if boiled with dilute acid, are broken down to a solution of simple sugars; when neutralized, this will give a red precipitate on heating with Fehling's solution.

Fats

These also are of importance as a source of energy, having a much greater calorific value than carbohydrates (see p. 233), and therefore being specially important in cold climates. Familiar examples are butter, lard, suet, olive oil, peanut butter. They do not dissolve in water, but form an emulsion, e.g. milk. Vegetable fats occur in seeds and fruit, e.g. palm fruit, coconuts, linseed oil (from flax). Fats are stored under the skin, especially in women, and around certain organs such as the heart, and serve as reserves of energy-producing material. Margarine (British) is as good a food as butter.

They are compounds of glycerol (glycerine) with certain complex organic acids, related to acetic acid, known as "fatty acids." Liquid fats are mostly compounds of unsaturated fatty acids, and can be converted into solid fats by reacting with hydrogen in the presence of a nickel catalyst (pp. 101 and 293).

Fats are split up on digestion, or in *soap*-making, into their constituents. If mutton fat, which contains glyceryl stearate, is boiled for some time with an equal volume of caustic soda solution, it reacts to form glycerol and the sodium salt of the fatty acid ($CH_3(CH_2)_{16}COO^-Na^+$, soap).

$$\underset{\text{(fat)}}{\underset{\text{Stearate}}{\text{Glyceryl}}} + \underset{\text{(caustic soda)}}{\underset{\text{Hydroxide}}{\text{Sodium}}} = \underset{\text{(glycerol)}}{\underset{\text{Hydroxide}}{\text{Glyceryl}}} + \underset{\text{(soap)}}{\underset{\text{Stearate}}{\text{Sodium}}}$$

Expt. 107D. Test for Fats.

If the above reaction mixture is examined after half an hour, three layers will be noticed; these are (i) unchanged fat (on top), (ii) soap, (iii) glycerol+unchanged alkali. These layers can be separated by using a tap-funnel. The soap sets to a solid, which can be dissolved in water and treated as below.

If common salt is added to soap solution, the soap becomes less soluble and floats on top as a solid. When cold, it sets to a hard mass and may be pressed into suitable shapes, and perfumed if desired.

Commercially, vegetable oils such as palm oil and olive oil are used instead of mutton fat, and the salt and the glycerol are recovered from the solution.

Mineral Salts

The human body is such a complex organism that at least ten other elements are required besides C, H, O, N (and S), which are the indispensable constituents of protein (for flesh).

Sodium and *chlorine*, in the form of sodium chloride, are required for the bodily fluids such as blood, which contains about $\frac{1}{2}\%$ of salt; every person eats about 5 kilograms (11 lb.) of salt per year.

Calcium and *phosphorus* are used in the formation of calcium phosphate for bones and teeth (provided that vitamin D is available), about 300–500 gm. of each element being required per person per year. Milk is a good source of these elements. Calcium compounds are necessary for the clotting of blood, and must be removed by precipitation before blood can be stored for transfusion purposes. *Magnesium* is also needed, to a somewhat lesser extent.

Iron, together with smaller amounts of *copper* and *manganese*, is needed to the extent of about 5 gm. per year for making haemoglobin, the red oxygen-carrying pigment of the blood. Many people, especially women of ages fifteen to forty-five, do not get enough iron in their diet (see p. 376).

Iodine, to the extent of about 1 milligram per year, is necessary for the functioning of the thyroid gland (see p. 425); whilst *silicon* and *fluorine* occur as calcium silicate+calcium fluoride in the enamel which forms the protective outer coating of teeth.

The presence of inorganic substances ("ash") in foods may be shown by heating strongly in a crucible. A white residue is left after all the organic matter has burned away

Vitamins (see table overleaf)

A diet which provides enough water, body-building food, mineral salts, and energy may still be inadequate because of the lack of vitamins. These are substances required in very small amounts (e.g. $0 \cdot 1$ gm. of vitamin C per day, and far less of the others) to control growth and to prevent disease (see p. 237). For example, complete lack of vitamin C (from fresh fruit and vegetables) causes scurvy; whilst a mild lack of vitamin B_1 causes tiredness and the feeling that a holiday is needed. The chemical formulae and structure of all the common vitamins are now known, e.g. vitamin C is $C_6H_8O_6$; vitamins B_1, B_2, and C (and B_5, B_6, etc.) are prepared synthetically on a fairly large scale, i.e. hundreds of tons per year, worth millions of pounds sterling.

In 1938 nearly half the population of Great Britain were suffering from a lack of some vitamins, and so the advantages of the increased supplies of fresh vegetables and milk and the issue of orange juice (fig. 128B, p. 359) and free cod-liver oil are clearly seen from the table. Also, the importance of reducing the smoke nuisance is seen, because it results in less sunshine and so less vitamin D, thereby producing ill-formed bones and teeth in children, or even the disease of rickets, which was formerly known as "The English Disease."

The table below shows the principal vitamins, together with some of their sources and uses:

VITAMIN	FOODS CONTAINING IT	USE	PROPERTIES
A	Cod-liver oil, milk, butter, margarine, eggs, carrots, tomatoes	For growth; prevention of "night-blindness"	Soluble in fats; destroyed by heat
B_1 B_2	Brown bread, yeast, milk, yolk of egg	Nerves and muscles	Soluble in water
C	Green vegetables, fruit, especially black-currants, lemons and oranges, potatoes	General resistance to disease. Healing of wounds	Lost in bad cooking, because soluble in water and destroyed by heat
D	Cod-liver oil, milk, butter, margarine, eggs; is formed in body by sunlight	Formation of teeth and bones	Soluble in fats

This is only a fragment of the story, but is sufficient to show something of the fascinating chemistry of the living creature; for further details, see Frank Wokes: "Food the Deciding Factor" (Penguin).

Suggestions for Practical Work

Expts. 103–105, and 107 (*a, b, c, d*).

QUESTIONS ON CHAPTER XVIII

1. How would you prepare (*a*) marsh gas, (*b*) acetylene? Compare the properties of these gases, and explain clearly how each may be distinguished from hydrogen. (D.)

2. How is ethylene usually prepared and collected? Compare its properties with those of hydrogen. How would you demonstrate that ethylene is a compound of carbon and hydrogen? (L.)

3. What are hydrocarbons?
What is the chief source of such compounds?
Name three hydrocarbons or mixtures of hydrocarbons in everyday use and describe the uses and importance of such substances.

How would you show that when a candle burns, carbon dioxide and steam are formed? (C.)

4. What do you understand by combustion? Give examples. Describe experiments which show that "combustible substance" and "supporter of combustion" are only relative. State the approximate composition of gunpowder, and account for the explosive nature of the substance. (L.)

5. Describe, using diagrams, the structure of the flame of a bunsen-burner. How do you account for the differences in the flame when the air holes of the bunsen-burner are closed? Indicate experiments which might be carried out in support of your answer.

6. Describe what you would do to prove that when a candle burns it produces water and carbon dioxide.
Draw a sketch showing the structure of a candle flame. (O. Gen. Sc.)

7. Describe and explain the burning of (a) coal gas, (b) paraffin, (c) coke, under conditions involving (i) partial combustion, (ii) complete combustion. (L. Gen. Sc.)

8. Draw a labelled diagram showing the structure of a non-luminous bunsen flame.
(a) Describe one experiment to demonstrate the presence of unburnt gas in such a flame.
(b) Why are smoky flames wasteful? How can this be prevented?
(c) Name the final products of combustion of coal gas, and describe how you would show that they are formed in a bunsen-burner. (C. Gen. Sc.)

9. What are the principal elements found in plants, and how does the plant obtain each of these during its growth?
Describe exactly how any two of the constituent elements could be obtained in a reasonable state of purity from a piece of wood. (L.)

10. Describe the principal properties of cane-sugar and of starch. What changes occur in these substances within the human body?
Calculate the weight of oxygen required for the complete oxidation of 1 gm. of glucose, $C_6H_{12}O_6$. (A.)

11. What do you know of the chemistry of alcohol, sugar, and starch? From where does a wheat plant derive the starch which it stores in its grains, and what becomes of the starch after it has been eaten by man?

12. If you were provided with a paste of starch and water and the necessary laboratory materials, how would you obtain from it an aqueous solution of (*a*) sugar, (*b*) alcohol?

What steps would be necessary for the separation of the alcohol from the water?

How would you distinguish between starch and sugar, and between water and alcohol? (D.)

13. Give an account of two fermentation processes, and of the uses to which the products are put.

14. Comment (*a*) on the disadvantages of a diet consisting of white bread, dripping, potatoes, and tea; and (*b*) on the advantages which would result from milk consumption in this country being doubled.

CHAPTER XIX

THE FIXATION OF NITROGEN. AMMONIA

The importance of nitrogen compounds to plant and animal life has already been mentioned (pp. 301, 304). The most abundant source of nitrogen is the atmosphere (p. 28), and processes for using this source are known as "the fixation of nitrogen."

THE NITROGEN CYCLE

In nature, when dead plants and animals decay, bacteria convert the proteins into ammonia (NH_3) and then into nitrates; broken-down proteins, excreted by higher animals in the

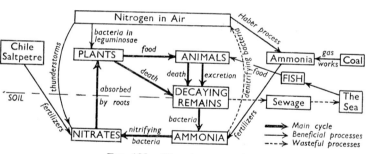

FIG. 105. The nitrogen cycle.

form of urea (CON_2H_4, dissolved in urine), behave similarly. The nitrates dissolve in the soil water, and so are absorbed by the roots of plants for building up once more into proteins; this completes the "Nitrogen Cycle" (fig. 105).

In addition, certain plants such as peas, beans, clover, etc. ("Leguminosae") have colonies of bacteria which live in easily visible nodules on their roots (PLATE 19), and which make atmospheric nitrogen directly available to the plant.

Also thunderstorms cause the combination of some nitrogen and oxygen in the air to form nitric oxide (p. 336), which comes down in the rain as very dilute nitric acid, and is therefore available as nitrates.

These beneficial processes are balanced by a certain small

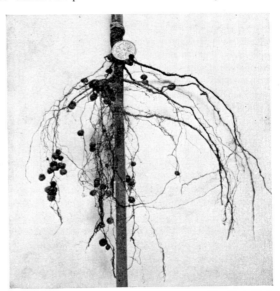

[Photo by courtesy of Dr. Hugh Nicol

PLATE 19. HELPING THE NITROGEN CYCLE

Nodules containing nitrogen-fixing bacteria on a soya-bean plant's roots (compared in size with a sixpence). Most other nodules are much smaller.

waste, which occurs when *denitrifying bacteria* convert ammonia into atmospheric nitrogen. Now the *nitrifying* bacteria which form nitrates from ammonia require both air and alkaline conditions:

$$NH_3 + 2O_2 = HNO_3 + H_2O$$

Ammonia Nitric acid

$$CaCO_3 + 2HNO_3 = Ca(NO_3)_2 + H_2O + CO_2$$

Limestone Calcium Nitrate

so that the above waste of nitrogen occurs specially on undug soils which are acidic, i.e. in need of liming (p. 270).

Much more serious waste occurs when foodstuffs are consumed miles away from the scene of their growth, because the nitrogen in them cannot be returned to the soil. Moreover, a large amount of excrement is wasted by being cast into the sea as sewage. These losses have to be made good by the application of fertilizers, now mostly obtained by the "*fixation*" of *atmospheric nitrogen*.

Nitrogenous Fertilizers

There are three main sources of supply of nitrogen compounds:

(*a*) The nitrogen of the atmosphere, mostly "fixed" by the Haber process (see below) for making ammonia; this, and the cyanamide process (p. 271), account for 75% of the total.

(*b*) Ammonia recovered as a by-product from coal gas at gas-works (p. 260): 17%.

(*c*) Naturally occurring deposits of sodium nitrate ("Chile saltpetre," p. 333), which are slowly becoming exhausted: 8%.

Historically, Chile saltpetre was used first (about 1840), then by-product ammonia (about 1850), then early fixation processes (1905, see p. 336), and most recently the Haber process (1914). The world production of nitrogen compounds in 1920 was equivalent to about 1 million tons of *nitrogen*; this had risen to 2 million tons by 1930, and 3 million tons by 1940 (fig. 161, p. 527), i.e. about 14 million tons of $(NH_4)_2SO_4$ or its equivalent.

AMMONIA

The Manufacture of Ammonia (Haber process)

The principles underlying the direct combination of nitrogen with hydrogen to form ammonia,

$$N_2 + 3H_2 = 2NH_3 + heat,$$

have been thoroughly explained in Chapter XV (pp. 229, 231, 234).

Nitrogen (obtained from the atmosphere, p. 33), and

hydrogen (from water gas, p. 93) are mixed in the correct proportions (p. 200) and subjected to a high pressure (250 atmospheres) in the presence of an iron catalyst. The lowest temperature at which the reaction proceeds sufficiently fast is about 500° C.

Only about 15% of the gases are converted into ammonia. This is removed by liquefaction (p. 322) or by dissolving in water (see below), and the unchanged gases are passed once more over the catalyst.

There are three main uses for the ammonia: (a) it is converted into *ammonium sulphate* (p. 375), which is used as a fertilizer; (b) it is oxidized to *nitric acid* (p. 325), which makes fertilizers or explosives; (c) when liquefied under pressure, it is used for *refrigerators* (p. 322).

This process was worked out by the German, Fritz Haber, just before the 1914 war, and enabled Germany to be independent of supplies of Chile saltpetre for explosives; these supplies were cut off by the blockade. The Haber process is operated at Billingham-on-Tees (FRONTISPIECE, p. ii) in this country, and in most other countries of the world. It is a classic example of a scientific discovery which can be used either for good or for evil purposes; ammonium nitrate is equally valuable as a fertilizer or as an explosive, and so the same chemical compound can save life or can kill, depending on the political decision to use it to produce food or to produce frightfulness.

Laboratory Preparation of Ammonia

Expt. 108. Ammonia gas is evolved when any ammonium salt is heated with a base. It is usually prepared by heating ammonium chloride, or sulphate, with slaked lime (fig. 106). The two solids are mixed thoroughly and heated in a round-bottomed flask or test-tube. Steam is formed during the reaction and the flask should be sloped slightly downwards to prevent condensed steam from running back on to the hot glass. As the gas is lighter than air (molecular weight=17; air—average M.W.=28·8) and very soluble in water, it is collected by displacement of air in an inverted gas-jar. The gas is dried by *quicklime* contained in a drying-tower. The usual drying agents are unsuitable because ammonia is an alkaline gas and combines directly with concentrated sulphuric acid; it also forms an addition compound with calcium chloride in the cold:

$$2NH_4Cl + Ca(OH)_2 = 2NH_3\nearrow + 2H_2O\nearrow + CaCl_2$$

To test when the jar is full, a piece of damp red litmus-paper is held below the jar; this turns blue as soon as the gas begins to escape from the jar.

Properties of Ammonia, (NH_3, M.W.$=17$)

(a) It is a colourless gas, with an extremely pungent smell, and is poisonous in large amounts, though smaller doses are stimulating (e.g. smelling-salts, p. 283).

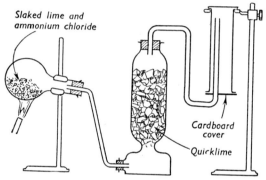

Slaked lime and ammonium chloride

Cardboard cover

Quicklime

FIG. 106. Laboratory preparation of ammonia.

(b) It is the only common alkaline gas, and so is detected by turning damp red litmus-paper blue. A very sensitive test for ammonia in solution is "Nessler's reagent," which gives a red-brown precipitate; this is used for testing drinking water, because if there is contamination with sewage ammonia will be present (fig. 105, p. 311).

(c) It is one of the gases which are extremely soluble in water (p. 114), as may be shown by the "fountain experiment":

Expt. 109. A flask (A) is filled with ammonia gas (fig. 107) and then fitted with a rubber stopper carrying a glass tube drawn out to a jet This glass tube is connected by rubber tubing, clipped at B, with a bottle of water coloured by red litmus. By blowing with the mouth at C (both clips being open), a small amount of water is forced up the tube and through the jet, dissolving much of the ammonia in the flask. This produces such a reduced pressure in the flask that water rises in a brisk fountain, which continues until the flask is almost full. As ammonia gives an alkaline solution, the litmus in the flask goes blue in colour.

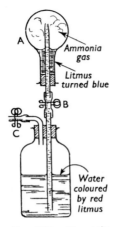

FIG. 107. Fountain experiment.

Ammonium Hydroxide Solution

Expt. 110. A solution of ammonia gas in water, known as ammonium hydroxide solution (p. 66), is prepared by passing the gas into water through an inverted funnel, as shown in fig. 108. The open end should just dip below the surface of the water in a beaker. This device effectively prevents any danger of the water "sucking back" into the apparatus used to generate the gas. As the gas in the funnel dissolves and the water is forced upwards by the reduction in pressure, the open end of the funnel very quickly becomes above the water-level outside. The external pressure, which forces the water into the funnel, then sends in air; this equalizes the pressure inside and out. If a narrow tube was used, no air could make its way past the water, and water would rapidly go up the tube, as in the fountain experiment.

At room temperature (15° C.), one volume of water will dissolve about 800 volumes of ammonia, producing a solution of density 0·880 gm. per c.c., which contains 35% of ammonia by weight.

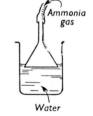

FIG. 108. Dissolving a very soluble gas.

Ammonium hydroxide solution smells strongly of ammonia, and as the solubility of ammonia decreases as the temperature rises (fig. 37, p. 108), a convenient way of preparing ammonia gas in the laboratory is to heat the solution.

$$NH_4OH = H_2O + NH_3 \nearrow$$

The name "ammonium hydroxide" is given to the solution of ammonia in water because it is alkaline to litmus and because it reacts as if it contains (a) ammonium ions (NH_4^+) and (b) hydroxyl ions (OH^-).

(a) With acids, *ammonium salts* are formed:

$$NH_4OH + HCl = H_2O + NH_4Cl \text{ (ammonium chloride)}$$
i.e. $$OH^- + H^+ = H_2O$$

cf. $$NaOH + HCl = H_2O + NaCl \text{ (sodium chloride)}$$

The ammonium "radical," i.e. NH_4 group of atoms, behaves here like a metallic atom such as sodium. The student must distinguish clearly between the *ammonia molecule* (formula NH_3) and the *ammonium radical* (NH_4); the latter cannot exist alone, but occurs only in the ammonium compounds.

(b) With solutions of metallic salts, *metallic hydroxides* are precipitated:

Expt. 111A.

$$3NH_4OH + FeCl_3 = 3NH_4Cl + Fe(OH)_3 \downarrow$$
i.e. $$3OH^- + Fe^{+++} = Fe(OH)_3$$
cf. $$3NaOH + FeCl_3 = 3NaCl + Fe(OH)_3 \downarrow$$

⎧ferric hydroxide: ⎫
⎨ see p. 65, ⎬
⎩ red-brown ppt. ⎭

This reaction occurs with the salts of all metals except potassium and sodium.

There are, however, two important differences in behaviour between ammonium hydroxide and sodium hydroxide:

(1) **Expt. 111B.** Excess ammonium hydroxide dissolves the precipitates first formed from solutions of copper or silver salts: sodium hydroxide does *not* do this:

$$Cu(OH)_2 + 4NH_4OH = Cu(NH_3)_4^{++} 2(OH)^- + 4H_2O$$

Pale-blue precipitate
of copper hydroxide

Deep blue solution of
cuprammonium hydroxide

(2) **Expt. 112.** Ammonium hydroxide is not a strong enough alkali to redissolve the precipitates of the amphoteric hydroxides (see p. 391) of aluminium, tin, or lead; sodium hydroxide *does* do so. (Zinc hydroxide will dissolve in both, giving zinc ammonium ions and sodium zincate respectively) (see p. 462).

11*

Preparation of Ammonium Salts

(a) From Ammonium Hydroxide (General Method)

Expt. 113. Ammonium chloride is formed when dilute ammonium hydroxide solution is run into hydrochloric acid until the smell of ammonia indicates excess. The excess is then driven off during partial evaporation of the solution to obtain crystals.

(b) From Ammonia

Expt. 114. If a jar of ammonia gas and one of hydrogen chloride (hydrochloric acid gas) are brought together mouth to mouth, dense white fumes are formed, which are small solid particles of ammonium chloride ("sal ammoniac"). This may be used as a test for ammonia.

$$NH_3 + HCl = NH_4Cl$$

If the tops of the jars are vaselined before the experiment, the formation of a solid from the two gases causes a large reduction in pressure, and so the jars stick tightly together. If hydrogen chloride gas is not available, rinse a few c.c. of concentrated hydrochloric acid round in a gas-jar and pour away the liquid.

(c) By Double Decomposition

A solution of ammonium carbonate or bicarbonate (prepared from ammonia, carbon dioxide, and water) is useful for this:

$$NH_4HCO_3 + NaCl = NaHCO_3 \downarrow + NH_4Cl \text{ (Solvay process, p. 281)}$$

$$(NH_4)_2CO_3 + \underset{\substack{\text{(naturally occurring,} \\ \text{slightly soluble)}}}{CaSO_4} = CaCO_3 \downarrow + (NH_4)_2SO_4 \text{ (see fig. 94, p. 271)}$$

General Properties of Ammonium Salts

(a) Action of Alkalis and Bases

Expt. 115. Ammonia gas is evolved from *all* ammonium salts on heating with an alkali or base (expt. 108, p. 314), and this is the best *test* for ammonium compounds. Any such compound (e.g. "sulphate of ammonia") is heated in a test-tube with sodium hydroxide solution; ammonia is a gas and so is driven off, and can be detected by its smell and by its action on damp red litmus-paper.

(b) Action of Heat

The sulphate and chloride (see below), and the carbonate (see p. 283) decompose into ammonia and the corresponding acid. The nitrate decomposes to nitrous oxide ("dental gas," see p. 338), and the nitrite to nitrogen (expt. 21, p. 33).

Expt. 116.   *Ammonium chloride* when heated turns directly into a gas without first melting; when cooled the gas re-forms the solid without first condensing to a liquid. This process of "sublimation" is shown by only a few substances, notably carbon dioxide (p. 251), and iodine and flowers of sulphur under certain conditions. Fig. 109 illustrates how this property may be used to purify ammonium chloride from a non-volatile impurity such as sodium chloride.

In the vapour state ammonium chloride is completely *dissociated* into ammonia and hydrogen chloride; but on cooling the two gases unite once more:

$$NH_4Cl \rightleftharpoons NH_3 \nearrow + HCl \nearrow$$

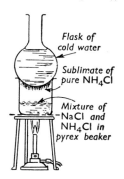

Flask of cold water

Sublimate of pure NH_4Cl

Mixture of NaCl and NH_4Cl in pyrex beaker

FIG. 109.
Sublimation.

Expt. 117A.   Solid ammonium chloride is strongly heated in a test-tube which has a tightly fitting plug of glass-wool in the middle, some wet red litmus-paper projecting above the plug, and some wet blue litmus-paper below it. The lighter ammonia (M.W. 17) diffuses faster (see p. 102) than the heavier hydrogen chloride (M.W. 36·5). The upper litmus-paper therefore turns blue and the lower one red.

Expt. 117B.   Solid ammonium sulphate when strongly heated in a test-tube gives off ammonia (test with damp litmus) and leaves a colourless liquid (ammonium bisulphate) which crystallizes on cooling:

$$(NH_4)_2SO_4 \rightleftharpoons NH_3 \nearrow + NH_4HSO_4$$

Nitrogen dioxide ($N_2O_4 \rightleftharpoons 2NO_2$) and phosphorus penta-chloride ($PCl_5 \rightleftharpoons PCl_3 + Cl_2$) similarly undergo reversible *thermal dissociation*.

(c) Action of Water

All ammonium salts are soluble.

(*d*) Other properties are discussed under the headings of the acids in question (carbonate, p. 283; nitrate, p. 334; nitrite, p. 340; sulphide, p. 351; sulphate, p. 375; chloride, p. 402).

The Oxidation of Ammonia

(*a*) *The Burning of Ammonia*

Ammonia will not burn in air unless a flame is held to it, but it will do so in oxygen.

Expt. 118. Dry ammonia is passed in through the long tube of the apparatus shown in fig. 110, while oxygen is passed in through the shorter tube. The glass-wool immediately above this makes the oxygen fill the wide tube evenly. The ammonia issuing from the long tube will burn, if lighted, to form nitrogen and water:

$$4NH_3 + 3O_2 = 2N_2 + 6H_2O$$

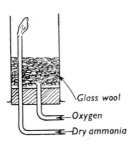

Glass wool

Oxygen

Dry ammonia

FIG. 110. Ammonia burning in oxygen.

(*b*) *Action of Oxides on Ammonia*

Expt. 119. Red-hot copper oxide, and certain other metallic oxides, will also convert ammonia to nitrogen, the other products being steam and the metal. If the steam is condensed in a cooled U-tube (fig. 111) and if the ammonia was originally dry, this reaction is a proof that ammonia contains both nitrogen and hydrogen:

$$2NH_3 + 3CuO = 3Cu + 3H_2O + N_2$$

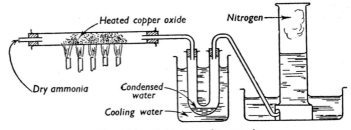

Heated copper oxide

Nitrogen

Dry ammonia

Condensed water

Cooling water

FIG. 111. Oxidation of ammonia.

The gas in the jar is colourless and gives negative tests with a burning splint, litmus, and lime-water, showing that it must be nitrogen.

(c) The Catalytic Oxidation of Ammonia

This reaction is of immense practical importance, because ammonia from the Haber process is used, and the nitric oxide first formed can easily be converted (see p. 337, and PLATE 15A, p. 234) into nitric acid and nitrates. It is used industrially on a very large scale:

$$4NH_3 + 5O_2 = 4NO + 6H_2O$$
$$4NO + 3O_2 + 2H_2O = 4HNO_3$$

Expt. 120. Excess of air is drawn, by means of the pump, through the concentrated solution of ammonia (fig. 112), and the mixture of air and ammonia gas passes over the platinum gauze, which is heated at the beginning of the experiment. The reaction is exothermic, i.e. gives out heat, so that once it has started the

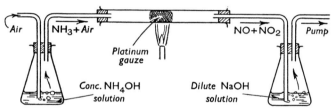

FIG. 112.   Catalytic oxidation of ammonia.

platinum is kept red hot without external heat, and the bunsen-burner may be turned off. The oxides of nitrogen produced are bubbled through a solution of caustic soda, which dissolves the nitrogen dioxide, forming sodium nitrate and nitrite:

$$2NO + O_2 = 2NO_2; \quad 2NO_2 + 2NaOH = NaNO_2 + NaNO_3 + H_2O$$

Nitrogen Dioxide   Sodium Nitrite   Sodium Nitrate

(d) Oxidation by Chlorine (see expt. 73, p. 189)

This shows the formula to be NH_3 (see p. 198).

(e) Decomposition of Ammonia by Sparking

At high temperatures ammonia is completely decomposed into nitrogen and hydrogen, $2NH_3 = N_2 + 3H_2$; this is why even at high pressures as in the Haber process, only 15% of ammonia is formed. If ammonia gas, confined over mercury, is sparked continuously from platinum wires connected to an induction coil, it will be found that the volume of gas is eventually doubled (see p. 206, qu. 2).

Other Uses of Ammonia

(a) Liquefied Ammonia for Refrigerators

At atmospheric pressure ammonia liquefies at $-33°$ C., and if compressed (e.g. p. 314) it can become a liquid at room temperature. This liquid is used in ice-factories and in some forms of refrigerators. The principle underlying its use is that if a liquid is turned to a gas, the latent heat necessary to produce the change will be taken from the surroundings. The cooling effect which results maintains a low temperature in the refrigerator. Fig. 113 illustrates the cycle of operations. Corresponding to that cooling effect, there is heat developed once more when the gas is liquefied by compression (compare liquid air, p. 30); this heat is dissipated either to the air or to cooling water. The liquefied ammonia then evaporates once more, and again cools the refrigerating chamber.

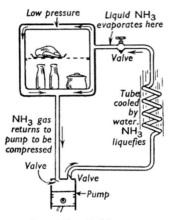

FIG. 113. Refrigerator.

The *non-poisonous*, *non-combustible*, *odourless* gas "Freon," CF_2Cl_2, which has a similar boiling-point, is now gradually replacing ammonia.

(b) Cleansing

Ammonium hydroxide softens temporary hardness in water by reacting with the calcium bicarbonate (compare calcium hydroxide, p. 276).

$$Ca(HCO_3)_2 + 2NH_4OH = CaCO_3 \downarrow + (NH_4)_2CO_3 + 2H_2O$$

It also neutralizes acids left in fabrics as the result of perspiration.

Note : The more important reactions of ammonia, nitric acid, and the oxides of nitrogen referred to in this chapter and the next are shown in fig. 115, p. 326.

Suggestions for Practical Work

Expt. 108 and properties of ammonia; test solubility by inverting a gas-jar of it over water. Expts. 110–117, 119.

QUESTIONS ON CHAPTER XIX

1. Give, with the aid of a diagram, an account of the nitrogen cycle. (L. Gen. Sc.)

2. Describe a method which can be used industrially for converting the nitrogen of the air into *either* (*a*) nitrates *or* (*b*) ammonium compounds.

Why is this fixation of atmospheric nitrogen of great importance to plants and animals? (C. Gen. Sc.)

3. How would you prepare ammonia gas, (i) in the laboratory, (ii) on the industrial scale? By reference to the equation:

$$N_2 + 3H_2 \rightleftharpoons 2NH_3 + 20,000 \text{ cal.}$$

Show how the yield of ammonia is affected by change in (*a*) pressure, (*b*) temperature. (Navy)

4. Give an account of the industrial preparation of ammonia from nitrogen and hydrogen, indicating the manner in which the nitrogen and hydrogen are obtained. What is done with the ammonia? (Sketches of plant are *not* required.) (O.)

5. Describe in outline the manufacture of ammonia from nitrogen and hydrogen. Why is this process of great importance? Write equations for the reaction which takes place, and name the products of the reaction when ammonia gas reacts with (*a*) hydrogen chloride, (*b*) hot copper oxide. (C.)

6. How is ammonia produced in nature? How could you prepare a solution of ammonia in the laboratory?

Explain why an aqueous solution of ammonia is described as an alkali. (O. Gen. Sc.)

7. How is ammonia recovered as a by-product in the manufacture of coal gas?

Mention and explain the purposes for which ammonia is commonly used. (A.)

8. How is the gas ammonia prepared in the laboratory?
What is its action on (a) litmus solution, (b) nitric acid?
Why is it inadvisable to apply, at the same time, lime and manure to the soil of a garden?
What principles underlie the use of ammonia (a) in refrigerators, (b) as a cleansing agent? (L. Gen. Sc.)

9. Give a labelled diagram and equation to illustrate the laboratory preparation of ammonia. State three tests by which you would identify the gas. Outline in each case one process by which ammonia is oxidized to give (a) nitrogen, (b) nitric acid.

10. Starting from ammonium chloride, how would you prepare an aqueous solution of ammonia? Describe the preparation, from this solution, of dry crystals of ammonium nitrate. How would you determine the weight of ammonia in a litre of its aqueous solution? (L.)

11. How would you prepare and collect several jars of dry ammonia? Sketch the apparatus you would use.
What laboratory experiments would you perform to show that ammonia (a) is very soluble in water, (b) contains hydrogen? Give one experiment in each case. (N.)

12. Sketch and label the apparatus that you would use to prepare and collect dry ammonia gas from ammonium chloride. Write the equation for the reaction.
State what takes place when ammonia gas is (a) mixed with hydrogen chloride, (b) shaken with a small quantity of copper sulphate solution.

13. What reactions take place, and what industrial process do you associate with each, when:
(a) a saturated solution of sodium chloride is treated first with ammonia and then with carbon dioxide;
(b) a suspension of calcium sulphate in water is treated with ammonia and carbon dioxide;
(c) a mixture of ammonia and air is passed through red-hot platinum gauze?
Give a *brief* outline of *one* of these industrial processes. (O.)

14. Give the names and formulae of *three* ammonium salts and explain their usefulness.

CHAPTER XX

NITRIC ACID. OXIDES OF NITROGEN

NOTE: The more important reactions of nitric acid, nitrates, the oxides of nitrogen, and ammonia (referred to in this chapter and Chapter XIX) are shown in fig. 115, overleaf.

NITRIC ACID

The Preparation of Nitric Acid

Expt. 121. Nitric acid can be prepared in the laboratory by distilling sodium nitrate (about 25 gm.) with concentrated sulphuric acid (just enough to cover it) in a retort (fig. 114). No cork or rubber must be used in the apparatus, because nitric acid rapidly attacks them both

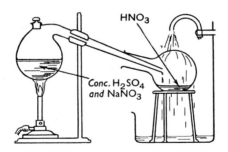

HNO₃

Conc. H₂SO₄
and NaNO₃

FIG. 114. Laboratory preparation of nitric acid.

The volatile nitric acid comes over at first as an almost colourless vapour, gradually turning brown as the experiment proceeds, and condensing to a straw-coloured liquid. Sodium bisulphate remains behind in the retort with the excess sulphuric acid.

$$NaNO_3 + H_2SO_4 = NaHSO_4 + HNO_3 \nearrow$$

At higher temperatures two molecules of sodium nitrate can be made to react with each molecule of sulphuric acid, leaving the normal sulphate (Na_2SO_4). Although this results in a larger yield of nitric acid for a given quantity of sulphuric acid, the reaction is

COMPOUNDS OF NITROGEN

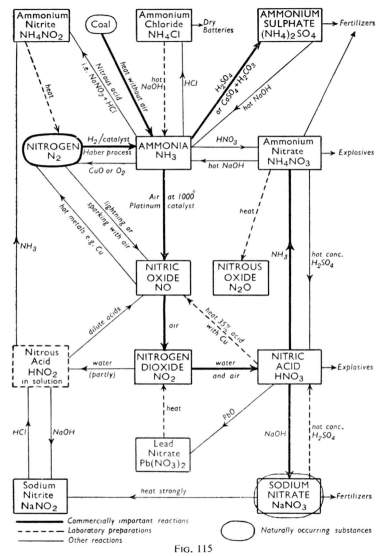

FIG. 115

326

not allowed to proceed so far, since at the higher temperature some of the nitric acid is decomposed (expt. 122); also the sodium sulphate left, being a solid at the temperature of the reaction, is less easily removed from the retort than the easily fusible bisulphate.

The brown fumes seen in the receiving flask are nitrogen dioxide (NO_2), formed by the decomposition of some of the nitric acid; the yellow, or straw, colour of the liquid is due to the dissolving of some of this gas.

Industrial Production of Nitric Acid

Nitric acid is now very largely made by the catalytic oxidation of synthetic ammonia to nitric oxide (p. 321), and the reaction of this with air and water (p. 337).   Some is still made by the method of expt. 121 from Chile saltpetre, using iron retorts, which are not attacked by the *concentrated* acids.

Properties of Nitric Acid

Pure nitric acid has a boiling-point of 86° C. and a density of 1·5 gm. per c.c.; but the ordinary concentrated acid is a solution in water containing 68% of pure nitric acid, and having a boiling-point of 120° C., density 1·4 gm. per c.c.   (It is convenient to remember that, roughly speaking, the strengths of the three common concentrated acids are: hydrochloric 33%, nitric 66%, sulphuric 99%.)   It is colourless if pure, but is usually slightly yellow, as in expt. 121.   Nitric acid reacts both as an acid (monobasic) and as an oxidizing agent.

Reactions of Nitric Acid as an Acid

(*a*) Its solution turns litmus red.

(*b*) It reacts with an *alkali or base* to form a salt (the nitrate) and water:

$KOH + HNO_3 = H_2O + KNO_3$ (potassium nitrate, see p. 70)
$PbO + 2HNO_3 = H_2O + Pb(NO_3)_2$ (lead nitrate, see p. 69)

(*c*) With metallic *carbonates* it sets free carbon dioxide and forms the corresponding nitrates:

$Na_2CO_3 + 2HNO_3 = H_2O + CO_2\nearrow + 2NaNO_3$ (sodium nitrate)
$CuCO_3 + 2HNO_3 = H_2O + CO_2\nearrow + Cu(NO_3)_2$ (copper nitrate)

(*d*) Extremely dilute nitric acid can be made to give hydrogen with magnesium metal, but in all other reactions with metals nitric acid acts as an oxidizing agent (see below) and hydrogen is *not* formed.

Reactions of Nitric Acid as an Oxidizing Agent

These reactions are more readily understood if the *decomposition* of nitric acid *by heat* is first considered:

Expt. 122. Concentrated nitric acid is allowed to trickle down from the bowl of a long clay-pipe, through the stem which is strongly heated (Fig. 116). The wire gauze is used to spread out the flame, or a long burner may be used   The nitric acid is decomposed, by

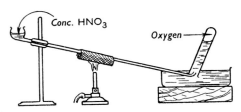

FIG. 116.   Decomposition of nitric acid by heat.

the strong heating, into water, nitrogen dioxide (which dissolves), and oxygen (which is collected in the test-tube):

$$4HNO_3 = 2H_2O + 4NO_2 + O_2$$

It is important that the mouthpiece of the pipe is only *just* below the surface of the water, as otherwise the pressure will be too great for the oxygen to escape.   When the mouthpiece is removed from the water, brown fumes of nitrogen dioxide are seen.

If nitric acid is treated with a substance which can take up oxygen, i.e. "be oxidized," then the oxygen which came off in expt. 122 is taken up instead of being set free, as in the following examples:

(*a*) *Metals.*   Nearly all metals are attacked by concentrated nitric acid (see p. 140), the products being the nitrate, water, and nitrogen dioxide; these may be explained as follows:

(i) The metal is oxidized to its oxide:

$2HNO_3 = H_2O + 2NO_2 + O$ (for oxidizing)
$Cu + O$ (from above) $= CuO$

(ii) The oxide reacts with more acid:

$CuO + 2HNO_3 = Cu(NO_3)_2 + H_2O$
∴ $Cu + 4HNO_3 = Cu(NO_3)_2 + 2H_2O + 2NO_2 ↗.$

The trivalent metals (iron, chromium, and aluminium) are rendered "passive" by the formation of an extremely thin film of oxide, which prevents the surface of the metal from further attack.   In the case of aluminium, this occurs even with dilute nitric acid or with water, and accounts for this metal's resistance to corrosion.   The film of chromium oxide is formed on the surface of stainless steel, and of course on chromium plating also.

If the nitric acid is more dilute, other products, such as nitric oxide (NO, see p. 337), etc., are formed.

(b) *Non-metals.*   Many of these are oxidized to their highest oxide, e.g.

$C + 2O = CO_2$ (red-hot charcoal burns vigorously to carbon dioxide)

$2P + 5O = P_2O_5$ ($+ 3H_2O = 2H_3PO_4$, phosphoric acid, see p. 431)
$S + 3O = SO_3$ ($+ H_2O = H_2SO_4$, sulphuric acid, see below):

Expt. 123.   Boil a small quantity of powdered sulphur with concentrated nitric acid in an evaporating basin in the fume cupboard for a few minutes.   Cool, dilute, and filter.   Test the solution for sulphuric acid by adding dilute hydrochloric acid and barium chloride solution; a white precipitate is obtained (see p. 374).

(c) *Sawdust*
Expt. 124.   A few drops of pure nitric acid (prepared in expt. 121) are dropped on to warm, dry sawdust.   This consists mostly of cellulose (p. 301), and takes fire, burning strongly.   Clouds of brown nitrogen dioxide, carbon dioxide and steam are given off.

(d) *Hydrochloric acid.*   A mixture of $\frac{3}{4}$ concentrated hydrochloric acid and $\frac{1}{4}$ concentrated nitric acid is called *aqua regia,* because of its power to dissolve gold, "the royal metal." The hydrochloric acid is oxidized by the nitric acid to chlorine, which then attacks the gold, e.g. a fountain pen-nib.

$$2HCl+O=H_2O+Cl_2 \quad ; \quad 2Au+3Cl_2 = 2AuCl_3$$
Chlorine   Gold Chloride

(*e*) *Ferrous Sulphate* (see "brown-ring" test, p. 332)

Reactions of Nitric Acid with some Organic Compounds

$$C_6H_5.CH_3+3HNO_3=C_6H_2(CH_3)(NO_2)_3+3H_2O$$
Toluene (p. 295)   Tri Nitro Toluene ("T.N.T.")

$$C_3H_5(OH)_3+3HNO_3=C_3H_5(NO_3)_3+3H_2O$$
Glycerol (p. 306)   Glyceryl Nitrate ("nitroglycerine")

The above reactions also form water, and are therefore helped by the presence of concentrated sulphuric acid, which acts as a dehydrating agent (p. 368).

Warning: The above reactions are dangerous and should not be attempted by anyone without much experience. Even the famous French scientist Dulong (p. 166) lost an eye and three fingers in research on explosives.

The above compounds, and also tri-nitro-phenol ("picric acid") and cellulose nitrate ("guncotton") are important as *explosives* because they contain a large amount of oxygen; this helps them to burn quickly without the aid of outside oxygen, to give large amounts of hot gas in a fraction of a second, e.g.

$$4C_3H_5(NO_3)_3 \quad \text{(1 c.c. of liquid "nitroglycerine")}$$
$$\downarrow$$
$$12CO_2+10H_2O+6N_2+O_2 \quad \left(\begin{array}{l}\text{1200 c.c. of gas, expanded to} \\ \text{12,000 c.c. at 3000° C.}\end{array}\right)$$
$$+ \ 1,729,600 \ \text{calories}$$

see PLATE 9, p. 126.

Apart from their misuse for war, explosives are very important in mining (see PLATE 20), quarrying, and in constructional work, such as the making of the Simplon Railway Tunnel and the Panama Canal.

[*Photo by courtesy of the National Coal Board*

PLATE 20.   EXPLOSIVES FOR PEACEFUL USE

The machine shown here bores a deep hole in the coal-face, ready for an explosive charge.   30 tons of coal are then obtained from the blast.

NITRATES

Heat	Tests

$\left.\begin{array}{l}K \\ Na\end{array}\right\} \rightarrow$ metal nitrite $+$ oxygen

$NH_4 \quad \rightarrow N_2O + H_2O$

$\left.\begin{array}{l}All \\ others\end{array}\right\} \rightarrow$ metal oxide $+ NO_2 + O_2$

(1) all are soluble in water;

(2) all give nitric acid with hot conc. H_2SO_4 (expt. 125);

(3) all give "brown-ring" test (expt. 126).

(1) *All nitrates are soluble in water,* and so cannot be tested by precipitation reactions.

(2) *Action of Hot Concentrated Sulphuric Acid*

Expt. 125. Any solid nitrate when heated in a test-tube with concentrated sulphuric acid gives off nitric acid, as in expt. 121. If the upper part of the test-tube is strongly heated, this will be decomposed to give brown fumes of nitrogen dioxide, as in expt. 122. If a few copper turnings are added, as in expt. 62, p. 140, far more brown fumes are given off.

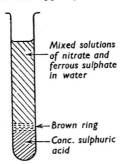

Mixed solutions of nitrate and ferrous sulphate in water

Brown ring

Conc. sulphuric acid

FIG. 117. Brown-ring test for nitrates.

(3) *The "Brown-Ring" Test*

Expt. 126. A solution of any nitrate in water is added to a solution of ferrous sulphate in water (preferably freshly made, see p. 470) in a test-tube, both being cold. Concentrated sulphuric acid is then poured *very gently* down the side of the test-tube so as to form a separate layer at the bottom (density 1·84 gm. per c.c.). Where the two liquids meet, a brown layer is formed, which appears from the outside like a brown ring round the test-tube (fig. 117). This indicates that a nitrate is present, and is explained as follows:

(*a*) Where the concentrated sulphuric acid meets the nitrate solution, some nitric acid is formed:

$$Zn(NO_3)_2 + H_2SO_4 = ZnSO_4 + 2HNO_3$$

(b) This nitric acid oxidizes some of the ferrous sulphate to ferric sulphate, and is itself reduced to nitric oxide:

$$2HNO_3 = H_2O + 3O + 2NO \text{ (nitric oxide)}$$
$$O + H_2SO_4 + 2FeSO_4 = H_2O + Fe_2(SO_4)_3 \text{ (ferric sulphate)}$$

(c) The nitric oxide so formed reacts with the unchanged ferrous sulphate solution to form a deep-brown compound ($FeSO_4.NO$) which constitutes the "brown-ring":

$$NO + FeSO_4 = FeSO_4.NO$$

Preparation of Nitrates

All may be made by the action of nitric acid on the carbonate, or oxide, or hydroxide of the metal (p. 67), or in many cases on the metal itself (pp. 140, 335).

Potassium Nitrate, KNO_3 ("saltpetre" or "nitre"). When strongly heated, this decomposes to potassium nitrite and oxygen:

$$2KNO_3 = 2KNO_2 + O_2 \nearrow \text{ (see expt. 10, p. 19)}.$$

This accounts for its use in gunpowder and fireworks. It supplies the oxygen to the other constituents, sulphur and charcoal, oxidizing them quickly to form large volumes of sulphur dioxide and carbon dioxide; the pressure of these gases provides the force of the explosion. It is more suitable than sodium nitrate, because it is not deliquescent. It is formed naturally in hot countries (e.g. India) from the decomposition of dung (fig. 105, p. 311); hence the name salt-petre=salt-rock. It is manufactured by warming together hot solutions of the minerals potassium chloride and sodium nitrate; sodium chloride is the least soluble substance present when hot (fig. 37, p. 108) and so crystallizes out; potassium nitrate, which is the least soluble substance in the cold solution, crystallizes out on cooling.

$$KCl + NaNO_3 = NaCl \downarrow + KNO_3$$

Sodium Nitrate, $NaNO_3$, "Chile saltpetre." This occurs naturally as "caliche" in the Chilean desert, which is entirely rainless, and so the very soluble nitrate is not washed away. It is blasted from the deposits, extracted from the rocky impurities with water, and purified by crystallization, the solution being allowed to evaporate in the sun. Before processes were developed for the "fixation of nitrogen" (p. 313), Chile enjoyed an almost complete monopoly in the supply of this vital chemical. It is still used to a large extent as a fertilizer (see p. 301). Like potassium nitrate, it also decomposes when heated to form the nitrite and oxygen.

Ammonium Nitrate, NH_4NO_3, is used for preparing nitrous oxide (p. 338).

$$NH_4NO_3 = 2H_2O + N_2O \nearrow$$

It is also important as a fertilizer (mixed with limestone as "Nitrochalk," fig. 94, p. 271, to make it less hygroscopic). As an ingredient of explosives, a large amount of it is mixed with substances such as T.N.T. (p. 330) which have not enough oxygen of their own, because it can decompose explosively as follows:

$$14NH_4NO_3 = 14N_2 + 28H_2O + 7O_2$$
$$4C_7H_5(NO_2)_3 + 7O_2 = 28CO + 10H_2O + 6N_2$$

The Nitrates of Ca, Mg, Al, Zn, Fe, Sn, Pb, Cu all decompose on heating to give a metallic oxide, nitrogen dioxide, and oxygen (see expt. 127, p. 335), just as nitric acid (hydrogen nitrate) gives water (hydrogen oxide), nitrogen dioxide, and oxygen (see expt. 122, p. 328). All except lead nitrate are hydrated, i.e. have water of crystallization, and most of them are deliquescent:

$$2Cu(NO_3)_2.3H_2O = 2CuO + 4NO_2 \nearrow + O_2 \nearrow + 6H_2O \nearrow$$

The Nitrates of Mercury and Silver differ from the last class only because their oxides decompose on heating to give the metal and oxygen:

$$2Hg(NO_3)_2 = 2HgO + 4NO_2 \nearrow + O_2 \nearrow$$
$$2HgO = 2Hg + O_2 \nearrow$$

Silver nitrate is important as the only common soluble salt of silver, and so is used for making the silver bromide of photographic films. It oxidizes organic compounds, e.g. warts on the skin, bacteria in new-born babies' eyes, cellulose in linen, leaving a black stain of metallic silver ("marking ink"). It is also slowly decomposed by light, and so is kept in a brown bottle. It is made by dissolving silver in nitric acid.

THE OXIDES OF NITROGEN

All three of the oxides to be described here have remarkable formulae which would not be expected from the ordinary valencies of nitrogen: they are NO_2, nitrogen dioxide (or "peroxide"); nitric oxide, NO; and nitrous oxide, N_2O. For proof of these formulae, see p. 199.

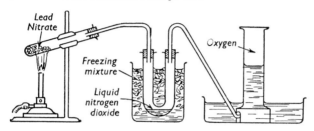

FIG. 118.   Laboratory preparation of Nitrogen Dioxide.

Nitrogen Dioxide, NO_2

This is formed whenever nitric oxide (NO) meets air, and so is an important intermediate in the manufacture of nitric acid from ammonia, and in the lead-chamber process for sulphuric acid. It may be prepared in the laboratory by heating a nitrate, usually lead nitrate because it is anhydrous (see above).

$$2Pb(NO_3)_2 = 2PbO + 4NO_2 \nearrow + O_2 \nearrow$$

Expt. 127. Powdered lead nitrate crystals are heated in a hard-glass test-tube as shown in fig. 118; they crackle loudly as they decompose, and later melt. The brown fumes of nitrogen dioxide condense in the U-tube, which is cooled in a freezing mixture of ice and salt, forming a pale-yellow liquid (b.p. 22° C.). The oxygen which is formed may be collected over water, any uncondensed nitrogen dioxide reacting with the water (see below). The yellow lead oxide which is left partly melts into the glass, with which some of it combines (see p. 435).

If samples of the gas are required, a little of the liquid is poured into a gas-jar, where it evaporates and displaces the lighter air upwards.

Properties of Nitrogen Dioxide. 1. When hot, nitrogen dioxide is a dark red-brown gas, with a vapour density of 23, i.e. a molecular weight of 46, corresponding to the formula NO_2. As it cools the colour becomes much paler, and the vapour density approaches 46, corresponding to a formula N_2O_4. These facts indicate that "thermal dissociation" (see p. 319) takes place on heating, $N_2O_4 \rightleftharpoons 2NO_2$, a mixture of the two kinds of molecules being present at intermediate temperatures.

2. It has an acidic smell, and is poisonous because it forms nitric acid in the lungs:

$$4NO_2 + 2H_2O + O_2 \text{ (air)} = 4HNO_3$$

This reaction is very important in the preparation of nitric acid.

3. In the absence of excess air or oxygen, it combines with water to form a *colourless* mixture of nitrous and nitric acids in solution:

$$2NO_2 + H_2O = HNO_2 + HNO_3$$

and similarly alkalis produce a mixture of nitrite and nitrate:

$$\left. \begin{array}{l} NaOH + HNO_2 = NaNO_2 + H_2O \\ NaOH + HNO_3 = NaNO_3 + H_2O \end{array} \right\} \text{ see p. 321.}$$

4. It is fairly easily decomposed, e.g. by red-hot metals and by burning magnesium or a burning splint, which burn more brightly in the gas than in air, e.g.

$$4Cu + 2NO_2 = 4CuO + N_2$$

5. It will oxidize sulphur dioxide in the presence of water to sulphuric acid (p. 364).

Nitric Oxide NO

At high temperatures, nitrogen and oxygen combine to form nitric oxide; some is therefore formed in thunderstorms, and the first commercial process for the fixation of nitrogen used a temperature of 3000° C. in an electric arc, maintained by cheap electric power (in Norway). The principles underlying this reaction were discussed on pp. 229, 231; a 2% yield was achieved.

Nowadays, nitric oxide is almost entirely manufactured by the catalytic oxidation of synthetic ammonia (expt. 120, p. 321) by air at 1000° C. over platinum gauze (PLATE 15B, p. 234). This is then made to react with air and water to form first nitrogen dioxide and then nitric acid:

$$4NO + 2H_2O + 3O_2 = 4HNO_3$$

Laboratory Preparation

Expt. 128. When copper turnings are treated with *moderately dilute* nitric acid (equal volumes of concentrated acid and water), the main gaseous product is nitric oxide. The apparatus shown in fig. 119 is suitable.

An equation representing this reaction is:

$$3Cu + 8HNO_3 =$$
$$3Cu(NO_3)_2 + 4H_2O + 2NO \nearrow$$

though the reaction is more complex than this, forming some NO_2 and N_2O also, so that the *quantities* shown in the equation are not accurate.

As soon as the reaction has warmed itself up, a gas comes

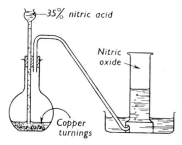

FIG. 119.   Preparation of nitric oxide.

off which is brown; this is due to the air in the apparatus combining with the nitric oxide to form nitrogen dioxide. The latter reacts with the water, and the gas which comes off afterwards is colourless nitric oxide which collects in the gas-jar.

Properties of Nitric Oxide (M.W.=30).   1. On exposure to air nitric oxide immediately forms brown fumes of nitrogen dioxide, NO_2:

$$2NO + O_2 = 2NO_2$$

For this reason it is difficult to perform experiments with the gas in a pure state. As soon as the cover is removed from a jar, nitrogen dioxide fumes are formed. Thus it is impossible to smell the gas.

2. Nitric oxide will support the combustion of strongly burning substances like magnesium and phosphorus, but not a burning splint or taper. The reason is that only substances which burn in air with a temperature high enough to decompose the gas are able to set free the oxygen in it, and so continue burning:

$$2Mg + 2NO = 2MgO + N_2$$

3. Nitric oxide is absorbed by ferrous sulphate solution, making the loosely united compound which occurs in the "brown-ring" test (p. 333):

$$FeSO_4 + NO = FeSO_4.NO$$

As the compound sets free nitric oxide once more on heating, this provides a ready means of purifying nitric oxide from other gases.

4. Like the other oxides of nitrogen, nitric oxide is reduced to nitrogen by hot metals, such as burning magnesium or red-hot iron (see expt. 77, p. 190, which proves its formula).

Nitrous Oxide, N_2O

Preparation

Expt. 129. When ammonium nitrate crystals are cautiously heated in a hard-glass round-bottomed flask (fig. 120) they decompose into nitrous oxide ("laughing gas") and steam:

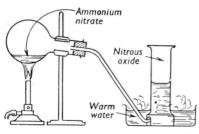

FIG. 120. Preparation of nitrous oxide.

$$NH_4NO_3 = N_2O + 2H_2O$$

The crystals first melt to a clear liquid, which appears to boil; nitrous oxide, a colourless gas, is evolved and is collected over luke-warm water because it is soluble in cold water. The decomposition of the ammonium nitrate may become explosive (p. 334) if the temperature is allowed to rise too high. This is unlikely to occur if an excess of the solid is used so that there is always some of the melted nitrate in the flask, and if it is only heated sufficiently to keep the liquid gently effervescing. The reaction is still safer if the ammonium nitrate is prepared in the flask by mixing and heating ammonium chloride and sodium nitrate in the correct proportions to give ammonium nitrate.

This method is also used for the commercial preparation.

Physical Properties (M.W.=44).   It is a colourless gas with a faint sweet smell, slightly soluble in cold water but much less so in hot water (see p. 115).   It is easily liquefied and is sold in steel cylinders for use as an anaesthetic for dental or other operations; it is administered together with oxygen and is regarded as very safe.

Chemical Properties.   1. Nitrous oxide will not burn, but will support the combustion of almost any substance which burns in air.   Feebly burning sulphur is said to be an exception, but even in this case if the sulphur is burning at all well it will often continue to burn in the gas. A strongly glowing splint may be relit by the gas, this may make it difficult to distinguish between nitrous oxide and oxygen (see below).

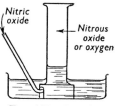

FIG. 121.   Test for oxygen.

Thus the oxide of nitrogen which contains the smallest proportion of oxygen appears to be the best supporter of combustion.   This is entirely due to the ease with which nitrous oxide can be decomposed into its elements on heating; a much lower temperature is necessary to liberate the oxygen from this oxide than is the case with the other two oxides.   One-third of the gas formed by the thermal decomposition of nitrous oxide is oxygen, and so the gas is richer in oxygen than air.

2. Like the other two oxides, nitrous oxide is readily reduced to nitrogen by passing it over heated iron or copper in a combustion tube:

$$N_2O + Cu = CuO + N_2 \text{ (compare expt. 76, p. 190).}$$

3. *To distinguish nitrous oxide from oxygen.* (*a*) If nitric oxide is blown into a jar of oxygen, as shown in fig. 121,

brown fumes of nitrogen dioxide are formed. No such reaction occurs between nitric oxide and nitrous oxide.

(b) When nitrous oxide is passed over iron heated in a combustion tube, nitrogen passes on and may be collected over water; if the experiment is repeated with oxygen, no gas remains to be collected.

Nitrous Acid and Nitrites

Sodium nitrite dissolves in dilute hydrochloric acid to form a solution which, if kept cool, contains nitrous acid and sodium chloride:

$$NaNO_2 + HCl = HNO_2 + NaCl$$

This is the form in which the acid is usually used, as for instance in the preparation of aniline dyes from aniline (compare p. vi).

The acid is unstable and cannot be isolated, existing only in solution. On heating it decomposes to form nitric acid and nitric oxide. This reaction involves oxidation of some of the nitrous acid at the expense of the rest, which is reduced to nitric oxide. This process of self-oxidation and reduction is called "autoxidation":

$$3HNO_2 = HNO_3 + 2NO + H_2O$$

Nitrites

The nitrites of sodium and potassium are formed by heating the nitrates (see p. 333). They are easily distinguished from the nitrates by their reaction with warm, dilute acids, when brown fumes of nitrogen dioxide are evolved. Nitrous acid is first formed in these reactions, and is then decomposed by the heat of the reaction forming nitric oxide ; the nitric oxide then combines with the air to give nitrogen dioxide.

Ammonium nitrite is the only other nitrite of any importance. It is not usually isolated, but is formed from a heated mixture of ammonium chloride and sodium nitrite, and decomposes to form nitrogen and water:

$$NH_4NO_2 = N_2 + 2H_2O \text{ (expt. 21, p. 33).}$$

Reduction of nitrogen compounds to ammonia

Nitrates, nitrites, and oxides of nitrogen are all reduced to ammonia if treated with "nascent hydrogen," e.g. aluminium+caustic soda solution (p. 92), and warmed.

Suggestions for Practical Work

Expt. 121 and properties of nitric acid. Expts. 125, 126. Preparation of lead nitrate, and expt. 127. Expt. 128, and pass a little nitric oxide into a jar of air over water.

QUESTIONS ON CHAPTER XX

1. Describe how, starting from nitre, you would prepare nitric acid in the laboratory.

State *two* industrial uses of nitric acid, and *two* examples of its action as an oxidizing agent.   (O. Gen. Sc.)

2. Nitric acid is said to be an oxidizing agent.   Explain and illustrate this term.   Describe *three* reactions in which nitric acid acts as an acid, and *three* in which it behaves as an oxidizing agent. (B.)

3. Describe a process by which nitric acid is prepared on a large scale from ammonia.   Outline experiments to show how nitric acid can behave (i) as an acid, (ii) as an oxidizing agent, (iii) as a nitrating agent.   Give equations where possible.   (Navy.)

4. You are provided with copper nitrate.   Describe fully the apparatus and methods you would use to prepare from this substance (*a*) cupric oxide, (*b*) liquid nitrogen dioxide, (*c*) oxygen containing only a small quantity of air.   (D.)

5. How would you prepare and collect a pure specimen of nitrogen dioxide in the laboratory?   Describe carefully the changes which occur when nitrogen dioxide reacts with (*a*) a solution of sulphur dioxide, (*b*) water, (*c*) phosphorus.

State the conditions necessary for each reaction.   (C.)

6. Describe in detail the laboratory method of preparing nitric oxide, and mention two experiments you would perform to illustrate important properties of the gas.

When iron wire is heated in nitric oxide the metal combines with the oxygen, leaving nitrogen, which occupies half the volume originally occupied by the nitric oxide.   The density of nitric oxide is 15.   Use these facts to find the formula of the gas.   (S.)

7. (*a*) Give a detailed account of the usual laboratory method of preparing and collecting nitric oxide.

(*b*) Explain the colour changes which occur during this experiment.

(*c*) What action, if any, has nitric oxide on (i) ferrous sulphate solution, (ii) burning sulphur, (iii) red-hot copper?   (L.)

8. Describe the preparation and collection of nitrous oxide. Mention *four* properties of this gas.

What *chemical* test could be used to distinguish between nitrous oxide and oxygen?   (C.)

9. Write the equation for the reaction by which nitrous oxide is usually prepared and give *one chemical* test to distinguish this gas from oxygen. Describe all that would be observed if a piece of potassium or phosphorus were ignited in a definite volume of nitrous oxide enclosed in a tube over mercury. What conclusion or conclusions could you draw from this experiment? The vapour densities of nitrous oxide and of nitrogen are, respectively, 22 and 14 $(H=1)$. Show clearly how, using all this information, you could deduce the molecular formula of nitrous oxide. (Atomic weights: N, 14; O, 16.) (L.)

10. Tabulate the properties of the three common oxides of nitrogen.

11. Describe the action of heat on (*a*) ammonium nitrate, (*b*) ammonium nitrite, (*c*) potassium nitrate, (*d*) copper nitrate. By what tests would you distinguish the solid products left in (*c*) and (*d*) from the original substances?

12. Describe, giving equations, the actions of (*a*) heat, (*b*) concentrated sulphuric acid, (*c*) caustic soda solution on ammonium nitrate.

Explain, with a sketch of the apparatus used, how you would show that the gas given off in (*c*) contains nitrogen. (L.)

13. Describe a method by which pure nitrogen may be prepared in the laboratory.

Name a compound of nitrogen with (*a*) oxygen, (*b*) hydrogen, and mention two reactions of each of the substances you have named. (C.)

14. How would you prepare a specimen of (*a*) calcium nitrate and (*b*) calcium sulphate from calcium carbonate, and how would you know that you had succeeded in the former case? (B.)

15. If you were given some lead nitrate, Pb $(NO_3)_2$, how could you prepare from it a specimen of each of the elements it contains? (Navy.)

16. How could you use a solution of potassium nitrate which is saturated at room temperature in order (*a*) to determine the solubility of potassium nitrate at room temperature, (*b*) to isolate well-formed crystals of the salt? Without giving experimental details, state the reactions by which, using potassium nitrate, you could obtain specimens of (i) oxygen, (ii) nitrous oxide, (iii) nitrogen. (L.)

CHAPTER XXI

SULPHUR AND THE SULPHIDES

Sulphur is a reactive non-metal which is similar to oxygen in some ways (fig. 14, p. 49): e.g. in its occurrence both free and combined, in its reactions with metals to form stable compounds, and in possessing a stable volatile hydride.

Occurrence of Sulphur and its Compounds

Sulphur is found free in volcanic regions, e.g. in Sicily near Mount Etna, and also in Texas and Louisiana in the U.S.A. America supplies about 95% of the world's elemental sulphur.

Its compounds with the metals, "sulphides," occur naturally when they are insoluble in water, e.g. ZnS, FeS_2 (iron pyrites), SnS, PbS, Cu_2S, HgS, Ag_2S. Iron pyrites is used in the manufacture of sulphuric acid (p. 356); the others, with the exception of SnS, are the main ores of the metals (see pp. 444–5, etc.).

Coal contains about 1% of its weight of sulphur, so that actually far more sulphur dioxide is produced unintentionally by the burning of coal than is manufactured as such. When coal gas is made (p. 260), the sulphur is recovered as "spent oxide" formed by the hydrogen sulphide (PLATE 21, p. 344).

Sulphates of calcium and magnesium are also important minerals.

NOTE: The more important reactions of sulphur, sulphides, and other compounds of sulphur (referred to in this chapter and in Chapter XXII), are shown in fig. 127, p. 356.

Extraction of Sulphur

The American deposits of sulphur occur under quicksands, and so cannot be mined directly. In the Frasch process use is made of the low melting-point of sulphur (114° C.), so that it is melted underground and then forced to the surface by pressure. A hole is drilled into the sulphur deposits, and in it

PLATE 21. GASWORKS COULD PROVIDE HALF THE SULPHUR WE NEED (see p. 260)
View of part of Beckton Gasworks. East Ham. London. the largest gasworks in the world.

are fitted three concentric pipes (fig. 122). Water, "superheated" to a temperature of 180° C., under 10 times atmospheric pressure to prevent it boiling, is forced down the outer pipe, and hot compressed air down the central pipe. The hot water melts the sulphur, but not of course the earthy impurities, while the combined pressure of water and air forces up the frothy mass of molten sulphur, water, and air. This is run into huge settling tanks, where the sulphur solidifies and the water may be run off. Large masses of purified sulphur are thus obtained ready for despatch to all parts of the world. The product is pure enough (99·9%) for almost all industrial uses.

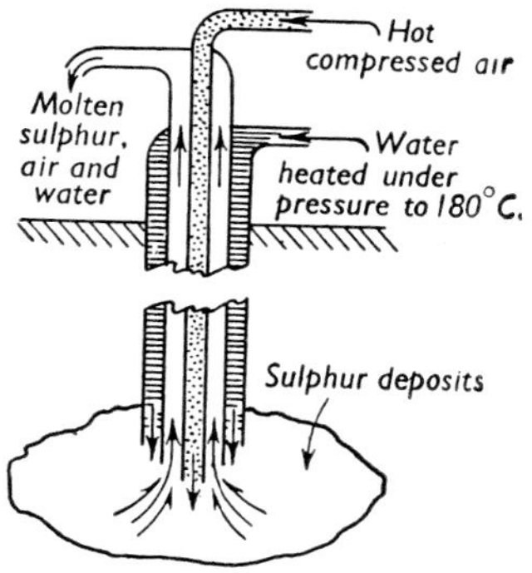

FIG. 122. Extraction of sulphur.

Uses of Sulphur

These depend on:

(a) the ease of burning to sulphur dioxide (uses 1, 2, 6);

(b) the reactivity of sulphur with rubber (use 3, compare the reaction of rubber with oxygen or ozone);

(c) the harmfulness of sulphur and its compounds to the lower forms of life (uses 4, 5).

1. The manufacture of sulphuric acid (p. 362), the most important chemical compound made in industry, accounts for over half the world's consumption of 4 million tons of sulphur per year.

2. Paper manufacture requires wood pulp to be purified with sulphur dioxide in the form of calcium bisulphite solution (p. 358). Paper from untreated pulp, e.g. newspaper, soon turns yellow when exposed to light.

3. Rubber is "vulcanized" by heating with sulphur, which combines with it to make it much tougher. Raw rubber, obtained by coagulating the milky liquid "latex" from the rubber-tree, rapidly perishes by combining with the oxygen of the air.

4. Fruit-trees, vines, and other crops are sprayed with sulphur or "lime-sulphur" to kill insects and fungi.

5. "Sulpha-drugs," such as M & B 693, used for killing the bacteria which cause pneumonia, etc., are complicated compounds of sulphur; so is penicillin. Sulphur ointment is also used medicinally.

6. The manufacture of matches (p. 430) and gunpowder (p. 19) both require sulphur.

7. Many other sulphur compounds are important, such as carbon disulphide (CS_2) for rayon manufacture (p. 367), photographic "hypo" ($Na_2S_2O_3.5H_2O$), and many dyes (p. vi).

The Action of Heat on Sulphur

Expt. 130. When sulphur is heated slowly in a test-tube it undergoes the following changes:

1. It melts to a pale yellow, free-flowing ("mobile") liquid (about 114° C.).

2. On further heating, its colour darkens until it is nearly black and it becomes thick ("viscous"). At this stage (about 160° C.) the test-tube can be turned upside-down without the liquid running out.

3. Still further heating makes the liquid mobile once again, but still very dark in colour.

4. At a temperature of 444° C. the molten sulphur boils to produce a pale yellow vapour. Where this vapour touches the cold sides of the test-tube, towards the top, it sublimes to form a fine yellow powder. Lower down, where the glass is hotter, the vapour condenses to the brown liquid which flows down the glass.

The changes in colour and viscosity (i.e. "thickness") of molten sulphur point to the existence of at least two different kinds ("allotropes"—see p. 241) of liquid sulphur. These are called sulphur-lambda and sulphur-mu (S_λ and S_μ) and the differences are due to their consisting of two different kinds of sulphur molecules.

$$\underset{\text{solid}}{S} \rightarrow \underset{\text{liquid}}{S_\lambda} \rightarrow \underset{}{S_\mu} \rightarrow \underset{\text{vapour}}{S}$$

The finely powdered yellow sublimate is the familiar "flowers of sulphur" which is made by rapidly cooling sulphur vapour.

When molten sulphur is allowed to cool and solidify, a hard, yellow, crystalline form of the element (see below) is made. This is the form known as "roll sulphur," because the molten sulphur is cast in wooden moulds into cylindrical rolls.

The Allotropic Forms of Solid Sulphur

(a) Rhombic or Octahedral Sulphur (" Alpha-Sulphur," S_α)

Expt. 131. Some crushed roll sulphur is dissolved in carbon disulphide in a beaker and the solution filtered into a clock-glass. It is then put into a fume cupboard to evaporate slowly, when well-defined crystals separate. Examined with a microscope they are seen to have the shape illustrated in fig. 123. Larger crystals are obtained if the evaporation is made slower by covering the clock-glass with an inverted filter funnel.

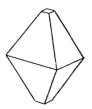

Careful examination shows roll sulphur to be composed of a mass of crystals of this shape, the normal crystalline form of sulphur. The crystals are, however, very small and only by crystallizing from carbon disulphide are crystals obtained which are large enough to be drawn.

FIG. 123.
Rhombic
α-sulphur crystal.

(b) Monoclinic or Prismatic Sulphur (" Beta-Sulphur," S_β)

Expt. 132. This second crystalline form of sulphur is obtained when molten sulphur is crystallized at temperatures only a little below its melting-point. The usual laboratory method of preparing it is to melt sulphur in a deep evaporating dish, having the dish almost full. (It will be noticed that the sulphur is a bad conductor of heat—characteristic of a non-metal.) The bunsen-burner is removed as soon as the whole mass is melted, and the sulphur is then allowed to cool until a crust forms most of the way over the surface.

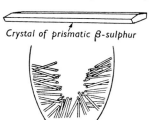

Crystal of prismatic β-sulphur

FIG. 124. Monoclinic sulphur.

All the still molten sulphur is then poured away. Inside the dish is found an interlacing mass of lemon-yellow needles.

Seen under the magnifying-glass they are observed to have the shape of the thin prisms illustrated in fig. 124. This form of sulphur is called monoclinic, prismatic, or β-sulphur

If rhombic (a) sulphur is heated to a temperature of 96° C. and kept there, it slowly changes its crystalline form to prismatic (β) sulphur. Similarly, when prismatic sulphur is kept at a temperature below 96° C. it slowly changes to rhombic sulphur, the stable form at lower temperatures. Each needle of prismatic sulphur retains its external shape, but changes into a mass of small rhombic crystals and so becomes opaque. The changes may be represented by the equation:

$$96° \text{ C.}$$
$$\text{Rhombic or } a\text{-sulphur} \rightleftharpoons \text{Prismatic or } \beta\text{-sulphur}$$

The temperature 96° C., at which the change of crystalline form occurs, is called the *transition temperature* for sulphur.

Like rhombic sulphur, prismatic sulphur dissolves in carbon disulphide, but on crystallizing its solution only rhombic crystals are obtained, because the temperature at which crystallization occurs is necessarily below 96° C. (Carbon disulphide boils at 46° C.)

(c) *Amorphous sulphur.* In reactions in which sulphur is slowly precipitated from solution, a white form is often obtained which passes through filter-paper. This "colloidal" sulphur is amorphous, i.e. non-crystalline, and is insoluble in carbon disulphide, e.g.

$$H_2S + O \text{ (e.g. from air)} = H_2O + S \downarrow$$

Flowers of sulphur (p. 346) are another amorphous form. Like a– and β–sulphur, they melt to the same liquid forms.

(d) Plastic Sulphur

Expt. 133. When boiling sulphur is rapidly cooled by pouring it in a thin stream into cold water, it cools so quickly that it has no time to crystallize before it has reached a temperature so low that the rate of crystallization is very slow indeed. A yellow-brown solid is formed which resembles india-rubber in being elastic. It is really supercooled liquid sulphur (S_μ, with its molecules still in confusion as in the liquid), and therefore not a new allotrope. On standing it slowly crystallizes to a hard, yellow solid insoluble in carbon disulphide.

To Prove that the Allotropes of Sulphur consist of Sulphur and nothing but Sulphur

(a) Convert equal weights of each into the same weight of sulphur dioxide (see allotropes of carbon, (p. 245).

(*b*) Convert one form into another by changing the physical conditions, without adding or subtracting any other substance.

Reactions of Sulphur

1. *With oxygen.* Sulphur burns in air or oxygen with a blue flame to form sulphur dioxide:

$$S + O_2 = SO_2 \nearrow \text{ (expt. 23, p. 47).}$$

2. *With oxidizing agents.* Concentrated sulphuric acid oxidizes sulphur to sulphur dioxide (expt. 140, p. 371); so does potassium nitrate in gunpowder (p. 333). Concentrated nitric acid converts it to sulphuric acid (expt. 123, p. 329).

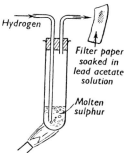

3. *With metals.* Nearly all metals combine directly with sulphur, e.g. iron (expt. 24, p. 51); copper forms cuprous sulphide (expt. 67B, p. 151); mercury when rubbed with sulphur in a mortar forms black mercuric sulphide:

$$Hg + S = HgS$$

4. *With hydrogen.*

Expt. 134. If hydrogen is passed through molten sulphur in a test-tube (fig. 125), a small proportion unites with the sulphur to form hydrogen sulphide, $H_2 + S \rightleftharpoons H_2S$. A test for this is to hold a filter-paper soaked in lead acetate (or lead nitrate) solution at the mouth of the exit-tube. This turns a brownish-black because of the formation of lead sulphide:

FIG. 125. Reaction of hydrogen with sulphur.

$$Pb\bar{A}_2 + H_2S = PbS \downarrow + 2H\bar{A}$$

(where $\bar{A}$ is used to mean "acetate," i.e. $CH_3.COO$.

HYDROGEN SULPHIDE, H_2S
("Sulphuretted hydrogen")

Preparation

The reaction of expt. 134 is unsuitable, because hydrogen sulphide is decomposed by heat and so the yield is small.

12*

Hydrogen sulphide is therefore prepared by treating ferrous sulphide with dilute hydrochloric or sulphuric acid:

$$FeS + 2HCl = FeCl_2 + H_2S \nearrow$$

Expt. 135. As the reaction occurs in the cold, a Kipp (fig. 25, p. 90) is used as the normal source of supply, but the apparatus of fig. 126 is also suitable. Ferrous sulphide nearly always contains free iron (from which it is prepared), and this reacts with the acid to give hydrogen. For chemical reactions, such as testing metallic salts, this impurity does not matter, but a low value would be obtained for the density (see p. 199).

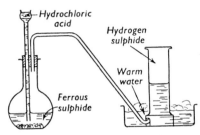

FIG. 126. Preparation of hydrogen sulphide.

If necessary, the hydrogen sulphide could be liquefied (b.p. −61° C.) by the use of solid carbon dioxide (−78° C.), the hydrogen passing on unchanged.

Physical Properties (M.W. = 34)

Hydrogen sulphide is a colourless gas, which is poisonous, and has an offensive smell of "bad eggs." As it is fairly soluble in cold water (p. 114), it is therefore preferable to use its solution for most reactions; for the same reason, in expt. 135, it was collected over *hot* water. It is produced by decaying proteins (p. 306), especially those in eggs.

The formula of hydrogen sulphide was proved on p. 199.

(i) Reactions of Hydrogen Sulphide as an acid

1. Hydrogen sulphide solution turns blue litmus to a wine-red colour, showing it to be weakly acidic: $H_2S \rightleftharpoons 2H^+ + S^{--}$.

2. When passed into a solution of sodium hydroxide, the gas is absorbed to form sodium sulphide; excess of hydrogen sulphide converts this into the acid sulphide, showing that hydrogen sulphide is a dibasic acid:

$$2NaOH + H_2S = Na_2S + 2H_2O \quad \text{(sodium sulphide)}$$

$$Na_2S + H_2S = 2NaHS \quad \text{(sodium hydrogen sulphide)}$$

3. By far the most important reaction of hydrogen sulphide is its *use in analysis* to precipitate metallic sulphides from solution $M^{++} + S^{--} = MS \downarrow$. As is seen from the table of sulphides on p. 353, these fall into three groups:

(*a*) K, Na, NH$_4$, Ca (also Sr, Ba), Mg, Al (and Cr), which are *not* precipitated.

(*b*) Zn, Fe (also Mn, Co, Ni), which are precipitated *only in* alkaline solution.

(*c*) Sn, Pb (also As, Sb, Bi), Cu (also Cd), Hg, Ag, which are precipitated *even in* the presence of dilute hydrochloric *acid*.

Within these groups the sulphides may be partially distinguished by their colours, e.g. those of antimony (Sb_2S_3 orange), arsenic (As_2S_3 yellow), cadmium (CdS yellow; used as a yellow pigment), and manganese (MnS pink), or by the colours of their original solutions.

$$H_2S + CuSO_4 = CuS \downarrow + H_2SO_4 \quad \text{(p. 151)}.$$
$$\text{blue solution} \quad \text{black ppt.} \quad \text{colourless solution}$$
$$2H^+ + S^{--} + Cu^{++} + SO_4^{--} = CuS \downarrow + 2H^+ + SO_4^{--}$$

The reaction with lead acetate solution (see expt. 134) to give a shiny, black-brown precipitate of lead sulphide is the standard **test for hydrogen sulphide** (apart from its smell!).

As free acid is produced in these reactions, those sulphides which react with acid (e.g. iron—see expt. 135, and zinc) will not be precipitated from acidic or neutral solutions. But if ammonium hydroxide is added to neutralize the free acid (or if ammonium sulphide solution is used) these sulphides *are* precipitated:

$$ZnSO_4 + (NH_4)_2S = ZnS \downarrow + (NH_4)_2SO_4$$
$$\text{(or NH}_4\text{OH} + H_2S) \quad \text{white ppt.}$$

(ii) Reactions of Hydrogen Sulphide as a Reducing Agent

4. (*a*) Hydrogen sulphide solution slowly turns cloudy on exposure to *air*, because atmospheric oxygen oxidizes it to sulphur: $2H_2S + O_2 = 2H_2O + 2S \downarrow$.

(*b*) Hydrogen sulphide gas, in a jar, burns with a blue flame when lit, forming steam and leaving a yellow deposit of sulphur on the sides of the jar.

(c) If it is burnt at a jet, the plentiful supply of oxygen converts most of it into sulphur dioxide:

$$2H_2S + 3O_2 = 2H_2O + 2SO_2 \nearrow$$

5. (a) *Nitric acid*, even when fairly dilute, gives a yellow precipitate of sulphur; concentrated acid gives brown fumes of nitrogen dioxide:

$$2HNO_3 = H_2O + 2NO_2 \nearrow + O \text{ (available for oxidation)}$$
$$H_2S + O = H_2O + S \downarrow$$

(b) Concentrated *sulphuric acid* also oxidizes it to sulphur and so should not be used for drying the gas, but phosphorus pentoxide (P_2O_5) may be used.

6. A purple solution of *potassium permanganate*, acidified with dilute sulphuric acid, is reduced to colourless potassium and manganous sulphates, and again a yellow precipitate of sulphur is formed:

$$2KMnO_4 + 3H_2SO_4 = K_2SO_4 + 2MnSO_4 + 3H_2O + \mathbf{5O}$$
$$\text{(available for oxidation)}$$
$$\mathbf{5O} + 5H_2S = 5H_2O + 5S \downarrow$$

7. Similarly, orange *potassium dichromate* solution, acidified with dilute sulphuric acid solution, becomes green owing to the formation of chromium sulphate, and sulphur is precipitated:

$$K_2Cr_2O_7 + 4H_2SO_4 = K_2SO_4 + Cr_2(SO_4)_3 + 4H_2O + \mathbf{3O}$$
$$\text{(for oxidation)}$$
$$3O + 3H_2S = 3H_2O + 3S \downarrow$$

8. (a) Jars of *chlorine* and of hydrogen sulphide when placed mouth to mouth give hydrogen chloride (which fumes with ammonia, see p. 318) and a deposit of sulphur:

$$H_2S + Cl_2 = 2HCl + S \downarrow$$

(b) The other halogen elements, bromine and iodine, if dissolved or suspended in water behave similarly (see pp. 418, 423).

9. Ferric chloride solution (yellow) is reduced to ferrous chloride (pale green), and a precipitate of sulphur is thrown down:

$$2FeCl_3 + H_2S = 2FeCl_2 + 2HCl + S \downarrow$$

10. Jars of sulphur dioxide and of hydrogen sulphide when placed mouth to mouth gradually give a deposit of sulphur. It is often necessary to add a trace of moisture to catalyse the reaction. As the equation shows, there is a considerable fall in pressure as a result of this reaction, and the gas-jars stick firmly together:

$$2H_2S + SO_2 = 3S \downarrow + 2H_2O$$

Metallic Sulphides

K Na NH₄ Ca Mg Al	Colourless solids	Soluble in water or decomposed to give H_2S	Unknown in nature
Zn	White ppt.	Precipitated in alkaline solution (decomposed by HCl)	Naturally occurring minerals (FeS_2 not FeS) (SnS uncommon) (Cu_2S usually)
Fe	Black ppt.		
Sn(ous) Sn(ic)	Brown ppt. Yellow ppt.	Precipitated even in presence of dilute HCl	
Pb Cu Hg Ag	Black ppts.		

The blackening of white lead paint (p. 389) and the tarnishing of silver (p. 459) are due to the action of hydrogen sulphide in the atmosphere forming the black sulphides. Zinc white paint (ZnS), used in factories and laboratories, is of course not affected by hydrogen sulphide (see p. 464).

The sulphides of calcium and zinc are used in making luminous paints, as they show the property of "phosphorescence," i.e. they appear luminous in the dark after being exposed to light. Zinc sulphide is also one of the substances used to coat the surface of the tubes used in modern fluorescent lighting (p. 480); when exposed to the ultra-violet radiation from an electric discharge through mercury vapour, it gives off light in the visible spectrum (i.e. it "fluoresces"). Sodium sulphide is used for hair removal.

Suggestions for Practical Work

Expts. 130–133. Preparation of hydrogen sulphide (expt. 135), and examination of its properties (test-tube reactions or gas-jars). Also expt. 24, p. 51 ; and expt. 67ʙ, p. 151.

QUESTIONS ON CHAPTER XXI

1. What do you understand by the term allotropy? Describe how you would prepare specimens of (a) rhombic, (b) monoclinic or prismatic crystals, from roll sulphur. How could it be shown experimentally that rhombic and monoclinic sulphur are both forms of the same element? (C.)

2. Carbon and sulphur are said to be typical non-metals. Compare their physical and chemical properties.

3. Describe the changes that take place when sulphur is gradually heated to its boiling-point in a test-tube.

Give an account of the reaction that takes place when iron and sulphur are heated together. What happens when the product is treated with dilute hydrochloric acid and the gas thus formed passed into a solution of copper sulphate? (O. and C.)

4. Describe the preparation of hydrogen sulphide in the laboratory. What is its chief use?

Describe what happens when hydrogen sulphide is (a) burned (i) in a gas-jar, (ii) at a jet; (b) passed through copper sulphate solution; (c) passed into chlorine water. (O.)

5. Explain the working of Kipp's apparatus when used for the preparation of hydrogen sulphide.

Describe what can be seen, and write equations for the reactions which occur when hydrogen sulphide is passed into (a) sulphur dioxide, (b) chlorine, (c) acidified potassium bichromate (= dichromate) solution, (d) lead nitrate solution. (D.)

6. What impurity is present in hydrogen sulphide prepared by the usual method? How would you prepare and collect several jars of the dry gas free from this impurity? Under what conditions and with what results does hydrogen sulphide react with (a) oxygen, (b) chlorine, (c) sulphur dioxide? (L.)

7. What is the evidence for writing the formula of hydrogen sulphide as H_2S?

CHAPTER XXII

THE OXIDES AND OXYACIDS OF SULPHUR

The most important reactions connecting sulphur and the sulphides with sulphur dioxide and sulphuric acid are summarized in fig. 127, overleaf.

SULPHUR DIOXIDE, SO_2

Industrial Preparation. 1. Sulphur or iron pyrites is burnt in air. Alternatively "spent oxide" from the gas-works (p. 260) is used, or metallic sulphides as the first stage of their conversion to metals.

$$S + O_2 = SO_2$$
$$4FeS_2 + 11O_2 = 2Fe_2O_3 + 8SO_2$$
$$2ZnS + 3O_2 = 2ZnO + 2SO_2$$

2. Another important raw material, which does not have to be imported, is calcium sulphate ("anhydrite"). On heating with coke and sand this is converted to calcium silicate (used for making cement) and sulphur dioxide is given off together with carbon dioxide:

$$2CaSO_4 + 2SiO_2 = 2CaSiO_3 + 2SO_2 \nearrow (+O_2)$$
$$O_2 + C = CO_2 \nearrow$$

Laboratory Preparation of Sulphur Dioxide

The gas is liquefied under pressure and sold in glass siphons, which are much the most convenient source. The following two methods, however, demonstrate important reactions and so are included here:

(a) From Concentrated Sulphuric Acid

Expt. 136. Concentrated sulphuric acid is poured on to 25 gm. of copper turnings in a round-bottomed flask (fig. 128A). On warming, sulphur dioxide is given off and is collected by displacing air upwards. To test when the gas-jar is full, wet blue litmus-paper is held at the top. (Sulphur dioxide cannot be collected over water because it is too soluble).

COMPOUNDS OF SULPHUR

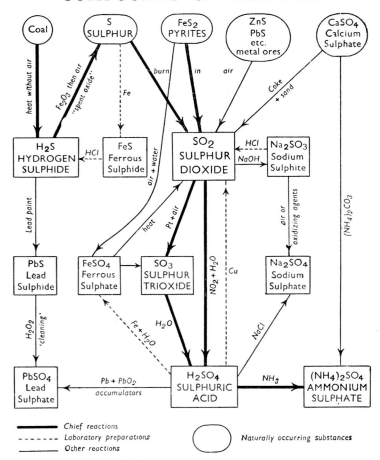

FIG. 127.

A simplified account of the reaction is as follows:

1. The sulphuric acid oxidizes the copper to copper oxide, being itself reduced to sulphurous acid, i.e. sulphur dioxide + water:

$$Cu + H_2SO_4 = CuO + H_2SO_3 \ (\rightarrow H_2O + SO_2 \nearrow)$$

2. The copper oxide at once reacts with more sulphuric acid to produce copper sulphate and water:

$$CuO + H_2SO_4 = CuSO_4 + H_2O$$
$$\therefore \ Cu + 2H_2SO_4 = CuSO_4 + 2H_2O + SO_2 \nearrow$$

The residue in the flask may be shown to contain anhydrous copper sulphate by cooling, pouring off the acid, dissolving in water and filtering; the blue solution may be crystallized in the usual way. On the filter-paper will be found black insoluble copper sulphide, showing that the reaction is more complex than the equation indicates.

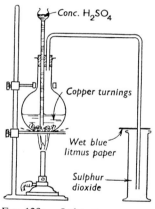

Fig. 128A. Laboratory preparation of sulphur dioxide.

(b) From Sodium Sulphite

Expt. 137. Sodium sulphite is warmed with concentrated hydrochloric acid in a round-bottomed flask. The sulphurous acid formed is decomposed by heat, and so the sulphur dioxide should be dried, in this case by passing through a washbottle of concentrated sulphuric acid.

$$Na_2SO_3 + 2HCl = 2NaCl + H_2SO_3$$
$$H_2SO_3 = H_2O \nearrow + SO_2 \nearrow$$

Properties and Uses of Sulphur Dioxide

Physical Properties (M.W. = 64). It is a colourless gas, more than twice as heavy as air, with a characteristic smell; it can easily be felt at the back of the throat, but is often mistaken for hydrogen chloride. It is poisonous, and atmospheric pollution is therefore very harmful to vegetation, but it can be used as a fumigant. At ordinary temperatures it liquefies under about 3 atmospheres pressure and is therefore used in some refrigerators (see ammonia, p. 322).

The formula of sulphur dioxide was proved on p. 198.

Chemical Properties. Like hydrogen sulphide, sulphur dioxide reacts both as an acidic gas and as a reducing agent.

(a) Acidic Properties of Sulphur Dioxide

1. Sulphur dioxide is very soluble in water (p. 114), forming sulphurous acid, which will turn blue litmus-paper red:

$$H_2O + SO_2 \rightleftharpoons H_2SO_3$$

This acid is unstable, evolving sulphur dioxide on heating. These reactions are the basis for the removal of sulphur dioxide from smoke, e.g. at the Battersea Power Station; the carbon dioxide also present is much less soluble (p. 114).

2. When bubbled into alkalis, like caustic soda and milk of lime, solutions of sulphites or bisulphites are formed, e.g. $Ca(HSO_3)_2$, p. 345. The gas may be regarded as first forming sulphurous acid with the water of the solution, and then reacting with the alkali to form a salt. On evaporating, the sodium sulphite may be crystallized out:

$$H_2O + SO_2 = H_2SO_3$$
$$H_2SO_3 + 2NaOH = Na_2SO_3 + 2H_2O$$

With excess of sulphur dioxide, the acid salt sodium bisulphite is formed:

$$Na_2SO_3 + H_2SO_3 = 2NaHSO_3$$

Both salts are soluble, but the bisulphite, like bicarbonates, is unstable to heat, and cannot therefore be obtained as a solid by methods involving heating.

The sulphites and bisulphites are readily decomposed on warming with dilute or concentrated acids (see expt. 137).

(b) Reducing Properties of Sulphur Dioxide

By far the most important reaction of sulphur dioxide is its conversion to sulphuric acid. In all cases except the

Contact process (p. 362), this occurs when sulphur dioxide *solution* is treated with an oxidizing agent:

$$H_2SO_3 \quad + \quad O \quad = \quad H_2SO_4$$

Sulphurous acid   from oxidizing agent   Sulphuric acid

The sulphuric acid produced in these reactions may be tested with barium chloride solution and dilute hydrochloric acid; a white precipitate of barium sulphate is obtained, showing the presence of a sulphate ("hydrogen sulphate"). Sulph*ites* (like many other substances) give a white precipitate of the barium salt with barium chloride solution, but this dissolves in hydrochloric acid to form sulphurous acid:

$$H_2SO_4 + BaCl_2 = 2HCl + BaSO_4 \downarrow$$ white precipitate

i e. $$SO_4^{--} + Ba^{++} = \qquad BaSO_4 \downarrow$$ *insoluble* in acid

$$Na_2SO_3 + BaCl_2 = 2NaCl + BaSO_3 \downarrow$$ } white precipitate
$$BaSO_3 + 2H^+ = Ba^{++} + H_2SO_3$$ *soluble* in acid.

3. *Bleaching.* Sulphur dioxide reduces some coloured substances by removing oxygen and converting them into colourless compounds. It is therefore used industrially as a bleaching agent for delicate goods such as wool, silk, straw, which would be injured by chlorine. Exposure to oxidizing conditions is liable to restore the original colour, e.g. the gradual yellowing of straw hats.

The remaining reducing reactions of sulphur dioxide should be compared with those of hydrogen sulphide (pp. 351-2).

4. *Oxygen of the air* slowly converts sulphurous acid to sulphuric; this accounts for the use of sulphur dioxide for preserving fruit (e.g. orange juice, fig. 128B) by preventing oxidation. Similarly the Contact process for making sulphuric acid uses air in the presence of a catalyst.

MINISTRY **MF** OF FOOD

CONCENTRATED

ORANGE
JUICE

This juice contains not less than 60 mg. of vitamin C per fl. oz. It is sweetened with added sugar and contains not more than 0·035% sulphur dioxide

6 fl. oz.

FIG. 128B. Sulphur dioxide as a preservative.

5. *Nitric acid* and *nitrogen dioxide* (as in the lead-chamber

process, p. 364) oxidize it to sulphuric acid, forming nitric oxide:

$$2HNO_3 = H_2O + 2NO + 3O$$
$$H_2SO_3 + O = H_2SO_4$$

6. Purple *potassium permanganate* solution (p. 352) is decolorized; no additional sulphuric acid is needed in this case because it is formed in the reaction.

7. Orange *potassium dichromate* solution (p. 352) is turned green; this is the standard **test for sulphur dioxide.**

8. *Chlorine water* is reduced to hydrochloric acid; solutions of bromine or iodine behave similarly (PLATE 25B, p. 419).

9. *Ferric chloride* solution (yellow) becomes ferrous chloride (green, very pale) **on warming;** if cold, brown $FeCl_3.SO_2$ appears.

(*c*) **Oxidizing Properties** (much less important)

10. The reaction with *hydrogen sulphide* (p. 353) is an example of the oxidizing action of sulphur dioxide, which is much less common.

$$S + \begin{array}{|cc|} \hline O & H_2 \\ \hline \end{array} S = 3S + 2H_2O$$
$$\begin{array}{|cc|} \hline O & H_2 \\ \hline \end{array} S$$

Here oxygen from the sulphur dioxide removes hydrogen from the hydrogen sulphide, thereby oxidizing it.

11. *Burning magnesium* is hot enough to decompose sulphur dioxide, forming magnesium oxide and sulphur (compare CO_2, N_2O, NO, NO_2).

$$2Mg + SO_2 = 2MgO + \underset{\text{White} \quad \text{Yellow}}{S}$$

SULPHUR TRIOXIDE, SO_3

Preparation

Expt. 138. Sulphur dioxide combines directly with oxygen, in the presence of a platinum catalyst, to form sulphur trioxide:

$$2SO_2 + O_2 = 2SO_3$$

This reaction is the basis of the Contact process for making sulphuric acid.

The catalyst, of platinised asbestos, is prepared by soaking asbestos fibres in a solution of platinum chloride and then heating strongly. The platinum chloride decomposes,* leaving metallic platinum as a very fine layer spread over the asbestos. In this form, platinum is very much more active as a catalyst than when in the compact state, because the surface area is so much greater.

Sulphur dioxide from a siphon and oxygen from a cylinder are dried by passing through concentrated sulphuric acid (fig. 129) and then passed over the platinised asbestos, which is heated in a combustion tube. White fumes of sulphur trioxide are formed and

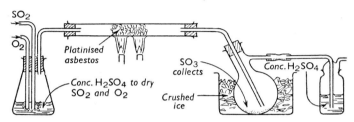

FIG. 129. Laboratory preparation of sulphur trioxide

condense in the receiver as white, silky needles. The receiver must be protected from atmospheric moisture by a wash-bottle of concentrated sulphuric acid, and must be cooled in ice to condense the sulphur trioxide (b.p. 45° C.), but not the sulphur dioxide (b.p. −10° C.).

Properties

Sulphur trioxide reacts with water to form sulphuric acid:

$$SO_3 + H_2O = H_2SO_4$$

The solid prepared in expt. 138 dissolves with a hissing sound when cautiously added to water, generating great heat. But if the delivery tube in fig. 129 is led directly into water, clouds of acid fumes are formed, consisting of tiny droplets of sulphuric acid. In the manufacture of sulphuric acid, therefore, some way had to be found to get over this difficulty.

* Compare compounds of other metals which are low in the electrochemical series (p. 223); e.g. mercuric oxide (p. 20), silver nitrate (p. 334).

The sulphur trioxide may be dissolved directly in concentrated sulphuric acid, forming "fuming sulphuric acid" (oleum):

$$H_2SO_4 + SO_3 = H_2S_2O_7$$

this is then cautiously diluted with water or dilute sulphuric acid:

$$H_2S_2O_7 + H_2O = 2H_2SO_4$$

SULPHURIC ACID

The Manufacture of Sulphuric Acid

There are two main processes for this; the Contact process is the more modern (PLATE 5, p. 62), but the Lead-Chamber process has some advantages also, and still accounts for about half the world production of over twenty million tons per year (fig. 131, pp. 372–3).

1. The Contact Process for Sulphuric Acid

The method is based on the production of sulphur trioxide (expt. 138), but *air* is used instead of oxygen, because it costs nothing.

(*a*) *Sulphur dioxide* is produced from one of the raw materials described on p. 355, preferably by burning sulphur, as this gives the purest product (FeS_2 usually contains FeSAs).

(*b*) The gases sulphur dioxide and air are now carefully *purified* to remove dust and traces of arsenious oxide, As_2O_3, which would otherwise "poison" the catalyst, i.e. remove its catalytic activity. This purification is done mostly by "electrostatic precipitation," i.e. submitting the gases in metal towers to a very high electrical potential difference between the walls and metal plates hung in the centre. As the particles of solid each carry small electrical charges, they are attracted by the plates and so removed. After treatment (washing with water, then precipitation, and finally drying with concentrated sulphuric acid) the gas is perfectly transparent when viewed through great lengths, although it is as black as domestic smoke when it comes from burning pyrites. Similar methods may be used to remove smoke and soot from the gases of factory chimneys.

(c) The purified sulphur dioxide and air now pass over the platinum catalyst at a temperature of 400° C. (fig. 130A). This temperature is chosen because it gives the best yield at a fairly reasonable speed according to the principles discussed on p. 231: 99% of the sulphur dioxide is *converted* to the trioxide.

The catalyst now most used is vanadium pentoxide, V_2O_5 (see PLATE 15B, p. 235), which is as efficient as platinum, but very much cheaper. If a less effective catalyst is used. such as iron oxide. which is very much cheaper, a temperature of

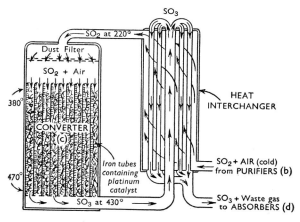

FIG. 130A.   Contact process

660° C. is needed, and this produces only a 60% yield. The platinum catalyst (or lead chambers) used in producing 100,000 tons of acid per year might today cost as much as £100,000.

Increased pressure is not used because of the difficulties of designing plant to withstand such reactive acid gases, but the amount of air used is three times the theoretical value, so as to increase the probability of the sulphur dioxide reacting (see p. 228).

As the reaction gives out heat, no external heat need be supplied because the hot outgoing gases are used to warm the cold incoming gases in a system of "heat interchangers."

(*d*) The sulphur trioxide is *absorbed* in concentrated sulphuric acid, which is diluted as required. The 1% of unchanged sulphur dioxide is not allowed to lay waste the countryside (p. 358), but is absorbed in "milk of lime," calcium hydroxide, which is the cheapest alkali.

The Contact process thus produces a very pure, concentrated acid, but the cost of the plant—especially the catalyst—is high.

2. The Lead-Chamber Process for Sulphuric Acid

NOTE: The chemical reactions in this process are highly complicated, and the account given below is a simplified version illustrating only the main principles.

The fundamental reaction in this process is the oxidation of sulphurous acid to sulphuric by nitrogen dioxide.

$$H_2SO_3 + NO_2 = H_2SO_4 + NO$$

The nitric oxide so formed is oxidized by the air to re-form nitrogen dioxide:

$$2NO + O_2 = 2NO_2$$

Thus the nitrogen dioxide plays the part of a "chemical" catalyst, emerging unchanged at the end, although it has undergone reactions during the process. (The platinum catalyst of the Contact process does not seem to react, and is called a "physical" catalyst.)

Fig. 130B shows in diagram form how the process is carried out industrially.

A. Hot sulphur dioxide, prepared by burning iron pyrites or spent oxide, and air are passed into B, the "Glover tower" lined with acid-resisting brick.

B. Here they are cooled by a stream of "chamber acid" (65% H_2SO_4) which they concentrate to 77% strength; this is the final product and is removed from the bottom of this tower. The hot gases also drive off nitrogen dioxide from its solution in 77% acid (obtained from a later stage, D).

C. The sulphur dioxide, air, and nitrogen dioxide pass into a series of three "lead chambers" where a spray of steam comes from the roof and the main reactions take place. Sheets of lead are chosen for the lining because they are much less attacked than any other metal (lead sulphate is insoluble). The quantity of steam is adjusted to produce acid of 65% strength ("Chamber acid") because stronger acid attacks lead much more.   The chambers are huge (50 ft. high x 100' x 20').

D. In the "Gay-Lussac tower" the nitrogen dioxide is recovered for re-use, by being dissolved in *some* of the cold 77% acid formed in the Glover tower (B).

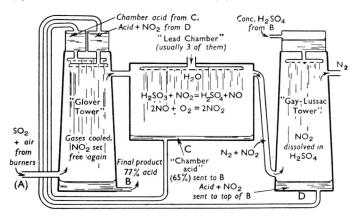

FIG. 130B.   Lead-chamber process.

The escaping gases consist mainly of nitrogen (from the air), but some brown nitrogen dioxide can be seen.   This has to be replaced by adding a little nitric oxide ($+air \rightarrow NO_2$) formed by the catalytic oxidation of ammonia (p. 320).

The Lead-Chamber process has the advantage that the gases do not require such thorough purification as in the Contact process; but the resulting acid is therefore not so pure, and may contain arsenic and lead compounds, the latter dissolved from the chambers as lead bisulphate ($Pb(HSO_4)_2$). The maximum possible strength of the acid is only 77%, but this is not such a disadvantage as it might seem, because for many purposes—such as the manufacture of fertilizers—a stronger acid is not needed.

Properties and Uses of Sulphuric Acid

Concentrated sulphuric acid ($98 \cdot 4\%$ strength) is a heavy, oily liquid, density $1 \cdot 84$ gm. per c.c., sometimes known as "oil of vitriol." It boils at $333°$ C., decomposing into sulphur trioxide and steam.

Its chemical reactions are those of (*a*) an acid, (*b*) a non-volatile acid, (*c*) a strong dehydrating agent, (*d*) an oxidizing agent. Reactions (*b*), (*c*), (*d*) only take place when the acid is concentrated.

(*a*) Acid Properties of Sulphuric Acid (these are listed on p. 62)

Dilute sulphuric acid behaves as a perfectly typical acid, turning litmus red, forming salts and giving hydrogen with metals such as iron (expt. 27A, p. 69), giving carbon dioxide with sodium carbonate, and forming salts with bases such as copper oxide (expt. 27B, p. 69). Concentrated sulphuric acid is very different (see below); it does not affect litmus-paper, and it does not give hydrogen with any metals.

The most important uses of sulphuric acid depend on its being an acid which is readily available (over a million tons per year being produced in Great Britain) and cheap (costing less than £10 per ton).

1. The manufacture of *fertilizers* (these account for about 50% of the total acid used in Great Britain in 1947).

(i) Calcium Phosphate $\quad + \quad$ Sulphuric acid
$\qquad Ca_3(PO_4)_2 \qquad\qquad\qquad 2H_2SO_4$
(naturally occurring " Phosphate Rock'
  —see fig. 94, p. 271)

$\quad = $ Calcium Acid Phosphate $\quad + \quad$ Calcium Sulphate
$\qquad\qquad Ca(H_2PO_4)_2 \qquad\qquad\qquad 2CaSO_4$

(" superphosphate " fertilizer)

The insoluble normal salt is converted by acid into the more soluble acid salt, which can more readily be used by plants, see p. 301. (Compare $CaCO_3$, insoluble; $Ca(HCO_3)_2$, soluble.)

(ii) Ammonium Hydroxide + Sulphuric acid
$$2NH_4OH \qquad\qquad H_2SO_4$$
(from gas-works)

$$=\text{Ammonium Sulphate} + \text{Water}$$
$$(NH_4)_2SO_4 \qquad\qquad 2H_2O$$
"sulphate of ammonia" fertilizer,

The volatile alkaline solution is thus converted by acid into a neutral solid salt, which is much easier to transport and to apply to the soil.

2. The manufacture of *Rayon* (10% of total acid used).

Rayon (so-called "artificial silk") is made from cellulose (from wood-pulp, p. 345). This is dissolved in sodium hydroxide solution combined with carbon disulphide. The highly alkaline solution of cellulose is then squirted through platinum jets into a bath of sulphuric acid; this precipitates the cellulose, which is drawn out as a continuous thread.

$$\underbrace{Cellulose + 2NaOH} + H_2SO_4 = Na_2SO_4 + 2H_2O + Cellulose \downarrow$$
("Viscose" solution)

3. The "pickling" of steel for *tinplating*, *galvanizing*, etc. (6%)
$$Fe_2O_3 + 3H_2SO_4 = Fe_2(SO_4)_3 + 3H_2O$$

The oxide on the surface, formed when the steel was red hot, dissolves in the acid much more rapidly than the metal itself; the clean surface will then allow a firm coating of tin or zinc (see p. 461) to be put on.

4. The *electrolytic preparation* of copper and zinc (2%)
$$ZnO + H_2SO_4 = ZnSO_4 + H_2O$$

The oxide, formed by roasting the ore, is converted by the acid into a soluble salt, capable of being electrolysed (p. 220).

5. In *accumulators* (1%)

$$Pb + PbO_2 + 2H_2SO_4 = 2PbSO_4 + 2H_2O(+\text{electrical energy})$$

The electrodes are converted into the insoluble lead sulphate; as the accumulator "runs down," acid is used up, as is shown by the density of the solution decreasing (usually from about 1·25 to 1·15 gm. per c.c.).

6. The formation of *salts* ("sulphates," see p. 374), many of which are important. (6% of acid used.)

(b) Properties of Sulphuric Acid as a non-volatile acid

Concentrated sulphuric acid (b.p. 333° C.) will displace more volatile acids such as nitric acid (b.p. 86° C.) and hydrogen chloride (b.p. −83° C.) from their salts (see expt. 121, p. 325, and expt. 149, p. 397); this happens even though the sulphuric acid is really the *weaker* acid.

7. Such reactions are important in *analysis*, when testing for acid radicals (see pp. 332, 401). Commercially, some *hydrochloric acid* and nitric acid are still made in this way (see pp. 327 and 398). (5% of acid used.)

(c) Dehydrating Properties of Sulphuric Acid

Concentrated sulphuric acid has a very great affinity for water, as is shown by its use for drying gases (p. 95), by its use in desiccators, and especially by the heat evolved when the acid is poured into water. When concentrated sulphuric acid has to be diluted, *it must always be poured into the water* and stirred well, so that the heat generated will be spread throughout the mass of liquid. If water is added to the much denser acid, all the heat will be generated at the junction of the two liquids; this would be enough to break the glass of a thick bottle and to boil the small amount of water added, thus making the acid splash dangerously.

8. Much sulphuric acid (6% of the total) is used as a dehydrating agent in the manufacture of *dyes, drugs, and explosives* (see p. 330), for removing the water formed when nitric acid reacts with organic compounds.

9. *Ether*, the anaesthetic, is manufactured by dehydrating alcohol (p. 302) by means of concentrated sulphuric acid:

$$2C_2H_6O - H_2O = C_4H_{10}O \text{ (ether)}$$

Ethylene, C_2H_4, may be prepared similarly (p. 292).

Expt. 139. Action on carbohydrates (see p. 300).

$$C_x(H_2O)_y - yH_2O = xC$$

When *sugar* is mixed with enough concentrated sulphuric acid to moisten it, the mixture slowly darkens in colour till it is almost black. The mass then swells to about six times its former bulk, and evolves clouds of steam. Amorphous carbon remains as a black porous solid, as a result of the removal of the elements of water from the carbohydrate.

Paper, wood, and cloth behave similarly. Dilute sulphuric has been used as an "invisible ink" because of this property. The writing dries without leaving any traces, but on warming the paper the acid becomes concentrated and so chars the paper, leaving black carbon. Thus the warmed writing stands out clearly.

Human skin is affected in the same way. Great care must therefore always be exercised when using the concentrated acid. If the skin happens to get any acid on it, it must instantly be washed under the tap; delay may be serious. Clothes (or the bench or floor) should be neutralized with sodium carbonate until no more "fizzing" takes place.

Blue copper sulphate crystals are slowly converted in the cold to the white anhydrous salt:

$$CuSO_4.5H_2O - 5H_2O = CuSO_4$$

This is why the copper sulphate formed in expt. 136 (p. 357) does not appear blue until the acid is removed and water added.

Oxalic acid and *formic acid* are dehydrated to form carbon monoxide (see p. 253); oxalic acid forms carbon dioxide also.

(d) Oxidizing Properties of Sulphuric Acid

Hot *concentrated* sulphuric acid attacks all *metals* except gold and platinum, to form the sulphate and sulphur dioxide (*not* hydrogen); the action is similar to that on copper, which was explained in expt. 136 (p. 357). *Gold* may be *purified* commercially in this way; hence the common phrase, "the acid test." More active metals, such as zinc, may reduce the sulphuric acid as far as hydrogen sulphide:

$$\begin{cases} 4Zn + H_2SO_4 = 4ZnO + H_2S \nearrow \\ 4ZnO + 4H_2SO_4 = 4ZnSO_4 + 4H_2O \end{cases}$$

[Photo by courtesy of I.C.I. Ltd.

PLATE 22. WEEDS SPRAYED BY SULPHURIC ACID

Very few weeds grew among the wheat which has been sprayed with 6½% sulphuric acid. The plots full of bright yellow charlock were left unsprayed as a control experiment.

Non-metals such as sulphur and carbon are also oxidized to their dioxides, but much more slowly than by nitric acid.

Cold concentrated sulphuric acid does not attack iron and so can be transported in tank cars, though it is usually seen in "carboys" (fig. 131) —large glass bottles—surrounded by an iron casing with straw packing.

Expt. 140. If a filter-paper soaked in orange potassium dichromate solution is held over the mouth of a test-tube in which sulphur is being boiled with concentrated sulphuric acid, it will slowly turn green, showing that sulphur dioxide is being evolved (see p. 360, reaction 7).

$$S + 2H_2SO_4 = 3SO_2 \nearrow + 2H_2O$$

Hydrogen bromide and *hydrogen iodide* cannot be prepared pure from their salts by the action of concentrated sulphuric acid because they are oxidized to bromine and iodine respectively (see p. 421). The sulphuric acid is reduced to sulphur dioxide, or even (by HI) to hydrogen sulphide.

$$\begin{cases} KBr + H_2SO_4 = KHSO_4 + HBr \nearrow \\ 2HBr + H_2SO_4 = 2H_2O + Br_2 \nearrow + SO_2 \nearrow \end{cases}$$

Hydrogen sulphide cannot be dried by concentrated sulphuric acid (p. 352), because it is oxidized to sulphur.

(e) Other Uses of Sulphuric Acid

A large amount of sulphuric acid (3% of the total in Great Britain, but far more in the U.S.A.) is used for *refining petroleum*, by removing unsaturated hydrocarbons such as ethylene (p. 292) and other impurities (evil-smelling sulphur compounds).

In agriculture, apart from the manufacture of fertilizers, sulphuric acid is important as a *weed-killer* (PLATE 22).

Practically every industry requires the use of some sulphuric acid at some stage in the manufacture (see pp. vi, 250, 293, 346, 362, 364, 407, 409); the amount of sulphuric acid used in a country is therefore a convenient measure of its industrial civilization (fig. 131, overleaf).

Production of Sulphuric Acid and World Population, 1947

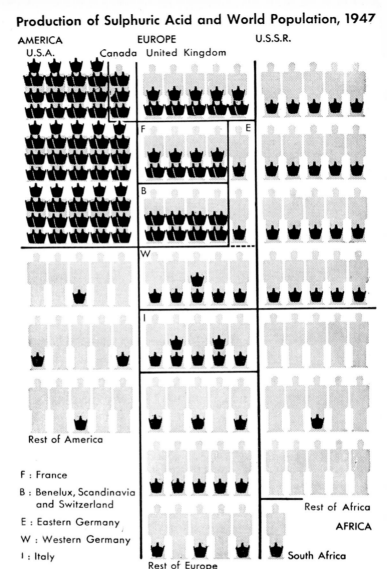

AMERICA EUROPE U.S.S.R.
U.S.A. Canada United Kingdom

F : France
B : Benelux, Scandinavia
 and Switzerland
E : Eastern Germany
W : Western Germany
I : Italy

Rest of America

Rest of Europe

Rest of Africa

AFRICA

South Africa

Each man symbol represents 10 million population

Each bottle symbol (carboy) represents 100,000 tons of 100 per cent sulphuric acid produced per year

Fig

ASIA

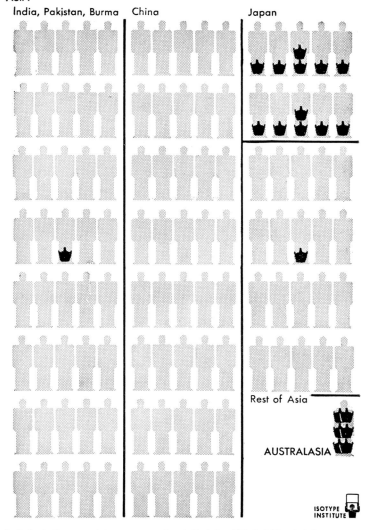

Production in Germany and Japan was more than double before 1940, in U.S.A. only half

Nearly all sulphuric acid is consumed in the producing country, as it is too corrosive to transport easily

Uses of Sulphuric Acid

UNITED KINGDOM, 1947

1. AGRICULTURE		50%
Superphosphate	32%	
$(NH_4)_2SO_4$	16%	
Spraying	2%	
2. RAYON		10%
3. METALS		7%
mostly Fe pickling		
4. DYESTUFFS, etc.		6%
Dyes	4%	
Drugs	1%	
Explosives*	1%	
5. ACIDS		5%
mostly HCl		
6. PAINTS		4%
including $BaSO_4$		
7. PETROLEUM REFINING†		3%
ETC.		15%

    * 11% in 1943.   † 10% in U.S.A.

SULPHATES

Test for Sulphates

Expt. 141. Solutions of sulphates (including sulphuric acid, of course: see p. 329) react with barium nitrate solution, even in the presence of dilute nitric acid, to form a dense white precipitate of barium sulphate. *No other salts do this.*

$$ZnSO_4 + Ba(NO_3)_2 = BaSO_4 \downarrow + Zn(NO_3)_2.$$

(Barium *chloride* or hydroxide solutions are often used with *hydrochloric* acid, but these will precipitate insoluble *chlorides*, e.g. $PbCl_2$ from solutions of lead compounds.)

Preparation of Sulphates

Sulphates may be prepared by the general methods described on pp. 67–72, i.e. (*a*) potassium, sodium, and ammonium sulphates by titration (expt. 28); (*b*) lead sulphate (and calcium or barium) by precipitation (expt. 29); (*c*) all others from the carbonate or oxide or metal (see ferrous and copper sulphates, expts. 27A and 27B) by neutralization of the acid.

Sodium Sulphate, Na_2SO_4, is manufactured from common salt (p. 398) by heating with concentrated sulphuric acid, and is used to treat wood-pulp for paper-making. Like "Epsom salt" (*Magnesium sulphate*, $MgSO_4.7H_2O$), it is used as a purgative, under the name of "Glauber's salt," $Na_2SO_4.10H_2O$.

Ammonium Sulphate, a very important fertilizer (see pp. 260, 301), is now mostly made by treating finely ground calcium sulphate with synthetic ammonia, carbon dioxide, and water:

$$CaSO_4+(NH_4)_2CO_3=CaCO_3\downarrow+(NH_4)_2SO_4$$

Nearly 10 million tons of it are produced in the world each year, and many countries, such as India, are now starting to manufacture it, so that they can produce more food for their rapidly increasing populations. Recent experiments have shown that in Scottish lochs the yield of fish per acre can be increased nearly forty-fold by the application of fertilizers, so that even wider uses for ammonium sulphate are within the bounds of possibility (see p. 526).

Calcium Sulphate occurs naturally as gypsum, $CaSO_4.2H_2O$, which is responsible for permanent hardness in water (p. 272). The anhydrous form is used (see fig. 127, p. 356) for making sulphur dioxide and ammonium sulphate. On careful heating, gypsum forms *Plaster of Paris*, $2CaSO_4.H_2O$, which unites again with water and sets to a hard mass of gypsum.

Barium Sulphate is used as a white pigment in paints, under the name of "constant white." See also "Lithopone" paint (p. 464).

Aluminium Sulphate, $Al_2(SO_4)_3.18H_2O$, like salts of other trivalent metals, will coagulate proteins, and so is commonly used as a "styptic pencil" for stopping the flow of blood from a cut, or for making insect stings less painful; its use for purifying sewage (see p. 114) is very important. It is manufactured by reacting *bauxite* or *china-clay*:

$$Al_2O_3+3H_2SO_4=Al_2(SO_4)_3+3H_2O$$

It forms a remarkable series of "double salts" known

as "alums." The commonest example is *potash alum*, $K_2SO_4.Al_2(SO_4)_3.24H_2O$, which can form very large crystals (p. 113), and which is used in solution as a "mordant" to help dyestuffs to "bite on" to a fabric. Other substances with similar formulae, e.g. $(NH_4)_2SO_4.Fe_2(SO_4)_3.24H_2O$ ("ammonium ferric alum"), crystallize in identical shapes (octahedra) and can be grown on top of crystals of potash alum or vice versa. " Chrome alum " has Cr in place of Al, and is purple.

Ferrous Sulphate, $FeSO_4.7H_2O$, "green vitriol," is made commercially by exposing heaps of iron pyrites to the action of air and water (compare p. 142), and is used with gallic acid in the manufacture of ink:

$$FeS_2 + 3O_2 + 7H_2O = FeSO_4.7H_2O + SO_2$$

Expt. 142. If powdered ferrous sulphate crystals are strongly heated in a hard-glass tube (sloping downwards), they decompose to form water, sulphur dioxide, and sulphur trioxide, leaving ferric oxide as a red-brown solid (the pigment " Indian Red "):

$$2FeSO_4.7H_2O = 14H_2O\nearrow + SO_2\nearrow + SO_3\nearrow + Fe_2O_3$$

By absorbing the gases in water, a solution is obtained which contains sulphuric acid; this was the way in which sulphuric acid was first made, over four hundred years ago.

Ferrous sulphate is the cheapest source of the iron required in the human body, if the diet is deficient (p. 307); most expensive "iron tonics" are no better.

Ferrous Ammonium Sulphate, $FeSO_4.(NH_4)_2SO_4.6H_2O$, is another example of a "double salt" (p. 174); like other double salts it behaves in solution like a mixture of the two single salts. It may be prepared as follows:

Expt. 143. Some dilute sulphuric acid is divided into two equal parts: one is treated with iron filings to form ferrous sulphate solution (expt. 27A, p. 69) and filtered into the other portion, which has previously been neutralized by ammonium hydroxide. After evaporation, the resulting solution crystallizes on cooling.

Copper Sulphate, $CuSO_4.5H_2O$, "blue vitriol," is the cheapest salt of copper, and is therefore used as the active ingredient in "Bordeaux mixture" for killing fungi on potatoes. It is prepared commercially by dissolving copper in dilute sulphuric acid through which air is blown (it does *not* dissolve in the absence of air):

$$2Cu+O_2+2H_2SO_4=2CuSO_4+2H_2O$$

In the laboratory, the anhydrous salt is used as a test for water (p. 80).

Sodium thiosulphate, $Na_2S_2O_3.5H_2O$ (Photographic "Hypo")

The prefix "thio-" means that one atom of oxygen in a sulphate has been replaced by a sulphur atom: $Na_2SO_3.O$; $Na_2SO_3.S$. It is manufactured by boiling a solution of sodium *sulphite* for several hours with sulphur:

$$Na_2SO_3+S=Na_2S_2O_3$$

and its main use is in photography for dissolving unchanged silver salts from a "developed" film or print, i.e. "fixing" the image which has been produced.

Like sodium sulphite, it is decomposed by dilute acids to give sulphur dioxide, but in addition it slowly gives a colloidal solution or precipitate of sulphur (pp. 114, 237):

$$Na_2S_2O_3+2HCl=2NaCl+H_2O+SO_2\nearrow +S\downarrow$$
$$Na_2SO_3+2HCl=2NaCl+H_2O+SO_2\nearrow$$

In the laboratory its most important use is for estimating iodine in solution (p. 424). It easily forms supersaturated solutions (p. 113). It does *not* respond to the sulphate test with barium nitrate.

Suggestions for Practical Work

Prepare sulphur dioxide (expt. 136) and examine the smell, solubility, density (expt. 78A, p. 196), and the effects on litmus, blue flowers, potassium dichromate, and burning magnesium. Try to obtain crystals of sodium sulphite. Examine the effect of leaving sulphur dioxide solution to stand in air for a few days.

Expts. 137, 139, 140, 141, 142, 143 and the preparation of various sulphates, including sodium bisulphate (expt. 31, p. 72). Expt. 123 (p. 329) by adding powdered sulphur to molten potassium nitrate in a crucible.

QUESTIONS ON CHAPTER XXII

1. Describe one method for making sulphur dioxide from each of the following substances: sulphur, sulphuric acid, iron pyrites.

Explain the use of sulphur dioxide in bleaching processes.

Briefly state how sulphur dioxide may be converted into sulphur trioxide. (W.)

2. How may a reasonably pure specimen of sulphur dioxide be prepared in the laboratory?

What reactions take place when sulphur dioxide is led into (a) sodium hydroxide solution, (b) chlorine water, (c) moist hydrogen sulphide? (C.)

3. When sulphur is burnt in oxygen, sulphur dioxide is formed and there is no change in volume. Show how far the formula for the gas can be deduced from this experimental fact. What other facts are needed?

4. Describe and give equations for reactions in which an aqueous solution of sulphur dioxide behaves as (a) an acid, (b) a reducing agent.

5. Compare and contrast the properties and general chemical behaviour of sulphur dioxide and carbon dioxide.

6. If you are given a ready supply of sulphur dioxide how would you prepare (a) sulphur trioxide, (b) dilute sulphuric acid? Describe what happens when sulphur dioxide reacts with a solution of (i) ferric chloride, (ii) hydrogen peroxide, (iii) chlorine. (L.)

7. How could you prepare a sample of sulphur trioxide? Describe the appearance of this substance, and state what happens when it reacts with water. (O.)

8. Describe *one* method for the manufacture of sulphuric acid on a commercial scale. What are its chief uses?

9. What facts can you deduce from the equation:

$$2SO_2 + O_2 \rightleftharpoons 2SO_3 + 64,320 \text{ cal.}$$

Describe briefly the industrial application of this reaction. (Navy.)

10. Describe and write equations for *two* examples each of sulphuric acid behaving as (a) a dehydrating agent, (b) an oxidizing agent.

11. Write an account of the action of sulphuric acid on metals. (A.)

12. Explain clearly why sulphuric acid is the most important chemical substance in industry.

13. You are provided with concentrated sulphuric acid, iron filings, sulphur, copper, water, a source of heat and any apparatus needed, but no other chemicals. Explain briefly how you would prepare gas-jars full of (a) hydrogen, (b) hydrogen sulphide, (c) sulphur dioxide. (N.)

14. Three unlabelled bottles contain concentrated sulphuric acid, concentrated nitric acid, and distilled water. How would you tell for certain which was which?

15. Describe the action of sulphuric acid upon the following substances: sodium sulphite, sodium nitrite, potassium nitrate, oxalic acid, copper sulphate crystals.

State the conditions under which the reactions are usually brought about, and express the changes by equations where possible. (L.)

CHAPTER XXIII

OXIDATION AND REDUCTION

Ozone and Hydrogen Peroxide. Oxides

In the last few chapters, frequent reference has been made to oxidizing agents, such as nitric and concentrated sulphuric acids, and to reducing agents such as hydrogen sulphide and sulphur dioxide. The most important feature of all their actions will also have been noticed:

An oxidizing agent gives oxygen and so becomes reduced (i.e. with less oxygen), whilst a reducing agent takes oxygen and so becomes oxidized, e.g.

$$CuO + H_2 = Cu + H_2O \quad \text{(expt. 47, p. 96)}$$

Oxidizing agent becomes reduced to Cu   Reducing agent becomes oxidized to H_2O

Oxidation

(*a*) The simplest type of oxidation is the *chemical addition of oxygen*:

$2H_2+O_2=2H_2O$ (p. 95)

$C+O_2=CO_2$ (O_2 obtained from air, p. 254)

$C+2O=CO_2$ (O obtained from nitric acid, p. 329)

$2SO_2+O_2=2SO_3$ (p. 360)

(*b*) The *removal of hydrogen* is evidently similar, even when oxygen itself is not the reagent:

$2H_2S+O_2=2H_2O+2S$ (O_2 from air, p. 351)

$H_2S+O=H_2O+S$ (O from nitric acid, p. 352)

$H_2S+Cl_2=2HCl+S$ (p. 352)

(*c*) *The addition of an acid radical or negative ion* to increase the valency of a metal is also oxidation:

$2FeCl_2+Cl_2=2FeCl_3$ (p. 400)

(ferrous chloride→ferric chloride)

$$2FeSO_4 + \boxed{O+H_2} SO_4 = Fe_2(SO_4)_3 + H_2O$$

(ferrous sulphate→ferric sulphate)

These changes are evidently similar to the oxidation:

$$2FeO + O = Fe_2O_3 \quad \text{(ferrous oxide→ferric oxide)}$$

because the ferrous salts can all be obtained directly from ferrous oxide and the ferric salts from ferric oxide:

$$FeO + H_2SO_4 = FeSO_4 + H_2O$$
$$FeO + 2HCl = FeCl_2 + H_2O$$
$$Fe_2O_3 + 6HCl = 2FeCl_3 + 3H_2O$$
$$Fe_2O_3 + 3H_2SO_4 = Fe_2(SO_4)_3 + 3H_2O$$

A substance is therefore said to be oxidized when it has its electro-negative part increased in proportion to its electro-positive part.

Reduction

This is the exact opposite of oxidation.

(a) *The removal of oxygen*, by hydrogen or other "reducing agent":

$$CuO + H_2 = Cu + H_2O \quad \text{(p. 96)}$$
$$CuO + CO = Cu + CO_2 \quad \text{(p. 256)}$$
$$Fe_2O_3 + 3CO = 2Fe + 3CO_2 \quad \text{(p. 465)}$$

(b) *The addition of hydrogen*, directly or indirectly:

$$O_2 + 2H_2 = 2H_2O$$
$$O_2 + 2H_2S = 2H_2O + 2S$$
$$Cl_2 + H_2S = 2HCl + S$$

(c) *The removal of an acid radical or negative ion* :

$$2FeCl_3 + H_2S = 2FeCl_2 + 2HCl + S \quad \text{(p. 352)}$$

$$2FeCl_3 + Zn = 2FeCl_2 + ZnCl_2 \text{ ("nascent hydrogen," p. 99)}$$

A substance is therefore said to be reduced when it has its negative portion decreased in proportion to its positive portion.

13*

Oxidizing agents

An oxidizing agent is one which can oxidize other substances, e.g.

1. Oxygen (see above examples), including the oxygen of the air, also in the presence of nitrifying bacteria, p. 312.

2. Nitric acid (p. 328).

3. Hot concentrated sulphuric acid (pp. 357, 369).

4. Potassium permanganate ($KMnO_4$, see pp. 352, 360).

5. Potassium dichromate ($K_2Cr_2O_7$, see pp. 352, 360).

6–8. Chlorine, bromine, or iodine (pp. 352, 360, and 410, 418, 423).

9–10. Ozone (O_3) or hydrogen peroxide (H_2O_2), described later in this chapter pp. 386, 389.

11. Water can also act as an oxidizing agent:

$$2Na + 2H_2O = 2NaOH + H_2 \quad \text{(expt. 37, p. 83)}$$

especially in the form of steam:

$$3Fe + 4H_2O = Fe_3O_4 + 4H_2 \quad \text{(expt. 34, p. 81)}$$

Reducing Agents

A reducing agent is one which can reduce other substances, e.g.

1. Hydrogen (see above examples).

2–3. Carbon or carbon monoxide (pp. 246, 256).

4–5. Hydrogen sulphide or sulphur dioxide (pp. 351, 358).

6. Hydrogen iodide (p. 424).

7. Stannous chloride (p. 402).

8. Metals

    (*a*) $N_2O + Cu = N_2 + CuO$ (p. 339).

    (*b*) $CO_2 + 2Mg = C + 2MgO$ (p. 249).

    (*c*) $2FeCl_3 + Zn = 2FeCl_2 + ZnCl_2$ ("nascent hydrogen," p. 100); similarly $2FeCl_3 + Cu$ (see p. 477).

    (*d*) $Fe_2O_3 + 2Al = 2Fe + Al_2O_3$ ("Thermit process" at high temperatures, see p. 459).

Some reducing agents can also *occasionally* act as oxidizing agents, e.g. sulphur dioxide can oxidize hydrogen sulphide or burning magnesium (p. 360); hydrogen sulphide can oxidize metals such as copper or tin:

$$Cu + H_2S = CuS + H_2 \quad \text{(expt. 70, p. 188)}$$

Hydrogen peroxide, which is normally an oxidizing agent (p. 389), can also reduce potassium permanganate solution or silver oxide (see (b) below).

Oxidation is always accompanied by reduction (but see p. 390).

(a) $\quad H_2SO_3 + Cl_2 + H_2O = H_2SO_4 + 2HCl$

Sulphurous acid (a reducing agent) becomes oxidized to sulphuric acid; chlorine (an oxidizing agent) becomes reduced to hydrogen chloride.

(b) $\quad\quad H_2O_2 + Ag_2O = O_2 + H_2O + 2Ag$

Hydrogen peroxide becomes oxidized to oxygen and water (by addition of oxygen) and so here acts as a reducing agent. Silver oxide (an oxidizing agent) becomes reduced to silver.

Tests for Oxidizing Agents (e.g. hydrogen peroxide)

All oxidizing agents will react in one or more of the following ways:

1. Hydrogen sulphide when bubbled through a solution of the substance and warmed gives a white or yellow precipitate of sulphur:

$$H_2S + O = H_2O + S \downarrow \quad \text{(e.g. } HNO_3, \text{ p. 352)}$$

2. Concentrated hydrochloric acid when warmed with the substance gives off chlorine (wet litmus-paper bleached):

$$2HCl + O = H_2O + Cl_2 \nearrow \quad \text{(e.g. } MnO_2, \text{ p. 404)}$$

3. Potassium iodide solution, acidified with dilute sulphuric acid and warmed with the substance, sets free iodine (brown solution or black precipitate; starch solution goes very deep blue):

$$2HI + O = H_2O + I_2 \quad \text{(e.g. } KMnO_4)$$

A very convenient form of this test is to use "starch-iodide paper," which contains both potassium iodide and starch and therefore turns blue with an oxidizing agent, *if wet*.

4. A *few drops* of *freshly prepared* ferrous sulphate solution, acidified with dilute sulphuric acid, are converted to ferric sulphate on warming with the substance; on adding sodium hydroxide solution, red-brown ferric hydroxide is precipitated (instead of green-blue ferrous hydroxide). See also p. 470.

$$O + H_2SO_4 + 2FeSO_4 = Fe_2(SO_4)_3 + H_2O$$
$$Fe_2(SO_4)_3 + 6NaOH = 2Fe(OH)_3 \downarrow + 3Na_2SO_4$$

Tests for Reducing Agents (e.g. sulphur dioxide)

All reducing agents will react in one or more of the following ways:

1. A *few drops* of ferric chloride or sulphate solution are reduced, on warming with the substance, to the ferrous salt. This gives a green-blue precipitate of ferrous hydroxide on treatment with sodium hydroxide solution (instead of red-brown ferric hydroxide).

$$2FeCl_3 + H_2O - O = 2FeCl_2 + 2HCl$$
$$FeCl_2 + 2NaOH = Fe(OH)_2 \downarrow + 2NaCl$$

2. A *few drops* of potassium permanganate solution, *acidified* with dilute sulphuric acid, will go from purple to colourless on warming with the substance:

$$2KMnO_4 + 3H_2SO_4 - 5O = K_2SO_4 + 2MnSO_4 + 3H_2O$$

3. A *few drops* of potassium dichromate solution, *acidified* with dilute sulphuric acid, will go from orange to green on warming with the substance:

$$K_2Cr_2O_7 + 4H_2SO_4 - 3O = K_2SO_4 + Cr_2(SO_4)_3 + 4H_2O$$

4. Red-hot copper oxide is reduced by the substance to copper. If pure, copper oxide will dissolve completely in hot dilute sulphuric acid, whereas copper is left as an insoluble red solid:

$$CuO - O = Cu \text{ (e.g. action of carbon)}$$

OZONE, O_3

When electrical machines are working, the air in the neighbourhood frequently has a curious smell. This is due to the formation of ozone, an allotrope of oxygen, which has the formula O_3.

Preparation

Expt. 144. Oxygen is partly converted into ozone when it is submitted to a high-potential difference across a thin layer of the gas. Some of the electrical energy goes into the reaction, forming

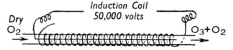

FIG. 132A. Preparation of ozonized oxygen.

ozone, which is more active than oxygen. Heat energy cannot be used because ozone is very easily decomposed, and actual sparking is no good for the same reason:

$$3O_2 + \text{energy} \rightleftharpoons 2O_3$$

In the apparatus shown in fig. 132A, one wire from an induction coil passes along inside a glass tube; the other wire is wrapped round the outside of the tube, so that there is no electrical contact between the two wires. The high voltage of the induction coil (about 50,000 volts) causes a so-called "silent electrical discharge," to pass through the oxygen, converting about 10% of it into ozone. (The loud noise accompanying this experiment actually comes from the working of the induction coil.) Any joints in the apparatus should be made with waxed corks, not rubber tubing (see below).

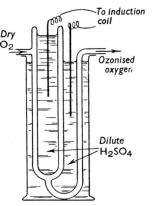

FIG. 132B. Another ozonizer

The gas emerging from the apparatus will turn moist starch-iodide paper blue, showing the presence of an oxidizing agent; but if it is first passed through a hot tube, it will no longer give the test, because all the ozone is then decomposed to oxygen.

Another common type of "ozonizer" is shown in fig. 132B.

Here again, there is no direct contact between the wires, and the discharge must pass through the gas. The same principle is used in commercial ozonizers.

Physical Properties (M.W.=48)

In high concentrations ozone is a poisonous blue gas, but as prepared in the laboratory it is harmless and colourless, with a smell rather resembling that of chlorine. It is much more soluble than oxygen in water, and—as expected—it has a higher boiling-point; by fractionally distilling ozonized oxygen, ozone has been obtained as an explosive liquid.

Chemical Properties

Ozone behaves as a strong oxidizing agent, responding to the tests on p. 383 with hydrogen sulphide, hydrogen chloride, hydrogen iodide and ferrous salts:

$$O_3 = O_2 + O \text{ (for oxidizing)}$$

Moist starch-iodide paper (p. 385) is turned blue by ozonized oxygen, but not by pure oxygen. Litmus is unaffected.

The fact that the only residue after oxidizing is gaseous oxygen has led to its use as a disinfectant for drinking-water, and for purifying the air of the early London tube railways.

Test for Ozone

In the presence of ozone, clean mercury in a dry flask or test-tube is partly converted into the oxide; this is shown by the mercury "tailing," i.e. sticking to the sides of the vessel, leaving tail-like streaks when shaken round. No other oxidizing agent does this.

Like hydrogen peroxide (p. 389), ozone converts lead sulphide (black into lead sulphate (white):

$$PbS + 4O_3 = PbSO_4 + 4O_2$$

but the solutions used to prepare the lead sulphide precipitate (on a filter-paper) must be very dilute.

Ozone reacts with "unsaturated" compounds (p. 292), destroying rubber very rapidly and being completely absorbed by turpentine.

When heated, it is completely converted into oxygen. These facts are the basis of the method for determining the formula of ozone, as it is difficult to obtain pure ozone and then find the molecular weight.

Formula of Ozone

The argument is illustrated diagrammatically in fig. 133. The two flasks are supposed to contain equal volumes of ozonized oxygen from the same supply. One is strongly heated to convert the ozone to oxygen, allowed to cool, and the increase in volume, say X c.c., measured. In

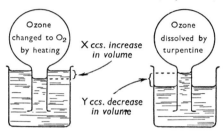

FIG. 133.   Formula of ozone.

the other the ozone is absorbed by breaking a small phial of turpentine in the flask. The decrease in volume, say Y c.c., is measured, and is clearly equal to the volume of ozone originally present.

Now in such experiments it is always found that $Y = 2X$, i.e. the increase in volume is $Y/2$ c.c.

∴ Y c.c. of ozone make $(Y + Y/2)$ c.c. of oxygen

∴ 1 c.c. of ozone makes $1\frac{1}{2}$ c.c. of oxygen.

Applying Avogadro's hypothesis,

1 molecule of ozone makes $1\frac{1}{2}$ molecules (i.e. 3 atoms) of oxygen.

∴ The formula of ozone is O_3.

HYDROGEN PEROXIDE. H_2O_2

Laboratory Preparation

Expt. 145. Add some barium peroxide gradually with stirring into ice-cold dilute sulphuric acid until it is only just acid to litmus. On filtering off the white precipitate of barium sulphate, a very dilute solution of hydrogen peroxide is obtained:

$$BaO_2 + H_2SO_4 = BaSO_4 \downarrow + H_2O_2$$

Barium peroxide is made by heating barium oxide in air to 500° C.:

$$2BaO + O_2 = 2BaO_2$$

Other "true" peroxides (see p. 392), notably sodium peroxide, Na_2O_2, also give hydrogen peroxide on treatment with dilute acids; they are less suitable for general use because their salts are soluble and so would contaminate the solution.

Commercially, hydrogen peroxide is made by a method involving electrolysis; the solution so obtained is concentrated by distilling off the water under reduced pressure, to avoid decomposing the hydrogen peroxide by heat. Hydrogen peroxide has been obtained 100% pure (b.p. 152° C., density 1·46 gm. per c.c.), but tends to decompose easily, and is usually sold as a solution in water containing 30% or less. In America and Germany, highly concentrated hydrogen peroxide (PLATE 23, p. 391) is available in 40-ton tank wagons.

Decomposition of Hydrogen Peroxide

Hydrogen peroxide solutions decompose slowly on standing, and more rapidly on heating, especially in the presence of a catalyst:

$$2H_2O_2 = 2H_2O + O_2 \nearrow$$

Dust, alkalis, charcoal, and finely divided metals are all such catalysts; manganese dioxide causes vigorous bubbling in the cold, and the decomposition with finely divided platinum may even be explosive.

"20 Volumes" Hydrogen Peroxide Solution

The strength of hydrogen peroxide solutions is quoted commercially in terms of the volume of oxygen available per unit volume of solution. Thus "20 volumes" hydrogen peroxide will yield 20 litres of oxygen from 1 litre of solution.

From the equation:

$$2H_2O_2 = 2H_2O + O_2 \nearrow$$

2×34 gm.   22·4 litres at N.T.P.

22·4 litres of oxygen at N.T.P. are obtained from 68 gm. of pure H_2O_2

∴ 1 litre of oxygen at N.T.P. is obtained from $\dfrac{68}{22\cdot4}$ gm. of pure H_2O_2

∴ 20 litres of oxygen at N.T.P. are obtained from $\dfrac{20 \times 68}{22 \cdot 4}$ gm.

   (i.e. 60·7 gm.) of pure H_2O_2

∴ 1 litre of "20-volume" hydrogen peroxide solution contains approximately 60 gm. of pure hydrogen peroxide.

"10 volumes" and "20 volumes" are the commonest commercial strengths, and "100 volumes" is sold for laboratory use.

Oxidizing Properties of Hydrogen Peroxide

Hydrogen peroxide is a strong oxidizing agent:

$$H_2O_2 = H_2O + O \text{ (for oxidizing)}$$

(a) It responds to the four *tests for an oxidizing agent* on p. 383, i.e. with hydrogen sulphide, hydrogen chloride, hydrogen iodide, and ferrous salts.

(b) **Expt. 146.**   Black *lead sulphide* is oxidized to white lead sulphate:

$$PbS + 4H_2O_2 = PbSO_4 + 4H_2O$$

A filter-paper moistened with lead acetate solution is treated with hydrogen sulphide from a Kipp, forming a black stain of lead sulphide. On adding hydrogen peroxide (or ozonized oxygen) this turns white (see p. 386).

This reaction is employed to restore old pictures in which the lead carbonate in the brighter colours has been changed in the course of time into lead sulphide (black), with consequent general darkening of the picture. Traces of hydrogen sulphide in the atmosphere are responsible for the change. Such a picture when sponged carefully with hydrogen peroxide has the black lead sulphide converted to white lead sulphate, thus restoring the original lightness.

(c) *Bleaching.*   Hair, silk, teeth, and other delicate materials are bleached with hydrogen peroxide owing to its oxidizing power. The great advantage of hydrogen peroxide as a bleaching agent lies in the harmless nature of the residue, water, left after oxidation.

For the same reason it finds frequent use as an antiseptic (e.g. "Sanitas").

(d) Test for hydrogen peroxide

Expt. 147. Potassium dichromate solution in a test-tube with dilute sulphuric acid, covered with a layer of ether, is oxidized by hydrogen peroxide to a blue "chromium peroxide." This dissolves in the ether, forming a bright blue layer. No other oxidizing agent behaves similarly.

Reducing Properties of Hydrogen Peroxide

(These are *much* less important than the oxidizing properties.)

(a) *Silver oxide* is reduced by hydrogen peroxide to silver. On the *usual* view, when hydrogen peroxide reacts with this or other oxidizing agents, *both* substances are reduced, and free oxygen is liberated.

$$Ag_2O-O=2Ag; \quad H_2O_2-O=H_2O; \quad O+O=O_2$$

On this view, therefore, reduction is *not always* accompanied by oxidation. An alternative view is given on p. 383.

(b) Acidified *potassium permanganate* solution is similarly reduced from its purple colour to a colourless mixture of potassium and manganous sulphate solutions; a similar reaction in V_2 rockets provided some of the necessary oxygen (PLATE 23).

$$2KMnO_4+3H_2SO_4=K_2SO_4+2MnSO_4+3H_2O+5O$$
$$5H_2O_2+5O=5H_2O+5O_2$$

Expt. 148. This reaction is very convenient for estimating the strength of a hydrogen peroxide solution, if the permanganate is of known strength. Alternatively, the volume of oxygen evolved from a given volume of hydrogen peroxide solution may be measured in the apparatus used for equivalents (expt. 59, p. 135), remembering that here half the oxygen comes from the potassium permanganate.

OXIDES

The chief distinction between the various kinds of oxides depends on their behaviour as acidic oxides or basic oxides (p. 47). A more complete classification is given here.

1. *Acidic oxides.* These are usually the oxides of non-metals, and usually dissolve in water to form acids, e.g. SO_2, SO_3, P_2O_5, CO_2, NO_2 (but see 6 below).

The oxides of chlorine (e.g. the explosive gas ClO_2; Cl_2O, Cl_2O_7) are acidic, as expected. Hydrogen peroxide is slightly acid to litmus (and see 5(a) below). Silicon dioxide, SiO_2 (sand) is insoluble in water and is only acidic at a high temperature (p. 437). *Higher* oxides of metals are acidic, e.g. CrO_3 which gives rise to salts such as $K_2O.2CrO_3=K_2Cr_2O_7$

potassium dichromate; $K_2O.CrO_3 = K_2CrO_4$, potassium chromate; similarly Mn_2O_7 gives $K_2O.Mn_2O_7 = 2KMnO_4$, potassium permanganate.

2. *Neutral oxides.* These are the *lower* oxides of many non-metals, e.g. H_2O, CO, N_2O, NO. They show neither acidic nor basic properties.

3. *Basic oxides.* These are the majority of the oxides of metals, and they react with acids to give a salt and water, e.g.

Photo by permission of the Controller H.M. Stationery Office

PLATE 23. HYDROGEN PEROXIDE FOR V_2 ROCKETS (p. 390)

This factory at Bad Lauterberg, carefully hidden away in the Harz mountains, Germany, produced hydrogen peroxide at 83% concentration

CuO, FeO, Fe_2O_3. They include such oxides as Na_2O, K_2O, CaO, which react with water to form *alkalis.*

4. *Amphoteric oxides.* The oxides of some metals (e.g. Al, Zn, Sn, Pb, see p. 49, note 2) dissolve both in acids and in alkalis and are called "amphoteric" (p. 459).

5. *Higher oxides.* Oxides which have more oxygen than would be expected from the usual valency of the element may conveniently be classed

as "higher oxides." In most cases they act as oxidizing agents (p. 382). They may be subdivided into:

(a) *True peroxides*, such as Na_2O_2, BaO_2 (p. 388), which give hydrogen peroxide when treated with dilute acids; and

(b) *Dioxides*, such as MnO_2, PbO_2 which do not give hydrogen peroxide.

6. *Mixed oxides* behave as compounds of two different oxides, e.g.:

$Fe_3O_4 = FeO + Fe_2O_3$ (p. 470);

$Pb_3O_4 = PbO_2 + 2PbO$ (p. 475);

$4NO_2 = N_2O_3$ (from HNO_2) $+ N_2O_5$ (from HNO_3) (p. 336, reaction 3).

Suggestions for Practical Work

Try the tests for oxidizing and reducing agents on pp. 383–84, using hydrogen peroxide and sulphur dioxide respectively.

Expts. 145–148.

QUESTIONS ON CHAPTER XXIII

1. Describe an apparatus for the preparation of ozonized oxygen. Compare the properties of oxygen and ozone.

How has it been proved that the molecule of ozone contains three oxygen atoms? (D.)

2. 1000 c.c. of ozonized oxygen were heated. When the temperature had regained its original value the volume of gas was found to be 1025 c.c. Calculate the volume of ozone in the original mixture. (O. and C.)

3. Define the term allotropy. Describe *one* method by which oxygen may be partially converted into ozone. Assuming complete conversion, what volume of ozone would be obtained from 600 c.c. of oxygen if both gases were measured at the same temperature and pressure?

What happens when ozone is strongly heated? State what you would observe if ozone were brought into contact with (a) mercury, (b) moist litmus-paper, (c) an aqueous solution of potassium iodide. What chemical changes occur in (c)? (L.)

4. Describe the preparation of a dilute solution of hydrogen peroxide. Describe an experiment (sketching the necessary apparatus) by which you could measure the volume of oxygen evolved when 5 c.c. of a hydrogen peroxide solution are treated with excess of acidified potassium permanganate solution. (C.)

5. How would you prepare a dilute solution of hydrogen peroxide? Describe, and explain briefly (by an equation if you like), what you see when this solution is treated with (a) manganese dioxide, (b) acidified potassium permanganate solution, (c) acidified potassium dichromate solution, (d) freshly precipitated lead sulphide. (O.)

6. Compare the properties of (a) hydrogen peroxide and water, (b) ozone and oxygen.

7. What do you understand by an oxidizing agent? Give *two* tests by which you could recognize a given substance as an oxidizing agent.

Describe how you would oxidize ferrous sulphate to ferric sulphate and how you would show that the oxidation was complete. (O.)

8. Describe shortly how each of the following may be oxidized: (a) hydrogen chloride, (b) ferrous sulphate, (c) copper, (d) sulphur.

9. What is a reducing agent? Give *three* examples of common reducing agents. Describe and explain any experiment in which sulphuric acid is reduced. (O. and C.)

10. Select from the following substances two examples each of an oxidizing agent and reducing agent and write an account of the experiments you would perform with them to illustrate your answer: hydrogen, carbon monoxide, chlorine, sulphur dioxide, nitric acid, potassium permanganate. (S.)

11. So-called "nascent hydrogen" is a more effective reducing agent than ordinary hydrogen. Illustrate and explain this statement.

12. What simple tests would you apply in order to decide whether a given substance is an oxidizing agent or a reducing agent? Some substances may be classified under both headings. Give two examples of such substances.

13. What is meant by the terms "reduction" and "oxidation"? Illustrate your answer by examples.

What tests would you apply to a given substance to show whether it is a reducing agent or an oxidizing agent? (C.)

14. Each of the following equations represents a simultaneous oxidation and reduction. (In section (c) and (d) the symbols X, Y, Z stand for three different elements.) State in each example which is the *oxidizer* and which is the *reducer*, and in each case give *a reason* which justifies your choice.

$$(a) \quad NaNO_3 + Pb = NaNO_2 + PbO$$
$$(b \quad H_2S + 2FeCl_3 = 2FeCl_2 + 2HCl + S$$
$$(c) \quad 2X + Fe_2O_3 = X_2O_3 + 2Fe$$
$$(d) \quad YCl_2 + ZCl_2 = Y + ZCl_4 \qquad \text{(N.)}$$

15. In the following equations, state, giving your reasons, whether the substances underlined have been oxidized or reduced:

(a) $H_2S + 2FeCl_3 = 2FeCl_2 + 2HCl + S$

(b) $PbO_2 + 4HCl = PbCl_2 + Cl_2 + 2H_2O$

(c) $2H_2S + SO_2 = 2H_2O + 3S$

Give *one* example of an application in industry of reduction, and *one* example of an application in industry of oxidation.   (C.)

16. Explain (with equations where possible) the following:

(i) Sulphur dioxide when passed into a solution of potassium dichromate turns the latter from red to green.

(ii) Hydrogen sulphide decolorizes dilute potassium permanganate solution.

(iii) A solution of potassium iodide, containing starch and hydrogen peroxide, on acidification gives a deep-blue solution which is decolorized on the addition of sodium thiosulphate.

(iv) A green solution of ferrous sulphate turns brown on the addition of a few drops of concentrated nitric acid, and on being heated this gives place to a clear yellow solution.   (Navy.)

17. Explain the meaning of the terms, and illustrate by examples: acid salt, basic salt, acidic oxide, basic oxide, neutral oxide.

18. What are the four chief classes of oxides?   Give *one* example of each class.   How do oxides of metals differ chemically from those of non-metals?

State briefly how you would prepare from suitable oxides (a) a solution of copper sulphate. (b) a dilute solution of hydrogen peroxide.

What happens when manganese dioxide is added to a solution of hydrogen peroxide?   (N.)

CHLORINE AND CHLORIDES

Occurrence of Chlorine Compounds

Chlorine is a poisonous gas which is so reactive that it never occurs free. By far the most important compound of chlorine is sodium chloride, "common salt," which is the source of almost all chlorine and sodium compounds. Its chief chemical uses are shown in fig. 134, overleaf.

Extraction of Sodium Chloride

Salt is extracted:

(*a*) from underground salt beds formed by the drying up of inland seas, e.g. in Cheshire and in Cracow, Poland. The Dead Sea is in the process of drying up and contains over 7% of salt;

(*b*) by the evaporation of sea-water, a process usually carried out in hot climates.

Sea-water contains approximately 2·8% NaCl, together with smaller quantities of other mineral salts, such as chloride and bromide of magnesium and of potassium (see p. 77).

The mining of salt from underground deposits is carried out in Cheshire by pumping down water to dissolve the salt. The solution, "brine," formed is pumped to the surface and evaporated in steam-heated pans. Even more than other methods of mining, this leads to subsidence of the ground above the deposits, which may have serious consequences. From some deposits the salt is obtained as a rock, "rock salt," by a process not unlike coal mining.

HYDROGEN CHLORIDE

Historically, this was made from sodium chloride and then converted into chlorine, until electrolysis became common. In the laboratory, this is still the most convenient method.

PRODUCTS FROM SALT

396

Laboratory Preparation

Expt. 149. Concentrated sulphuric acid is added, through a thistle funnel or dropping funnel, to small pieces of rock salt contained in a flask fitted with a cork and delivery tube (see fig. 135).

The name hydrogen chloride is given to the colourless gas which comes off, and the name hydrochloric acid is reserved for its solution in water.

Being heavier than air, the gas is collected by displacing air upwards. A wash-bottle of strong sulphuric acid is sometimes inserted; this shows how fast the gas is passing, but is not necessary for drying the gas, which should be dried by the acid in the generator. The reaction does not require much external heat, because a good deal of heat is generated during the reaction. The equation is:

$$NaCl + H_2SO_4 = NaHSO_4 + HCl \nearrow$$

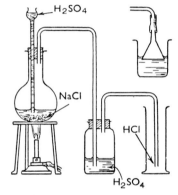

FIG. 135. Preparation of hydrogen chloride.

It will be noticed from this equation that the product left in the flask is sodium bisulphate. On a commercial scale the reaction is carried a stage farther to give sodium sulphate, thus giving another gram-molecule of HCl without using any more H_2SO_4, which is the more expensive of the two ingredients.

For this second stage to occur a temperature is required too high for ordinary laboratory glassware.

$$NaCl + NaHSO_4 = Na_2SO_4 + HCl \nearrow$$

Industrial Preparation

Nowadays hydrogen chloride is mostly made by direct synthesis, i.e. by burning hydrogen in an atmosphere of chlorine. These two elements are by-products obtained in the manufacture of sodium hydroxide by the electrolysis of brine (p. 405). The gaseous hydrogen chloride is then absorbed in water to form hydrochloric acid.

Hydrogen chloride is also a by-product formed in the conversion of sodium chloride to sodium sulphate for paper-making. The method is similar to the laboratory preparation (expt. 149).

Properties of Hydrogen Chloride (HCl, M.W.=36·5)

It is a colourless gas with a choking smell and an acid taste. When it meets moisture in the air, and especially when breathed upon, it dissolves in the moisture, producing a very visible mist of hydrochloric acid.

It also gives clouds of white smoke when brought into contact with ammonia (as given off by a glass rod previously dipped into a bottle of strong ammonia solution), due to the formation of fine white specks of solid ammonium chloride:

$$NH_3 + HCl = NH_4Cl$$

It does not burn in air, nor does it support combustion.

It is extremely soluble in water (p. 114), as can be shown by inverting a gas-jar of it over water or by the "fountain experiment" (expt. 109, p. 316) described for ammonia; in this case, blue litmus in the lower bottle is turned red.

Hydrochloric Acid

A solution of hydrogen chloride in water should be made, using an inverted funnel (fig. 135), as described for ammonia (p. 316), to prevent "sucking back."

"Fuming" hydrochloric acid (density 1·20 gm. per c.c.) is a solution almost saturated at 0° C., and containing about 40% by weight of the gas. Ordinary "concentrated" acid contains about 32% (density 1·16 gm. per c.c.). If such strong solutions are boiled, they lose hydrogen chloride until the strength reaches 20·2% HCl, when the solution boils unchanged at 110° C. (density 1·10 gm. per c.c.). If a dilute solution is boiled, it loses water until the same *constant boiling-point mixture* is obtained. Thus, unlike ammonia and most other gases, hydrogen chloride is not completely driven out of its solutions by boiling.

Metals in the electrochemical series (see p. 223) down to and including tin react readily with concentrated hydrochloric acid, giving off hydrogen and leaving a solution of the chloride of the metal:

$$Sn + 2HCl = SnCl_2 + H_2 \nearrow$$
Tin   Stannous Chloride

Hydrochloric acid is therefore transported in steel containers lined with rubber; the yellow colour of the commercial acid (*spirits of salt*) is due to ferric chloride, presumably formed by attack on exposed portions of rusty iron (ferric oxide).

The acid is monobasic, and its salts are called chlorides, e.g. sodium chloride, $NaCl$; magnesium chloride, $MgCl_2$; aluminium chloride, $AlCl_3$.

Many oxidizing agents (see p. 383) convert it into chlorine; e.g. MnO_2 (p. 404), PbO_2, Pb_3O_4, $KMnO_4$, $CaOCl_2$.

The uses of the acid are described on p. 413.

METALLIC CHLORIDES

Preparation

Solutions of chlorides may be obtained by the general methods for preparing salts (p. 67), i.e. by treating the metal or its oxide, hydroxide, or carbonate with hydrochloric acid:

$$CuO + 2HCl = CuCl_2 + H_2O$$

Lead chloride, $PbCl_2$, mercurous chloride, Hg_2Cl_2, and silver chloride, $AgCl$, are insoluble; they are therefore precipitated by treating a solution of a soluble salt (such as the nitrate) with sodium chloride solution or with hydrochloric acid:

$$Pb(NO_3)_2 + 2HCl = PbCl_2 \downarrow + 2HNO_3$$
(compare expt. 29, p. 70, $PbSO_4 \downarrow$)

Preparation of Anhydrous Chlorides

The chlorides of K, Na, NH_4, and Ca may be obtained anhydrous by evaporating their solutions (and in the case of calcium chloride, by heating the solid to drive off the water of crystallization).

Other chlorides (except of course the insoluble ones) are partly "hydrolysed," i.e. decomposed by water, under these conditions, e.g.

$$MgCl_2 + H_2O \rightleftharpoons MgO + 2HCl \nearrow$$

Hydrolysis can be prevented in this case by heating the hydrated chloride in a current of hydrogen chloride, which reverses the reaction (see Chapter XV). Alternatively the metal must be treated with hydrogen chloride gas or chlorine in the complete absence of water (see below).

Expt. 150.   Preparation of anhydrous ferric chloride.

Iron wire or iron filings, dry and free from grease, are heated in a stream of dry chlorine (p. 404).   The iron is placed in a combustion tube connected with an extension drawn out at both ends, as shown

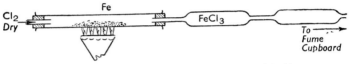

FIG. 136.   Preparation of anhydrous ferric chloride.

in fig. 136.   The ferric chloride sublimes into this tube as black lustrous crystals and may be kept permanently if the ends of the tube are sealed off by a blow-pipe before any moisture can get in.

$$2Fe + 3Cl_2 = 2FeCl_3 \nearrow$$

The anhydrous chlorides of Mg, Al, Zn, Pb, Cu, Hg may be prepared similarly. Tin, like iron, forms the *higher* chloride, $SnCl_4$, because any of the lower chloride first formed would be oxidized by chlorine to the higher chloride, e.g.

$$2FeCl_2 + Cl_2 = 2FeCl_3$$

Ferr*ous* and stann*ous* chlorides are formed as white solids if hydrogen chloride is used instead of chlorine in similar experiments:

$$Fe + 2HCl = FeCl_2 + H_2$$

Any of the higher chloride formed would be reduced by the hydrogen to the lower chloride, e.g.

$$2FeCl_3 + H_2 = 2FeCl_2 + 2HCl$$

Tests for Chlorides

1. All solid chlorides when warmed with concentrated sulphuric acid (see expt. 149) give off hydrogen chloride; this is easily detected by the fact that it fumes when breathed upon, and gives white clouds when a rod dipped in strong ammonia solution is brought into contact with it, e.g.

$$CuCl_2 + H_2SO_4 = CuSO_4 + 2HCl \nearrow$$

2. If manganese dioxide is added to the above hot mixture of a chloride and concentrated sulphuric acid, the hydrogen chloride is oxidized to the greenish-yellow gas chlorine (see expt. 152), e.g.

$$CuCl_2 + 2H_2SO_4 + MnO_2 = CuSO_4 + MnSO_4 + 2H_2O + Cl_2 \nearrow$$

3. **Expt. 151.** All chlorides in solution on treatment with dilute nitric acid and silver nitrate solution give a white precipitate; this is silver chloride, which darkens on exposure to light and readily dissolves in ammonium hydroxide: $Cl^- + Ag^+ = AgCl \downarrow$ (p. 214), usually written as $NaCl + AgNO_3 = NaNO_3 + AgCl \downarrow$ (see p. 78).

Addition of nitric acid is important, because many salts other than chlorides (e.g. carbonates, sulphites, oxalates, etc.) will give a white precipitate if silver nitrate is added alone, but not in the presence of nitric acid.

Potassium chloride, KCl, occurs in the ocean to a small extent, in salt lakes (e.g. the Dead Sea) and in salt deposits (especially at Stassfurt in Germany). It is an important fertilizer (p. 301) and is the chief source of potassium compounds.

Sodium chloride, NaCl, is very cheap (£1 per ton in U.K.), and so the chief source of compounds of sodium and chlorine. It is an important article of food (p. 306) and is used on a large scale also for the preservation of food such as fish, bacon, and meat. Common salt contains magnesium and calcium chlorides as impurities, which make it deliquescent. For table use, substances such as sodium phosphate are added to form a coating round each of the grains.

Sodium chloride is somewhat difficult to crystallize because its solubility varies so little with temperature (p. 108).

Ammonium chloride, NH₄Cl, is prepared by direct union of ammonia and hydrogen chloride gases (p. 318); it is used in Leclanché cells ("dry batteries"), and also as a flux in soldering, because the hydrogen chloride set free on heating cleans the metal surface by dissolving off any oxide.

Calcium chloride, CaCl₂, is a waste product from the Solvay process for making sodium carbonate. It is very deliquescent, and so is used for drying gases (see p. 38), except ammonia, which combines with it.

Magnesium chloride, MgCl₂, a constituent of sea-water, is the main source of magnesium metal (see p. 453). Like aluminium chloride, it may also be prepared by heating the oxide mixed with coke in a current of chlorine:

$$Al_2O_3 + 3C + 3Cl_2 = 2AlCl_3\nearrow + 3CO\nearrow$$

Aluminium chloride, AlCl₃, is an important catalyst in organic chemistry for cracking petroleum (p. 292) and for converting benzene to toluene (p. 295). A 20% solution in water or vanishing cream ("Odorono") is used to stop the flow of perspiration—compare aluminium sulphate (p. 114).

Zinc chloride, ZnCl₂, is used as a flux in soldering, because it dissolves metallic oxides. Its solution is used to protect timber from dry-rot.

Stannous chloride, SnCl₂, is a reducing agent which will convert ferric salts to ferrous:

$$2FeCl_3 + SnCl_2 = 2FeCl_2 + SnCl_4$$
$$\text{ferric} \quad \text{stannous} \quad \text{ferrous} \quad \text{stannic}$$

With mercuric salts it gives a white precipitate of mercurous chloride and then grey mercury:

$$2HgCl_2 + SnCl_2 = Hg_2Cl_2\downarrow + SnCl_4$$
$$Hg_2Cl_2 + SnCl_2 = 2Hg\downarrow + SnCl_4$$

Stannic chloride, SnCl₄, is interesting because it behaves like the chloride of a non-metal (compare the chlorides of phosphorus). It is a volatile liquid, b.p. 114°, which fumes strongly in moist air because of hydrolysis to hydrogen chloride. It provides a useful means of recovering tin (by reaction with chlorine) from salvaged tinplate.

Lead chloride, PbCl$_2$, is much more soluble in hot water than in cold (pp. 71, 108) and so can easily be recognized.

Cupric and mercuric chlorides, CuCl$_2$, HgCl$_2$, are soluble salts formed by the standard methods (but see p. 479). Both are poisonous, mercuric chloride being intensely so. On heating with the metal, they are converted into the lower chlorides, *cuprous chloride*, CuCl, most conveniently in the presence of concentrated hydrochloric acid which dissolves it, *mercurous chloride* by sublimation:

$$HgCl_2 + Hg = Hg_2Cl_2 \nearrow$$

Both the latter are white solids insoluble in water. Mercurous chloride is used as a purgative under the name of calomel.

A solution of cuprous chloride in ammonia is useful for absorbing carbon monoxide (p. 256).

CHLORINE

Laboratory Preparation

1. (**Expt. 152**). Concentrated hydrochloric acid is added to small lumps of manganese dioxide contained in a flask, fitted with

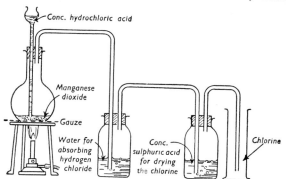

Fig. 137. Laboratory preparation of chlorine.

thistle funnel and delivery tube, as shown in fig. 137. As chlorine is very poisonous, the apparatus should be set up in a fume cupboard.

The contents of the flask are gently heated, and the chlorine evolved is passed through one wash-bottle containing a little water and then through another containing concentrated sulphuric acid to dry the gas. The object of the first bottle is to dissolve any hydrogen chloride which may be mixed with the chlorine. The chlorine is collected as shown, since it is much heavier than air.

The chemistry of the reaction is easily understood if the manganese dioxide is regarded as a basic oxide with an extra atom of oxygen. The former with hydrochloric acid will give a salt, manganese chloride, and water; whilst the extra atom of oxygen will oxidize some more hydrogen chloride, combining with its hydrogen to give chlorine, thus:

$$Mn O + 2H Cl \rightarrow MnCl_2 + H_2O$$
$$O + 2H Cl \rightarrow Cl_2 + H_2O$$
$$\overline{MnO_2 + 4HCl = MnCl_2 + Cl_2 + 2H_2O}$$

2. If desired, the hydrogen chloride for this experiment may be generated in the flask, by running concentrated *sulphuric* acid on to a mixture of sodium chloride and manganese dioxide, as in test no. 2 for a chloride (p. 401).

3. A very convenient oxidizing agent is solid potassium permanganate, which gives chlorine at once when cold concentrated hydrochloric acid is dropped on to it (fig. 138):

$$2KMnO_4 + 16HCl =$$
$$2KCl + 2MnCl_2 + 8H_2O + 5Cl_2 \nearrow$$

4. Another method, which can also be done in the cold, is to treat bleaching powder with a dilute acid:

$$CaOCl_2 + 2HCl = CaCl_2 + H_2O + Cl_2 \nearrow$$

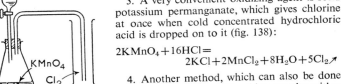

FIG. 138.
Laboratory preparation of chlorine.

Conc. HCl

$KMnO_4$

Cl_2

The Manufacture of Chlorine

Early industrial methods used the oxidation of hydrogen chloride by manganese dioxide, or by air in the presence of a copper chloride catalyst. Nowadays, chlorine is manufactured by the electrolysis of sodium chloride solution

(PLATE 24A), the main product being sodium hydroxide, with hydrogen and chlorine as by-products:

$$\underset{\text{energy}}{\overset{\text{Electrical}}{}} \underset{2\times 58\cdot5 \text{ gm.}}{+2NaCl} \underset{2\times 18 \text{ gm.}}{+2H_2O} = \underset{2\times 40 \text{ gm.}}{2NaOH} + \underset{2\times 35\cdot5 \text{ gm.}}{Cl_2} + \underset{2\times 1 \text{ gm.}}{H_2}$$

(p. 215, example 8).

The above equation provides an excellent illustration of the Law of the Conservation of Mass. For every 4 million tons of sodium hydroxide manufactured in the world per year, 3·55 million tons of chlorine would necessarily also be formed in this process. Actually the demand for chlorine and its compounds (except NaCl) is only about one-half of this, and so much sodium hydroxide is still made from sodium carbonate (p. 283).

[*Photo by permission of the Controller, H.M. Stationery Office*

PLATE 24A.   CHLORINE OBTAINED BY ELECTROLYSIS

Each knob in the photograph is one terminal of an electrolytic cell. The fifty-eight cell complexes shown produce 200 tons of chlorine per day (i.e. 14 tank wagons, p. 408) at this German factory at Burghausen.

The chief difficulty in applying this reaction lies in the fact that chlorine will react with the sodium hydroxide (p. 411) unless the electrolytic cell is designed to prevent this. Two types of cell are in common use:

1. *The Porous Diaphragm Cell* (fig. 139)

The sodium chloride solution is contained in a porous asbestos vessel. The anode consists of carbon rods, and the cathode is a steel net covering the outer surface of the asbestos. Electrical contact is made by the solution, which oozes through the asbestos and so reaches the cathode. The solution is electrolysed hot to reduce the resistance.

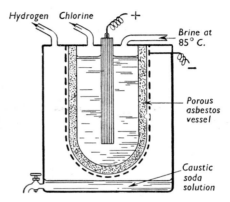

Fig. 139. Electrolysis of brine—1.

During electrolysis the chlorine ions are discharged at the anode, forming chlorine molecules, which are led away through a tube as shown. Sodium ions carry the current through the porous diaphragm to the cathode; here *hydrogen* ions are discharged (see pp. 221–22), because they have a lower discharge potential than the sodium ions. More water molecules then dissociate, and the hydroxyl ions remaining behind form sodium hydroxide, which is drained off in solution.

$$Na^+; \ OH^- + H^+ \rightleftharpoons H_2O \qquad Cl^-$$
$$\underbrace{\quad\quad\quad}_{\displaystyle NaOH} \qquad \downarrow \qquad\qquad\qquad \downarrow$$
$$H_2 \qquad\qquad\quad Cl_2$$

2. *The Mercury Cathode Cell* (fig. 140)

At a mercury cathode, hydrogen has a high overvoltage and the electrical potential required to discharge hydrogen ions is *greater* than that for sodium ions.   The latter are therefore discharged and dissolve in the mercury to form sodium amalgam.

This is continuously run out into a tank of water, where the sodium reacts to form caustic soda and hydrogen, leaving the mercury to be used again.   As in the first type of cell, the chlorine is evolved at the carbon anode.

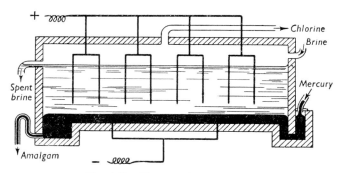

FIG. 140.   Electrolysis of brine—2.

Properties of Chlorine (Cl_2, M.W.$=71$)

Chlorine is a greenish-yellow gas, about $2\frac{1}{2}$ times as heavy as air.   It is easily liquefied under pressure, and is stored in iron cylinders which it does not attack if it has been dried by concentrated sulphuric acid (see PLATE 24B, p. 408).

It has an unpleasant irritating smell, and is extremely poisonous.   It is therefore used to destroy bacteria in water (p. 78), and was used as a poison gas in the 1914 war.

Chemical activity

Chlorine is an extremely reactive element.   It combines directly with all metals (see p. 408), even including gold and platinum, and with all non-metals except oxygen, nitrogen, carbon, and the inert gases.   (When chlorine is prepared by electrolysis, an anode of carbon rather than a metal is therefore used.)   It is a vigorous oxidizing agent (see p. 383), especially in its removal of hydrogen from compounds.

{*Photo by courtesy of I.C.I., Ltd.*

PLATE 24B. 14 TONS OF LIQUID CHLORINE

Chlorine, liquefied under a pressure of about 5 atmospheres, can be safely transported in steel tank wagons, so long as it is perfectly dry.

Combination of Chlorine with Metals (see also pp. 330, 400)

Expt. 153. (*a*) Burning magnesium ribbon continues to burn in a jar of chlorine, forming magnesium chloride:

$$Mg + Cl_2 = MgCl_2$$

(*b*) A piece of "Dutch metal" (imitation gold leaf, an alloy containing copper and a little zinc, i.e. very thin brass) bursts into flame when placed in a jar of the gas, producing a cloud of fine smoke which is anhydrous copper chloride:

$$Cu + Cl_2 = CuCl_2$$

(*c*) Finely powdered antimony gives a shower of sparks when shaken into a jar of chlorine:

$$2Sb + 3Cl_2 = 2SbCl_3$$

Combination of Chlorine with Non-Metals

Expt. 154. (*a*) White phosphorus, in a deflagrating spoon, takes fire in chlorine, forming white clouds which are partly phosphorus trichloride (liquid) and partly phosphorus pentachloride (solid):

$$2P + 3Cl_2 = 2PCl_3$$
$$2P + 5Cl_2 = 2PCl_5$$

(b) A jet of hydrogen, from a Kipp, which is burning in air will continue to burn in a jar of chlorine:

$$H_2 + Cl_2 = 2HCl$$

If hydrogen and chlorine are mixed in approximately equal volumes (see expt. 72, p. 189), they will combine slowly and quietly in ordinary daylight; if they are exposed to sunlight or lit with a flame, there may be a violent explosion.

Removal of Hydrogen from Compounds by Chlorine

Chlorine will remove hydrogen from the hydrides of all the other non-metals (except fluorine), forming hydrogen chloride and the non-metal.

Expt. 155. (a) A piece of glass-wool (or cotton-wool) dipped into a *hydrocarbon* such as turpentine and warmed will catch fire in chlorine, burning with a rather red flame, forming clouds of black soot and hydrogen chloride. The fine soot scatters light of short wavelengths, so that the longer wavelength (red) is transmitted to the eye. The hydrogen chloride can be tested, as usual, with ammonia.

$$C_{10}H_{16} + 8Cl_2 = 10C \downarrow + 16HCl$$

A burning taper or candle behaves similarly.

(b) Other hydrocarbons such as methane, CH_4 (p. 291), can react either as above or by a process of "substitution" in which chlorine replaces hydrogen:

$$\underset{\text{Methane}}{CH_4} + Cl_2 = \underset{\text{Methyl Chloride}}{CH_3Cl} + HCl$$

Similar reactions are important for preparing organic compounds containing chlorine, e.g. the insecticide "D.D.T." (Dichloro-Diphenyl-Trichloroethane) which is prepared from chlorine, benzene, and alcohol, using concentrated sulphuric acid as a dehydrating agent.

Ethylene, C_2H_4, reacts by "addition" with chlorine or bromine to give $C_2H_4X_2$ (p. 421).

(c) $\underset{\text{Ammonia}}{2NH_3} + 3Cl_2 = \underset{\text{Nitrogen}}{N_2} + 6HCl$ (→6NH_4Cl, see expt. 73, p. 189)

(d) $2H_2O + 2Cl_2 = O_2 + 4HCl$ (see below, expt. 156 (c))

(e) $H_2S + Cl_2 = S \downarrow + 2HCl$ (see p. 352)

(f) $\underset{\text{Hydrogen Iodide}}{2HI} + Cl_2 = \underset{\text{Iodine}}{I_2} \downarrow + 2HCl$ (see below, expt. 157)

Chlorine Water

Expt. 156. (*a*) Chlorine is *soluble* in water to the extent of about 3 volumes of gas in 1 volume of water at room temperature and pressure (p. 114). If chlorine is passed into water, this solution, known as "chlorine water," is formed. It has a pale-green colour and smells strongly of chlorine.

(*b*) This solution will turn blue litmus-paper red and then *bleach* it. Other coloured materials, such as cloth, flowers, and ink are bleached, but not printer's ink (p. 245), which consists of carbon. These effects are due to the fact that there is a certain amount of

FIG. 141. Decomposition of chlorine water.

chemical action when chlorine dissolves in water, giving a mixture of hydrochloric and hypochlorous acids. The latter, HClO, readily gives up its atom of oxygen and oxidizes the colour to a colourless substance.

$$H_2O + Cl_2 \rightleftharpoons HCl + HClO$$

$$HClO + colour = HCl + oxidized\ colour$$

This is why *dry* chlorine has no bleaching power.

(*c*) Chlorine water when exposed to *sunlight* gradually loses its colour, giving off oxygen and leaving hydrochloric acid. This can be demonstrated if chlorine water is placed in a retort as shown in fig. 141 and allowed to remain for several days. The oxygen should be tested, as usual, with a glowing splint.

(*d*) When *litharge* (PbO) is warmed with chlorine water, the orange colour gradually darkens, as it is oxidized to lead dioxide (PbO_2, "lead peroxide") which is a chocolate coloured powder.

$$PbO + \overline{Cl_2 + H_2}O = PbO_2 \downarrow + 2HCl$$

(*e*) Similarly a solution of *sulphur dioxide* in water is oxidized to sulphuric acid (test for sulphate with barium chloride and hydrochloric acid, expt. 141).

$$SO_2 + H_2O = H_2SO_3$$
$$\overline{Cl_2 + H_2}O + H_2SO_3 = H_2SO_4 + 2HCl$$

Chlorine as an Oxidizing Agent (see p. 380)

The above two reactions and the bleaching action are oxidations which require the presence of water. Dry chlorine, however, reacts as an oxidizing agent in its reactions with hydrides of non-metals and in combining directly with metals. It should be noticed that it gives three of the tests for an oxidizing agent (p. 383, nos. 1, 4, and 3—see expt. 157b, below).

Replacement of Bromine and Iodine by Chlorine

Expt. 157. (*a*) When chlorine gas is passed into a solution of potassium bromide (preferably saturated), this colourless solution rapidly turns red, due to bromine formed in solution. This solution soon becomes saturated and then bromine itself is deposited as a heavy dark-red liquid:

$$2KBr + Cl_2 = 2KCl + Br_2 \downarrow \quad \text{i.e.} \quad 2Br^- + Cl_2 = 2Cl^- + Br_2 \text{ (p. 222)}$$

(*b*) Similarly, if a solution of potassium iodide is used instead of the bromide, then iodine is set free. This at first dissolves in unchanged potassium iodide to give a very deep-brown solution, but as more of the potassium iodide reacts, the iodine, which is only slightly soluble in water, is deposited as a black solid. Chlorine will therefore turn moist starch-iodide paper blue:

$$2KI + Cl_2 = 2KCl + I_2 \downarrow$$

The solutions in the above tests do *not* need to be acidified, though less chlorine will dissolve if they are.

The Action of Chlorine on Alkalis

Expt. 158. (*a*) When chlorine is passed into a fairly *dilute cold solution* of caustic soda or caustic potash a colourless solution with a characteristic smell is obtained. The solution contains a *hypochlorite* and is a useful bleaching agent and disinfectant, which is sold under a large variety of trade names as " Milton," " Domestos," "Parozone," "Ink Eradicator," etc.

$$2NaOH + Cl_2 = NaClO + NaCl + H_2O$$

It gives off chlorine when dilute acid is added to it (test with moist blue litmus):

$$NaClO + 2HCl = NaCl + H_2O + Cl_2 \nearrow$$
$$NaClO + NaCl + H_2SO_4 = Na_2SO_4 + H_2O + Cl_2 \nearrow$$

(*b*) If chlorine is passed into a *hot, strong solution* of the caustic alkali a different reaction occurs. The resulting solution does not give chlorine with dilute acid. If concentrated and allowed to cool, both cubic crystals of the chloride and wedge-shaped crystals of the chlorate can readily be seen side by side, when examined under the microscope.

$$6KOH + 3Cl_2 = KClO_3 + 5KCl + 3H_2O$$

Potassium
Chlorate

Potassium Chlorate, $KClO_3$

This used to be manufactured by the above reaction; the present method involves electrolysing a boiling solution of potassium chloride, and the chlorine is never set free. On cooling, the potassium chlorate separates out, because it is so much less soluble (fig. 37, p. 108), and any unchanged potassium chloride solution can be used again.

Its uses all depend on the fact that under suitable conditions it goes to potassium chloride and oxygen: (a) the laboratory preparation of oxygen (expt. 18, p. 29); (b) in explosives and matches (p. 430 ; also compare potassium nitrate, p. 333); and (c) in sore-throat tablets (for oxidizing bacteria and so killing them).

Bleaching Powder, $CaOCl_2$

This substance is prepared by passing chlorine over moist slaked lime, and is given the above formula (which suggests $Ca(OCl)_2 + CaCl_2$) for convenience rather than accuracy. If pure, treatment with a dilute acid would give 56% of its weight of "available chlorine," whereas in fact only 36% is obtained, because unchanged $Ca(OH)_2$ is present and also H_2O.

$$Ca(OH)_2 + Cl_2 = CaOCl_2 + H_2O$$

$$CaOCl_2 + 2HCl = CaCl_2 + H_2O + Cl_2 \nearrow \text{ (see p. 404, method 4)}$$

$$CaOCl_2 + H_2SO_4 = CaSO_4 + H_2O + Cl_2 \nearrow$$

Bleaching powder is of great importance in British history, because it provided the means of bleaching the cotton and linen goods which were exported in huge quantities in the nineteenth century, and which were one of the foundations of British commercial supremacy. Chlorine had been discovered in 1776 by oxidizing hydrochloric acid with manganese dioxide (expt. 152), and was converted into this easily transportable, innocuous powder by treatment with the cheapest alkali, made from home-produced limestone.

The unbleached cotton or linen was immersed in a solution or suspension of bleaching powder in water. Then, in a bath of dilute sulphuric acid, chlorine was set free inside the pores of the fabric, thus bleaching the colour. The chlorine did not remain long enough to harm the cellulose of which the fibres of the material are made. The cloth was then washed completely free from chemicals, and sometimes treated with an "anti-chlor" (e.g. photographic "hypo") to remove free chlorine.

Before the use of bleaching materials, fabrics had to be exposed to the oxidizing action of air and light in fields; this was far more costly and took several months!

If a bleaching powder solution is heated with a cobalt salt (which acts as a catalyst), it is decomposed to give off oxygen:

$$2CaOCl_2 = 2CaCl_2 + O_2 \nearrow$$

Uses of Chlorine

The greatest amount of chlorine is used for bleaching cotton and linen (*not* wool, silk, or straw), and also wood-pulp for paper or rayon. Chlorine itself (transported in liquid form—PLATE 24B) is now the commonest reagent, although sodium hypochlorite solution and bleaching powder are also important. The treatment of water supplies has already been mentioned (p. 78).

Hydrochloric acid (largely made from chlorine) is a cheap acid which can be used in place of dilute sulphuric acid for many purposes, e.g. "pickling" steel (p. 367). It is important in the extraction of glue from bones (see p. 432). It is useful in forming soluble salts ("hydrochlorides") from many drugs, such as the local anaesthetic "Novocaine" (used in the extraction of teeth), which are insoluble organic bases; a solution of the salt can then be used in the form of an injection. A recent such example (1948) is "Antrycide," a solution of which is used for inoculating cattle against tsetse flies, and which has vast political implications because it makes it possible eventually for the equatorial half of Africa

14*

to be adequately used, and for Europe to get great food supplies from non-dollar areas.

Large numbers of important organic compounds contain chlorine: e.g. chloroform, $CHCl_3$; carbon tetrachloride, CCl_4 (p. 251); D.D.T. (p. 409); "TRIchlorethyLENE," as a solvent for dissolving grease from clothes; "chloroxone," for selective weed-killing; and antiseptics such as "T.C.P.," "Dettol," etc., which are chlorinated compounds made from coal-tar products. Men can therefore use chlorine, not for killing one another (p. 407), but for "killing" pain, fire, insect pests, dirt, weeds, and bacteria.

Suggestions for Practical Work

Expt. 149 and the properties of hydrogen chloride. Prepare a solution of it, test with litmus, boil, and test again.

Examine the action of the following oxides on concentrated hydrochloric acid: PbO, Pb_3O_4 (red lead), MnO_2, CuO. Also prepare potassium chloride.

Expts. 151–158 inclusive.

QUESTIONS ON CHAPTER XXIV

1. Common salt is the basis of much of the chemical industry of England. Discuss this statement, showing how (i) sodium carbonate, (ii) caustic soda. and (iii) sodium nitrate are manufactured from this source.

What are the chief uses of these three substances? (Navy.)

2. How may hydrogen chloride be obtained in a pure, dry state? Describe clearly, with a sketch, how a strong solution of this gas in water can be made in the laboratory. Under what conditions and how does the aqueous solution of this gas react with (*a*) marble, (*b*) lead peroxide, (*c*) nitric acid, (*d*) bleaching powder? (W.)

3. How would you prepare a solution of hydrochloric acid, starting from sodium chloride?

Describe the chief properties of this solution, pointing out those which are common to all acids and those which are peculiar to hydrochloric acid. (C.)

4. Give *three* uses of hydrochloric acid and *three* properties by which it could be distinguished from nitric acid. (O. Gen. Sc.)

5. Describe the physical properties of hydrogen chloride.

How would you demonstrate that it is very soluble in water?

What happens when (*a*) a concentrated solution, (*b*) a very dilute solution of this gas in water is heated?

6. Describe in outline *three* distinct methods which are available for the preparation of the chlorides of metals.

Which of the methods you have mentioned could be used to prepare the following salts: sodium chloride, lead chloride, ferric chloride?

Give full experimental details for the preparation of *one* of these salts. (C.)

7. How would you prepare pure dry chlorine from hydrochloric acid? (Sketch the necessary apparatus.) How does chlorine react with (*a*) potassium iodide solution, (*b*) heated metallic iron, (*c*) a cold dilute solution of sodium hydroxide? (C.)

8. How is the electrolysis of brine carried out on a large scale? What products are formed by this method? Describe *briefly* how you could prepare (*a*) solid sodium hydroxide, (*b*) hydrochloric acid, (*c*) a solution of sodium hypochlorite from these products. (C.)

9. Describe an electrolytic method for the preparation of chlorine. Explain what happens when:

(*a*) Chlorine is passed over red-hot iron.

(*b*) Chlorine reacts with ammonia.

(*c*) Chlorine and ethylene are mixed together. (C.)

10. Describe, giving chemical equations, the reactions that occur when chlorine is passed into aqueous solutions of the following: (*a*) ferrous chloride; (*b*) hydrogen sulphide; (*c*) ammonia; (*d*) sodium sulphite. Explain how you would isolate one product in *one* of these reactions. (O. and C.)

11. Describe one method used for the preparation of chlorine on a large scale. How is chlorine used for the preparation of (*a*) bleaching powder, (*b*) potassium chlorate? (D.)

12. It was formerly supposed that chlorine was an oxide of hydrochloric acid gas. Give evidence to prove that this is not so.

13. (*a*) Write down the equation for the production of chlorine by the action of hydrochloric acid on manganese dioxide. (*b*) What volume of chlorine measured at N.T.P. would be produced on treating 10 gm. of pure manganese dioxide with excess of hydrochloric acid?

(Mn=55, Cl=35·5, O=16. One gram-molecule of chlorine at N.T.P. occupies a volume of 22·4 litres.)   (L. Gen. Sc.)

14. What reaction occurs when chlorine water is exposed for a length of time to direct sunlight? Describe the experiment and the tests you would carry out to confirm your statement.

Calculate the volume of chlorine, measured at 12° C. and 74 cm. pressure, which will react with the whole of the hydrogen generated by the solution in sulphuric acid of 5 gm. of magnesium; also calculate the weight of the product.   (L.)

15. Write equations for the action of chlorine on the following substances: (*a*) dry slaked lime, (*b*) cold sodium hydroxide solution, (*c*) boiling potassium hydroxide solution.

In the case of (*c*), how would you isolate the two crystalline substances formed in a reasonable state of purity?   (O.)

16. How may pure oxygen and pure chlorine be made from potassium chlorate?

Compare the properties of these two gases.   (W.)

17. A woman, who was cleaning out a bath, failed to get the stain off with *Parozone*. She then mixed this with *Harpic* (sodium hydrogen sulphate) in spite of a notice in large red letters stating that the latter must not be used with any other chemical cleaner. A gas was liberated, and as she was bending over the bath, she breathed in the gas and died. When the case went to court, the judge ruled that the makers of the substances were not to blame.

Explain clearly, with the aid of a chemical equation, what must have happened.

18. One gallon (10 lb.) of sodium hypochlorite solution (which will set free 14·2% of its weight as chlorine) was put into a pure clean swimming pool at 9.0 a.m. on a bright sunny day when no bathing was taking place. By 10.30 a.m. there was no free chlorine remaining. How much oxygen has been set free by the action of the sunlight?

CHAPTER XXV

BROMINE, IODINE, FLUORINE
THE HALOGEN FAMILY

Bromine and iodine are elements which are very closely related to chlorine, but are less common and less reactive. Fluorine, the most reactive element known, is too difficult to handle in an elementary laboratory, and only in the last seven or eight years has it been used to any extent industrially (in the United States).

These four elements (the Halogens) all occur in the same group of the Periodic Table (fig. 14, p. 49), and their properties are compared in the table on p. 426.

BROMINE

Sodium bromide occurs in the sea and in salt lakes and salt deposits, together with sodium chloride, but in far smaller quantities. As large amounts of bromine are now required for use in petrol (see p. 421), the only adequate source is sea-water (PLATES 25A and B). Two hundred million tons of sea-water are treated every year with chlorine, which sets free the bromine:

$$2NaBr + Cl_2 = 2NaCl + Br_2 \text{ (expt. 157 (}a\text{), p. 411)}.$$

Laboratory Preparation of Bromine

Expt. 159. The method is similar to that for chlorine (p. 404, method 2). A mixture of potassium bromide and manganese dioxide is heated with strong sulphuric acid in a glass retort (fig. 142). The bromine vapour is condensed in a flask cooled by water. Sometimes a little water is placed inside the flask and the bromine collects as a heavy dark red liquid below the layer of the paler red " bromine water."

$$2KBr + 2H_2SO_4 = 2KHSO_4 + 2HBr \nearrow$$
$$\left\{ \begin{array}{l} MnO + H_2SO_4 = H_2O + MnSO_4 \\ O + 2HBr = H_2O + Br_2 \nearrow \end{array} \right.$$

Properties of Bromine (Br_2, M.W.$=160$)

Bromine is a heavy red volatile liquid, density 3·2 gm. per c.c., boiling at about 60° C. It has a considerable vapour pressure, even at room temperature, and that part of the bromine bottle which does not contain liquid is filled with red vapour. The liquid causes painful sores if allowed to touch the skin. The

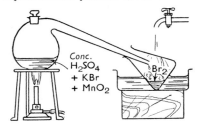

vapour is poisonous and has an extremely irritating smell (Greek *bromos*=a stench).

FIG. 142. Laboratory preparation of bromine.

Bromine Water

Bromine, like chlorine, is slightly soluble in water (3% by weight). The solution, "bromine water," is rather more stable, although small amounts of hydrobromic and hypobromous acids are present. Thus the solution turns blue litmus red and, after a time, bleaches it:

$$H_2O + Br_2 \rightleftharpoons HBr + HBrO$$
$$HBrO + colour = HBr + oxidized\ colour.$$

Expt. 160. (*a*) Hydrogen sulphide, when passed into bromine water containing an excess of liquid bromine, forms a dilute solution of hydrogen bromide (colourless), and precipitates sulphur.

$$H_2S + Br_2 = 2HBr + S \downarrow$$

If the yellow precipitate is filtered off and the excess hydrogen sulphide boiled away, the solution will respond to tests for acids (p. 63) and for bromides (p. 421). It may be concentrated by distillation.

(*b*) Sulphur dioxide also reduces bromine (see PLATE 25B opposite).

(*c*) Potassium iodide is oxidized to iodine:

$$Br_2 + 2KI = I_2 + 2KBr \quad (compare\ expt.\ 157,\ p.\ 411)$$

Other Reactions of Bromine

Bromine will combine directly with phosphorus (see expt. 161 below), with very many metals, and with alkalis. The products are similar to those from chlorine.

[*Photo by courtesy of the Dow Chemical Corporation, U.S.A.*

PLATE 25A.   SEA-WATER FOR MAKING BROMINE (p. 417)

1000 tons of sea-water per minute are sucked in by these four giant pumps.

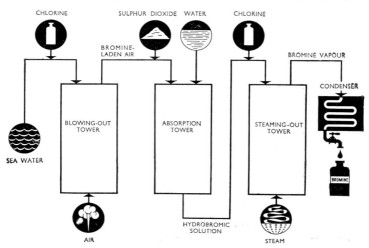

[*By courtesy of the Dow Chemical Corporation, U.S.A.*

PLATE 25B.   BROMINE FROM SEA-WATER

Hydrogen Bromide

Bromine combines directly with hydrogen to form hydrogen bromide, but the reaction requires heat, and the mixture does not explode in sunlight, as is the case with chlorine:

$$H_2 + Br_2 = 2HBr$$

Hydrogen bromide is partly oxidized to bromine by concentrated sulphuric acid, and cannot therefore be prepared from the sodium salt in this way (see expt. 162, p. 421).

It is best prepared by the action of water on phosphorus bromide. (Phosphorus chlorides, being the chlorides of a non-metal, see p. 45, behave similarly.)

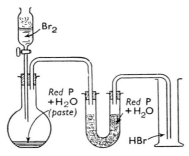

FIG. 143.   Preparation of hydrogen bromide.

Expt. 161. Bromine is added from a tap-funnel to a flask containing red phosphorus mixed with a little water (fig. 143). Phosphorus bromide is formed, and at once decomposed by the water. Any unchanged bromine in the outgoing vapours is similarly converted into hydrogen bromide in the U-tube of damp red phosphorus.

$$2P + 3Br_2 = 2PBr_3$$

Phosphorus Tribromide / Water = Phosphorous acid (H_3PO_3) / Hydrogen Bromide

Properties of Hydrogen Bromide (HBr, M.W.$=81$)

Hydrogen bromide, like hydrogen chloride, is a heavy colourless gas, which fumes in moist air and with ammonia gas. It is very soluble in water, forming a constant-boiling-point mixture (47% HBr, b.p. 125° C.), and its solution is a strong monobasic acid whose salts are the bromides.

Tests for Bromides

Bromides, like chlorides, are mostly soluble crystalline salts; those of silver, mercurous mercury, and lead are insoluble.

1. **Expt. 162.** Solid bromides, when heated with concentrated sulphuric acid, give white fumes of hydrogen bromide, mixed with the heavier red fumes of bromine (see p. 371). If manganese dioxide is also added, then bromine only is obtained (expt. 159).

2. **Expt. 163.** Bromides in solution, when treated with dilute nitric acid and silver nitrate solution, give a precipitate of silver bromide, which is very pale yellow, and only dissolves in much concentrated ammonium hydroxide.

$$NaBr + AgNO_3 = NaNO_3 + AgBr \downarrow \quad (Br^- + Ag^+ = AgBr \downarrow)$$

3. When chlorine is passed into a solution of a bromide, bromine is set free (expt. 157 (a), p. 411); if chloroform or carbon disulphide is now added, the bromine dissolves to form a brown solution which sinks to the bottom of the tube.

Uses of Bromine

The most important use of bromine is in combining with ethylene, C_2H_4 (p. 294), to form ethylene bromide, $C_2H_4Br_2$; this is used together with tetraethyl lead, $Pb(C_2H_5)_4$, in "ethyl" petrol. The tetraethyl lead reduces the chances of "engine knock," but deposits lead or lead oxide in the cylinders unless a bromine compound is present to give the more volatile lead bromide ($PbBr_2$, b.p. 916° C.).

Silver bromide is decomposed by light and so is important for making photographic films and papers. Potassium bromide is a sedative for nerves, and so is used in medicine. Many dyestuffs (e.g. that in red ink) are compounds of bromine.

IODINE

The minute amount of sodium iodide in sea-water is extracted by certain sea-weeds. Sea-weed ash ("kelp"), containing about 0·1% of NaI, was formerly the most important source of iodine.

Most of the commercial iodine is now made from the deposits of Chile saltpetre (p. 333), which contain about 0·1% of sodium iodate, $NaIO_3$. This, on treatment with sulphur dioxide in solution, is reduced to iodine, which is precipitated:

$$NaIO_3 + 3H_2SO_3 = NaI + 3H_2SO_4$$

$$NaIO_3 + 5NaI + 3H_2SO_4 = 3I_2 \downarrow + 3H_2O + 3Na_2SO_4$$

This second equation is the reverse of the reaction between sodium hydroxide and iodine:

$$3I_2 + 6NaOH = NaIO_3 + 5NaI + 3H_2O$$

(compare chlorine, expt. 158 (b), p. 411).

Laboratory Preparation

1. **Expt. 164.** When a mixture of potassium iodide and manganese dioxide is warmed with concentrated sulphuric acid, iodine is evolved as a purple vapour. The reaction may be carried out in a glass retort, as in the preparation of bromine (expt. 159), but the iodine is liable to condense too easily in the stem of the retort and so block it up.

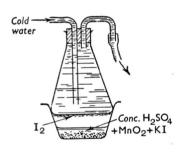

Fig. 144. Laboratory preparation of iodine.

A convenient method is to heat the mixture in a basin covered by an inverted funnel for collecting the iodine; or the latter may be condensed on the bottom of a conical flask through which cold water is circulating (fig. 144).

2. Alternatively, iodine may be prepared by the action of chlorine on potassium iodide solution (expt. 157B, p. 411) and filtered off.

Properties of Iodine (I_2, M.W.$=254$)

Iodine is a black, crystalline solid, with a lustre rather like that of a metal.

Expt. 165. A few crystals of iodine are gently heated in a large flask loosely plugged with cotton-wool. A violet vapour is formed which sublimes back to a solid on the cooler parts of the flask. This affords a good method of purifying iodine; if a little solid potassium iodide is added, this reacts with traces of any other halogens which are present.

Iodine and Water

Iodine is almost insoluble in water, but dissolves very easily in solutions of potassium iodide, giving a deep red-brown colour. This solution, or a suspension of iodine in water, will oxidize hydrogen sulphide or sulphur dioxide (compare bromine, expt. 160, p. 418). (Iodine also dissolves easily in chloroform or carbon disulphide to give deep violet solutions, and in alcohol to give the familiar brown "tincture.")

Test for Iodine

Expt. 166. Iodine in solution gives a very deep blue colour with starch solution (p. 301). The latter is best prepared by boiling a little starch with water in a boiling-tube, and pouring a little of the product into some boiling water contained in a beaker. The starch solution must be cold before being used for the test because the blue colour is destroyed by heat; it reappears on cooling.

Other Reactions of Iodine

Iodine combines directly with phosphorus (see below), with most metals (e.g. iron and mercury), and with alkalis. The reactions are less vigorous than those of bromine.

Hydrogen Iodide

Although hydrogen combines with iodine to some extent on heating, especially in the presence of a platinum catalyst, the reaction is easily reversible; the hydrogen iodide is itself dissociated into hydrogen and iodine on heating:

$$H_2 + I_2 \rightleftharpoons 2HI$$

Hydrogen iodide is best prepared by a method similar to that of hydrogen bromide (expt. 161, p. 420), except that as iodine is a solid, water must be added from the tap-funnel to a mixture of red phosphorus and iodine in the flask.

Properties of Hydrogen Iodide (HI, M.W. = 128)

Hydrogen iodide in solution, hydriodic acid, is similar to the other halogen acids, but is also a strong *reducing agent* (p. 382). Almost any oxidizing agent will convert it or an acidified solution of potassium iodide to iodine. As the amount of iodine formed can easily be found by its reaction with sodium thiosulphate ("hypo," see below), this provides an excellent method for estimating the strength of an oxidizing agent.

Estimation of Oxidizing Agents

Expt. 167. Obtain 6d. or 1s. bottles of as many domestic bleaching agents (see expt. 158 (*a*)) as possible. Compare their strengths as follows: dilute half the contents to $2\frac{1}{2}$ litres in a Winchester Quart bottle by adding distilled water. Mix well. Take a 10-c.c. portion by means of a pipette and put it in a 100-c.c. conical flask which already contains about 5 c.c. each of potassium iodide solution and dilute sulphuric acid (the strengths of the latter should be about "normal." see p. 498). Run in "N./10" sodium thiosulphate solution from a burette until the brown colour of the iodine fades to yellow and just disappears. The last trace of iodine can be shown by adding a few drops of starch solution.

$$2Na_2S_2O_3 + I_2 = \underbrace{2NaI + Na_2S_4O_6}_{\text{(colourless)}}$$

Sodium Thiosulphate   (brown)

Repeat with the other bottles, including 10% NaOCl solution as supplied to laboratories (cost about 1s. for 500 c.c.). Comparison of the results may prove to be very illuminating!

Tests for Iodides

Iodides are mostly colourless crystalline solids, easily soluble in water. Those of silver, mercury, lead (p. 71), copper, and bismuth are insoluble and brightly coloured; mercuric iodide, HgI_2, is used as a pigment ("pure scarlet").

1. **Expt. 168.** Solid iodides, when heated with concentrated sulphuric acid, give violet fumes of iodine (even without the addition of manganese dioxide).

2. **Expt. 169.** Iodides in solution, when treated with dilute nitric acid and silver nitrate solution give a precipitate of silver iodide which is pale yellow and does not dissolve even in concentrated ammonium hydroxide.

3. When chlorine (or bromine) is added to a solution of an iodide, iodine is set free (see expt. 157 (b), p. 411). This gives a violet solution in chloroform or carbon disulphide, or the characteristic blue colour with starch.

Uses of Iodine

Nearly three-quarters of the uses of iodine are in the field of medicine, the most familiar being "tincture of iodine" (a 10% solution in dilute alcohol) as an antiseptic. Combined iodine is necessary in human and animal food (see p. 307); foods grown in limestone or chalk districts inland may be deficient in it, so giving rise to goitre ("Derbyshire neck"). In some parts of Oxfordshire where the amount of iodine in the water is one-tenth as much as that in others, the proportion of children with enlarged thyroids is found to be 10 times as great.

FLUORINE

Although the chemistry of fluorine is beyond the scope of this book, it is worth noting that such an element does exist, and that with atomic weight 19 it forms the first member of the halogen family; its properties, with one or two important exceptions, are in accord with this position.

The element occurs as fluor-spar, CaF_2, in cubic crystals often tinted blue or yellow due to traces of impurities, and also as cryolite, Na_3AlF_6; its existence was suspected for a long time before it was isolated by Moissan in 1886.

Since the element is very active and decomposes cold water, it is not surprising that its isolation proved to be difficult.

It can, however, be obtained by the electrolysis of fused anhydrous hydrogen fluoride with the addition of some potassium fluoride to make the liquid a conductor.

Fluorine is a pale green-yellow gas, less easily liquefied than chlorine. Chemically it is more reactive than chlorine, and it combines directly and usually vigorously with all elements except nitrogen and the inert gases.

It combines with hydrogen explosively even in the dark at $-253°$ C.; it reacts at once with water:

$$2H_2O + 2F_2 = 2H_2F_2 + O_2 \nearrow$$

Hydrogen Fluoride

This is evolved as a fuming acid gas when strong sulphuric acid is heated with a fluoride such as calcium fluoride:

$$CaF_2 + H_2SO_4 = CaSO_4 + H_2F_2 \nearrow$$

The vapour density of hydrogen fluoride gives the formula H_2F_2, and its solution is a dibasic acid. The pure acid boils as high as 19° C.

It also differs from the other halogen acids in giving an insoluble calcium salt and a soluble silver salt.

Further, although it is a weaker acid (i.e. less ionized) it dissolves silica, the chief constituent of glass, and is therefore used for etching glass;

$$SiO_2 + 2H_2F_2 = SiF_4 + 2H_2O$$

for this purpose the glass is covered with a thin coating of etching varnish or wax. Markings (e.g. on thermometers) may then be made by a fine point through the wax and exposed to the fumes of hydrogen fluoride.

Many fluorine compounds, e.g. UF_6 (p. 104), were required for the atomic bomb project, and the price of fluorine is now much lower as production has increased.

The occurrence of calcium fluoride in teeth has been mentioned on pp. 276 and 307, and the use of "Freon" (CF_2Cl_2) in refrigerators on p. 322.

N.B.—Compounds of fluorine are poisonous; 100 mg. of NaF is fatal, but up to 3 mg. per day *may* improve teeth.

THE HALOGEN FAMILY

ELEMENT	FLUORINE	CHLORINE	BROMINE	IODINE
Molecular weight	38	71	160	254
Appearance	Pale green-yellow gas	Green-yellow gas	Red liquid. Red vapour	Black solid. Violet vapour
Boiling-point	−188° C.	−35° C.	63° C.	184° C.
Density (gm./c.c.)	1·1 (liquid)	1·5 (liquid)	3·1	4·9
Solubility in water	Decomposes it instantly	Slightly soluble. Decomposes it slowly in sunlight	Slightly soluble. Less decomposition	Almost insoluble
Bleaching action	Too reactive	Good	Slight	None
Combination with hydrogen	Explosive in dark at −253° C.	Explosive in sunlight	At red heat	Reversible. Catalyst needed
Compound with hydrogen HX	All are gases above 20° C., dissolving in water to give:			
	weak acid. Not oxidized	strong acid. Oxidized by strong oxidizing agents	strong acid. Oxidized by most oxidizing agents	very strong acid. Oxidized by all oxidizing agents
Combination with metals	Extremely vigorous	Very vigorous	Vigorous	Less vigorous
Displacement of other halogens from halides	Displaces all others	Bromine and iodine	Iodine only	None

ELEMENT	FLUORINE	CHLORINE	BROMINE	IODINE
Compounds with silver	Soluble in water	White ppt., soluble in ammonium hydroxide	Pale-yellow ppt., just soluble in conc. ammonium hydroxide	Yellow ppt., insoluble in ammonium hydroxide
% abundance in earth's crust	0·08	0·20	0·01	0·00003
World production (tons per year)	<100	2,000,000	20,000	1000
Approximate cost per ton	£4000	£20	£100	£1000

Suggestions for Practical Work

Expts. 159–160, 162–169.

QUESTIONS ON CHAPTER XXV

1. Mention two natural sources of bromine, and indicate briefly how the element is obtained commercially.

Describe a laboratory method for preparing bromine.

Compare three physical properties of chlorine and bromine, and outline two sets of experiments you would perform to compare the chemical properties of these two elements. (S.)

2. What experiments would you carry out to ascertain whether a given gas was nitrogen dioxide or bromine vapour?

3. Describe one method by which iodine is obtained on a commercial scale. What are its chief properties and uses?

4. Describe the preparation of an aqueous solution of (*a*) hydrobromic acid, (*b*) hydriodic acid, stating the chemical changes in the form of equations. (C.)

5. How would you distinguish between aqueous solutions of hydrochloric, hydriodic and hydrobromic acids? Give two tests in each case.

It was found experimentally that 2·0517 gm. of potassium bromide precipitated from solution 3·2375 gm. of silver bromide. What is the atomic weight of potassium, if it be assumed that the element is monovalent? ($Br=80$; $Ag=108$.) (L.)

6. A white solid is either potassium chloride, potassium bromide, or potassium iodide. What experiments would you make to identify it?

7. Illustrate the resemblances of iodine to chlorine by reference to (i) its occurrence, (ii) its physical properties, (iii) its action on hydrogen sulphide, (iv) its preparation from an iodide. Mention one case in which iodine shows itself to be less reactive than chlorine. (L.)

8. By what properties would you identify bromine and iodine? It was early recognized that bromine and iodine belonged to the same chemical group as chlorine. Summarize the main points of similarity between the three elements. (Civil Service Commission.)

9. Element no. 85, Astatine (At) has recently been prepared, and is the heaviest member of the halogen family. State what properties you would expect it and its compounds to have. (It is not yet available in weighable quantities.)

10. It has recently (1950) been decided that all salt supplied for eating and cooking must contain one part of potassium iodide per 100,000 parts of salt. In 1944 there were about 100,000 children in England between the ages of 5–20 suffering from goitre. The fatal dose of 7% *tincture of iodine* is considered to be 4 c.c. taken at one time.

Using these facts and those given on pp. 425, 307, 306, calculate the effect of the decision. Do you consider that this is " Unjustifiable Interference with a Natural Food "?

11. The rocket fuel for launching satellites is said to be liquid hydrogen + liquid fluorine, giving a temperature of 3900° C. With the aid of the data on pp. 10, 30, 93, 425–6, comment on the advantages of the use of fluorine instead of oxygen, and the difficulties likely to be involved.

CHAPTER XXVI

PHOSPHORUS AND SILICON

Both phosphorus and silicon are non-metallic elements. Phosphorus compounds are essential constituents of living matter (pp. 301, 306); both phosphorus itself and some of its compounds are inflammable (p. 18) and so are used for matches. Silicon is the second most abundant element (p. 50); its compounds, the silicates, form the majority of rocks and are used for making glass, cement, bricks, pottery, etc.

PHOSPHORUS

Phosphorus is found chiefly as *rock phosphate*, $Ca_3(PO_4)_2$. CaF_2 (see fig. 94, p. 271), in the United States and in North Africa, and is mostly treated with sulphuric acid (p. 366) to form superphosphate fertilizers (p. 301).

The calcium fluoride associated with it is of course converted into hydrogen fluoride (p. 425); 4000 tons of this poisonous gas are thus set free into the air of the British Isles every year.

Manufacture of Phosphorus

Rock phosphate is heated in an electric furnace (cf. calcium carbide, p. 294) with sand and coke. The acidic oxide, sand (SiO_2), displaces phosphorus pentoxide from the phosphate because of its much higher boiling-point. The phosphorus pentoxide is reduced by the coke to phosphorus, which boils off and is condensed as white phosphorus.

$$\underbrace{3CaO.P_2O_5}_{Ca_3(PO_4)_2} + 3SiO_2 = \underbrace{3CaO.3SiO_2}_{3CaSiO_3} + P_2O_5\nearrow$$

$$\text{Sand} \qquad \qquad \text{Phosphorus Pentoxide}$$

$$2P_2O_5 + 10C = P_4\nearrow + 10CO\nearrow$$

Allotropes of Phosphorus

The properties of the two main forms are tabulated for convenience:

	White ("Yellow")	Red
Preparation	Condensation of vapour (of either form)	Heating yellow form to 240° C. in nitrogen
Appearance	Yellow-white waxy solid	Red amorphous powder
Action of hot caustic soda solution	Forms phosphine (PH_3)	No action
Action of air	Glows in dark (slow oxidation)	
Ignition temperature	Catches fire below melting point (about 35° C.)	Does not catch fire till about 240° C.
Melting-point	44° C.	⎫
Boiling-point	290° C.	⎬ sublimes at about 400° C.
Density	1·8 gm. per c.c.	2·2 gm. per c.c. ⎭
Solubility in carbon disulphide	Very soluble	Insoluble
Action on man	Very poisonous (0·1 gm. fatal)	Not poisonous

The proof that the allotropes consist of the same element is the same as for carbon or sulphur (pp. 245, 348).

White phosphorus catches fire so easily that it must only be handled with tongs (never fingers), and it is kept below the surface of water.

Matches

White phosphorus was used at first, but it is so poisonous (used in rat poison) that this is now illegal. The heads of ordinary "strike anywhere" matches contain phosphorus sulphide mixed with potassium chlorate, which oxidizes it when warmed by friction. The heads of "safety" matches contain sulphur mixed with potassium chlorate; they usually need to be struck on a prepared surface which contains red phosphorus, and so there is less danger of fire.

Compounds of Phosphorus (valencies 3 and 5)

Phosphine, PH_3, is a colourless, poisonous gas with a fishy smell, prepared by heating white phosphorus with sodium hydroxide solution in an atmosphere of coal-gas. Unlike ammonia, NH_3, it is inflammable, almost insoluble in water, and not basic.

Phosphorus trichloride, PCl_3, is prepared by passing dry chlorine over white phosphorus which has been melted in a retort in an atmosphere of nitrogen or carbon dioxide. It distils over as a colourless liquid. If it is dripped from a tap-funnel into a wide-mouthed bottle through which a stream of dry chlorine is passing, it is converted to *phosphorus pentachloride*, PCl_5, a white solid. Both these compounds fume in moist air, and are hydrolysed violently by water to the corresponding acids.

$$2P + 3Cl_2 = 2PCl_3 \text{ (see p. 408)} \qquad PCl_3 + Cl_2 = PCl_5$$

$$PCl_3 + 3H_2O = H_3PO_3 + 3HCl \nearrow \quad \text{(compare } PBr_3, \text{ p. 420)}$$
Phosphor*ous* acid

$$PCl_5 + 4H_2O = H_3PO_4 + 5HCl \nearrow$$
Phosphor*ic* acid

Phosphorus trioxide, P_2O_3, is a white solid formed when phosphorus is burnt in a limited supply of air:

$$4P + 3O_2 = 2P_2O_3$$

Phosphorus pentoxide, P_2O_5, is the most important oxide, formed by burning phosphorus in excess of air. It is a white, very deliquescent solid which is a powerful drying agent (p. 38):

$$4P + 5O_2 = 2P_2O_5$$

Ortho-phosphoric acid is the most important of the various (13 or more!) oxyacids of phosphorus, and is formed by the action of phosphorus pentoxide on warm water (much heat given out):

$$P_2O_5 + 3H_2O = 2H_3PO_4$$

(*Cold* water gives *meta*-phosphoric acid, HPO_3.) In the laboratory it may be made by oxidizing red phosphorus with half-strength nitric acid (p. 431); after the violent reaction is over, any excess nitric acid may be distilled off, leaving the much less volatile phosphoric acid.

It is a syrupy liquid and is a tribasic acid. As it is a rather weak acid, the "ordinary" sodium phosphate used as a bench reagent is Na_2HPO_4, which is almost neutral to litmus (compare $NaHCO_3$); on heating, this salt loses water and forms the *pyro*-phosphate $Na_4P_2O_7$.

Phosphates

As these are the salts of a weak acid, they are in general soluble in stronger acids because they form either acid salts or free phosphoric acid. There are two important consequences:

1. The "superphosphate" fertilizer industry (pp. 429 and 366).

2. The treatment of bones with hydrochloric acid (p. 413) to make glue. The mineral matter of bones is calcium phosphate, which dissolves, giving free phosphoric acid:

$$Ca_3(PO_4)_2 + 6HCl = 3CaCl_2 + 2H_3PO_4$$

the protein, gelatin, remains and forms glue.

Test for phosphates. Add concentrated nitric acid to the solution, heat, and pour into a hot solution of ammonium molybdate, $(NH_4)_2MoO_4$. Phosphates give a yellow precipitate of complex formula, possibly not immediately.

Phosphates—including basic slag (p. 468)—are very important fertilizers, and there is an undoubted need for a much greater use of them in this country, especially on grassland where they assist the action of nitrogen-fixing bacteria. Also, about 25% of the phosphate applied is actually taken up by the plant, and research is badly needed to increase this figure.

SILICON

The free element silicon is unimportant, but its oxide "silica," SiO_2, gives rise to an immense branch of chemistry of great fascination. Its complexity is due to the fact that it can form *large molecules*, which are as important in the mineral kingdom as those of carbon are in the animal and vegetable kingdoms (Chapter XVIII). In addition, it is an acidic oxide which can exist both in the free state (e.g. flint, sand, and quartz) and combined with a large variety of basic oxides as silicates (e.g. the felspar in granite, see p. 434).

Mineral Silicates

(*a*) *Long-chain* compounds containing the ions shown in fig. 145, e.g. the fibrous substance ASBESTOS used for fireproofing, where the corresponding positive ions are magnesium Mg^{++}. (Compare the long chains of carbon atoms in paraffin hydrocarbons, p. 290.)

(b) *Ring* compounds containing the ions, shown in fig. 146, of structure similar to benzene (p. 295). EMERALD, containing 3 beryllium ions Be^{++} and 2 aluminium ions Al^{+++} to neutralize the 12 negative charges shown, is of this type; its green colour was thought to be due to traces of chromium (pp. 352, 436) occurring as an impurity!

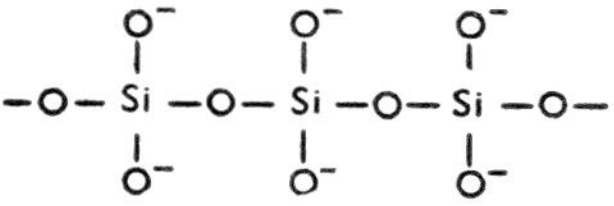

FIG. 145. Long-chain silicates. e.g. asbestos.

(c) *Layer* compounds (compare graphite, p. 243), of which the most notable example is MICA (PLATE 26) used in large quantities as thin sheets for electrical insulation and for the transparent "windows" of closed coal stoves. Crystals of it have been found with a diameter of 12 feet, and one weighed nearly 2 tons. Mica may contain any of the following elements: Li, Na, K, Ca, Mg, Mn, Fe, and Al, as well as Si and O.

(d) Three-dimensional *networks* (compare diamond, p. 243) such as FLINT, the very hard form of silicon dioxide used by Stone Age man for his tools. In certain complex aluminium silicates metallic ions (e.g. Na^+) are free to be washed out and replaced by other metallic ions without disturbing the structure; this is the basis of "Permutit" water-softening (p. 277).

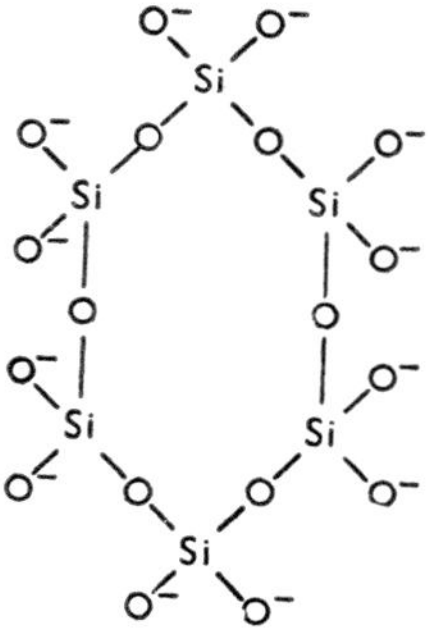

The most recent new type of plastics ("*Silicones*") are organic compounds based on a silicate skeleton, e.g.

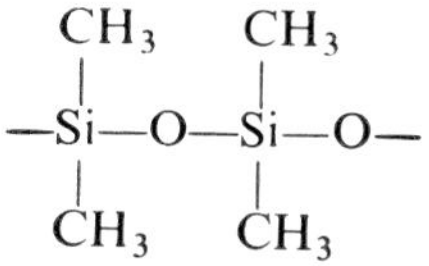

FIG. 146. Ring silicates, e.g. emerald.

$$-\underset{\underset{CH_3}{|}}{\overset{\overset{CH_3}{|}}{Si}}-O-\underset{\underset{CH_3}{|}}{\overset{\overset{CH_3}{|}}{Si}}-O-$$

which have entirely novel properties, some being soft like putty and yet allowing ball-bearings to bounce from them as if they were steel! Others are viscous water-repellent liquids which

PLATE 26.   NATURAL MICA CRYSTAL

One-half actual size, showing the hexagonal shape resulting from the arrangement of its atoms (compare fig. 146, p. 433).

can be used as lubricants at temperatures between $-40°$ C. and $+400°$ C.

Clay

This is a hydrated aluminium silicate formed by the action of water and carbon dioxide ("weathering") on more complex silicates such as granite:

$$K_2O.Al_2O_3.6SiO_2+2H_2O+CO_2$$
felspar (in granite)

$$=Al_2O_3.2SiO_2.2H_2O+4SiO_2+K_2CO_3$$
kaolinite (china-clay)   sand   (washed away)

Clay which has been hardened by compression in the earth is SLATE; the average house roof needs 4,000 slates.

When clay is mixed with water and sand or fine chalk, etc., it becomes plastic, and can be moulded into shapes such as cups, saucers, etc., and when heated makes POTTERY. The finest qualities of pottery, known as PORCELAIN, are made principally from the high-grade *china-clay* for which Cornwall and Devon are famous all over the world. BRICKS are similarly made by moulding clay, sand, and ashes into shape and heating to red heat; their normal red colour is due to the presence of 4% or more of ferric oxide, Fe_2O_3. Bricks cannot be remoulded because *combined* water has been lost. All such *earthenware* is porous (p. 102), and so most varieties are "glazed"; the surface is coated with materials such as sodium carbonate, lead oxide, etc., which combine to form a thin glassy layer (see below) of the corresponding silicate.

China-clay is also important in the manufacture of *paper*; the esparto-grass and wood-pulp (cellulose), after bleaching with chlorine, are "loaded" with a filler such as china-clay, which provides 25% of the weight of the paper in this book (and of most other paper, too). The use of clay in *cement*-making has already been mentioned (p. 270).

Sand

Sand consists almost wholly of *quartz* grains, i.e. silica formed by the weathering of silicate rocks (p. 434), and is coloured by traces of impurities. Over 30 million tons of sand and gravel are used every year in this country for making concrete, and sand is also very important in the manufacture of GLASS. This is made by melting together sand with sodium carbonate (or sodium sulphate), calcium carbonate, and broken glass in a furnace heated by producer gas to about 1500° C., to form a mixture of sodium and calcium silicates.

$$Na_2CO_3 = Na_2O + CO_2 \nearrow$$
$$Na_2O + SiO_2 = Na_2SiO_3$$

The product is a "supercooled liquid," not a crystalline solid, which can be softened at red heat and "rolled" to make *window glass* or "blown" to make bottles.

Sodium silicate itself is *water-glass*, which will dissolve in water. It is used for preserving eggs because it forms an impervious layer over the shell; also for "Chemical Gardens."

English crystal glass uses potassium oxide and lead oxide as the basic oxides, combined with the acidic silicon oxide. It is heavy and has a high refractive index ("flint glass"), thus making it brilliant (p. 242) and suitable for lenses and prisms.

"Pyrex" glass, which has a low coefficient of expansion and therefore does not crack easily when used for cooking or for chemistry, contains the oxide of boron (another non-metal) as well as 80% of silica and small amounts of sodium and aluminium oxides.

It is difficult to carry out any of the reactions of silica in the laboratory because of the very high temperatures and long periods of time required to make glass, pottery, or cement (and especially rocks!). The making of *coloured glass* may, however, be imitated by using borates instead of silicates.

Expt. 170. Borax beads.

Borax, which is a naturally occurring form of sodium borate, may be considered as a compound of sodium oxide and boron trioxide, $Na_2O.2B_2O_3.10H_2O$. A platinum wire is bent into a loop, heated, and dipped into powdered borax; on heating, the mass swells up and loses water, forming a white solid; on further heating, this melts to a colourless liquid, and on cooling forms a colourless bead. If the bead is dipped into a little of a compound of cobalt, so that a few particles stick to it, and then melted once more, cobalt borate is formed as a deep-blue bead, $CoO.B_2O_3$, i.e. CoB_2O_4.

Compounds of other metals with variable valency (fig. 14. p. 49) such as manganese, iron, nickel, and copper also give coloured beads; the most notable is chromium, which gives an emerald-green colour (p. 433).

Silica

Silicon dioxide can make a glass by itself, though it needs a very high temperature to melt it; it is useful because

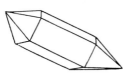

of its very low coefficient of expansion. Naturally occurring quartz crystals (fig. 147) are used in scientific apparatus, especially for keeping broadcasting stations at a constant frequency.

FIG. 147. Quartz crystal.

Chemically, silicon dioxide, as the oxide of a non-metal, is acidic, combining with basic oxides (see above) to form silicates. Also, being non-volatile (b.p. 2230° C.), it will drive off the volatile anhydrides even of stronger acids, e.g. CO_2 (p. 270), SO_3 (p. 355), and P_2O_5 (p. 429).

Silicosis

The almost universal occurrence of silica and silicates means that hard particles of these substances enter the lungs of most men engaged in mining. This results in *silicosis* ("dusty death"), which causes paralysis. Far more research is needed into ways of preventing this widespread crippling disease, and far more thoroughness in applying safeguards which are already known.

Soil

More complex even than the rocks, but also far more important, is the soil without which life could not exist. It consists of finely powdered rocks formed by the disintegrating action of the weather, mixed with *humus*. Humus is the decaying remains of animals and plants, together with a large population of living organisms—roots of living plants, insects and earthworms, and thousands of millions of bacteria in every gram. The proportion of humus varies from about 10% in the rich "black earth" of South Russia to negligible amounts in the sands of the desert. The mineral matter of English soil usually contains much clay, and is coloured brown by the humus and by ferric oxide. Other soils contain much sand or chalk.

The greatest danger to soil is *erosion*, the action of wind and water, which blow or wash the soil away, leaving shifting sands or bare rock where nothing can grow. In every year of recorded history land has been lost to cultivation, and the problem faces practically every country in the world outside North-West Europe. South Africa alone loses the equivalent of 300,000 acres (1% of the productive acreage of Great Britain) every year. Beside it, and the resulting threat to food supplies, political quarrels fade into complete insignificance.

Silicon

Silicon, the element, is now largely used in transistors which are replacing valves in electronic calculators, deaf hearing-aids, etc. It is made by heating silica with magnesium:

$$2Mg + SiO_2 = Si + 2MgO \text{ (a violent reaction)}$$

Some magnesium silicide Mg_2Si is also formed, but is removed by the action of hydrochloric acid.

Silicic acid

This (H_2SiO_3 for simplicity) is prepared by adding a dilute acid to a solution of "water-glass":

$$Na_2SiO_3 + 2HCl = H_2SiO_3 \downarrow + 2NaCl$$

It is an insoluble jelly, often called "silica gel," which is becoming increasingly used as a drying agent; it has the great advantage that after absorbing water, it can itself be dried simply by heating and then used again.

Suggestions for Practical Work

Preparation of glue, and testing the phosphoric acid for a phosphate (see p. 432). Also expt. 170.

QUESTIONS ON CHAPTER XXVI

1. Suggest reasons for the fact that, whereas nitrogen is very largely found in the free state in nature, phosphorus is always found combined with other elements.

Apart from colour, name *three* ways in which red and white phosphorus differ from each other. Describe how the red may be converted to the white variety.

Give an equation representing the reaction between moderately concentrated nitric acid and red phosphorus, and say how the solid product may be isolated. (D.)

2. What is the chief source of the element phosphorus? Briefly outline *one* method of preparing the element from a natural source.

The element is found to exist in several forms. Give in tabular form the chief properties of *two* of these forms. (W.)

3. Phosphorus is said to exist in allotropic modifications. What do you understand by this statement?

Starting with elementary phosphorus, describe *one* method in each case by which you could prepare (*a*) an oxide, (*b*) a chloride of phosphorus. What reactions occur when the oxide and the chloride you mention are brought into contact with water? (L.)

4. Describe the modern method for the extraction of phosphorus. Give an account of the chief properties and uses of this substance.

Under what conditions and with what results does phosphorus react with (i) caustic soda, (ii) chlorine, and (iii) nitric acid? (Navy.)

5. Starting with white phosphorus, how would you proceed to prepare: (a) red phosphorus, (b) phosphine, (c) phosphoric acid? (D.)

6. Given some phosphorus pentachloride, describe how you would obtain from it: (a) pure dry hydrogen chloride, (b) ortho-phosphoric acid free from hydrochloric acid. (O.)

7. Orthophosphoric acid has the formula H_3PO_4 and is capable of forming mono-, di-, and tri-sodium phosphates, i.e. NaH_2PO_4, Na_2HPO_4, and Na_3PO_4. The first in aqueous solution is acid to litmus, the second neutral, and the third alkaline. Given a supply of a solution of the acid, approximately decinormal, and of caustic soda solution of about the same strength, describe how you would obtain solutions of the three sodium phosphates. Explain the reasons for the various steps in your method. Ordinary laboratory apparatus such as measuring cylinders, pipettes, burettes, etc., are supposed to be available.

Can you suggest methods of making (a) microcosmic salt, $NaH(NH_4)PO_4.4H_2O$; (b) magnesium ammonium phosphate, $Mg(NH_4)PO_4.6H_2O$; (c) sodium pyro-phosphate, $Na_4P_2O_7$? (Navy.)

8. Name three varieties of silica which are found in nature. State some purpose for which silica is often employed and indicate the particular properties on which these uses depend.

State fully the reasons for regarding silica as an acid-forming oxide. (L.)

9. How would you proceed in order to find out the percentage of each substance in a mixture of sand and sodium carbonate? What would be the effect of heating such a mixture to bright redness?

What would be the properties of the substance produced and how would they be altered if some lime were added to the mixture before heating? (L.)

10. Contrast the physical and chemical properties of carbon dioxide and silica.

11. The wood for matches is said to have been treated with a solution of ammonium phosphate, so that it will not go on glowing after being blown out.

Suggest how you would try to test this statement experimentally, making sure by suitable **control experiments** that **all** wood and **all** solutions do not respond to the tests you choose (see pp. 432, 16, 31, 480–1, 318).

PART 4

THE METALS, ANALYSIS
AND REVISION

CHAPTER XXVII

THE METALS

The importance of the metals lies chiefly in their physical properties, especially their mechanical strength Chemical reactivity is usually a nuisance in a metal when it is used as such, the rusting of iron (p. 24) being the most obvious example. The extent to which a metal is used depends on these factors and also on (*a*) its abundance in the earth's crust (p. 50), and (*b*) the ease with which it can be extracted from its ores (p. 224).   The use of coke resulted in British iron production increasing 40-fold from 1790-1850; and more metal has been produced since 1900 than in all the ages before that date.

The Industrial Use of Metals

The table overleaf summarizes the main features of the industrial use of metals.   The arrangement of the first eleven is in order of the tonnage produced.   Notable features are shown in heavy type, and it must be remembered that many of the figures given (especially prices) are only *very* approximate.   (In February 1951, tin cost £1,435 per ton.)

Before the metals are considered separately, two sections of this book must be revised carefully.

(*a*) The differences between metals and non-metals (p. 45). Metals are usually strong, workable, bright-looking solids, good conductors of electricity and heat, often having high melting-points and densities.

(*b*) The relation between the chemical properties of a metal, especially the method of its extraction, with its place in the electrochemical series (pp. 223–24).   Those which are high up in the series (K, Na, Ca, Mg, Al) are extracted by electrolysis; the so-called "base" metals (Zn, Fe, Sn, Pb, Cu) by reduction of the oxide with carbon; and the more or less

THE INDUSTRIAL USE OF METALS

METAL (in order of importance)	Fe	Mn	Cu	Al	Zn	Pb	Cr	Na	Mg
World production, millions of tons/year	100	3	3	0·3 (1934) 2·0 (1943) 3·0 (1956)	2	2	0·3	0·3	0·005 (1934) 0·3 (1944)
Price in £ per ton	£3 (1934) £6 (1948)	£170 (93% Mn*) £30 as Fe/Mn	£30 (1934) £330 (1955)	£100 (1934) £65 (1946)	£23 (1934) £90 (1955)	£10 (1934) £103 (1955)	£570 (98% Cr) £160 as Fe/Cr	£70 (1945)	£125 (1934) £110 (1945)
% abundance in earth's crust	4	0·1	0·001	7	0·001	0·001	0·06	2·5	2
Chief ores	Fe_2O_3 Fe_3O_4	MnO_2	$CuFeS_2$	$Al_2O_3.2H_2O$	ZnS	PbS	$FeCr_2O_4$	$NaCl$	$MgCO_3$ $MgCl_2$
Average % of metal in ore	50	50	4	25	10	10	25	40	25
Main producers with % of world total	U.S.A., 40% U.S.S.R., 15%	U.S.S.R., 50% India, 15%	U.S.A., 50% Chile, 15% Rhodesia, 10%	U.S.A., 50% Canada, 25%	U.S.A., 50% Australia, 12%	U.S.A., 20% Australia, 15%	U.S.S.R., 20% Turkey, 15%	U.S.A., 50%	U.S.A., 50% (Germany)
U.K. production % of world total	8%	—	—	2%	3%	1%	—	10%	6%
Density, gm./c.c.	7·8	7·2	8·9	2·7	7·1	11·3	7·1	0·97	1·7
Melting-point, ° C.	1500°	1260°	1080°	660°	420°	327°	1610°	97°	650°
Boiling-point, ° C.	3000°	1900°	2300°	1800°	900°	1600°	2200°	880°	1100°
Chief uses	Steel for construction, machinery, tools, etc.	95% in steel *Rarely prepared as metal	60% as electrical conductor; 40% in alloys	Aircraft; electrical conductor; cooking; construction	50% galvanizing; 25% brass; 15% paint (ZnS)	20% batteries; 20% cable covering; 20% paints	75% in steel; Cr-plating	Na/Pb alloy for making lead tetraethyl in petrol; chemical reagent	Light alloys for aircraft; incendiaries or flashlights

METAL (in order of importance)	Ni	Sn	Ag	U	Hg	Au	Pt	Ca	K
World production, millions of tons/year	0·15	0·15	0·01	0·03	0·004	0·001	0·00001	0·001	*
Price in £ per ton	£320 (1949)	£230 (1934) £725 (1949)	£9,000 (1949)	£14,000	£400 (1934) £2,000 (1947)	£400,000 (1949)	£250,000 (1938) £800,000 (1948)	£600	£600*
% abundance in earth's crust	0·01	0·000,01	0·000,02	0·001	0·000,05	0·000,000,5	0·000,000,5	3	2·5
Chief ores	$NiCuFeS_3$	SnO_2	$Ag_2S.PbS$	U_3O_8	HgS	Au	Pt	$CaCO_3$	$KCl.MgCl_2.$ $6H_2O$
Average % of metal in ore	2	2	0·1	0·2	6	<0·001	0·0002	40	8
Main producers with % of world total	Canada, 85% U.S.S.R., 8%	S.E.Asia, 60% Bolivia, 18%	Mexico, 35% U.S.A., 25%	Congo Czecho-slovakia	Italy, 40% Spain, 30%	S. Africa, 40% U.S.S.R., 20%	U.S.S.R., 40% Canada, 40%	(Germany) France U.S.A.	*Not prepared in commercial quantities
U.K. production % of world total	—	1%	—	—	—	—	—	—	—
Density, gm./c.c.	8·9	7·3	10·5	18·7	13·6	19·3	21·4	1·55	0·85
Melting-point, ° C.	1450°	232°	960°	1850°	-39°	1060°	1770°	810°	62°
Boiling-point, ° C.	2900°	2300°	1950°	?	360°	2600°	4300°	1240°	760°
Chief uses	60% in steel	40% tinplate; 20% solder	67% coinage	Nuclear energy	33% scientific instruments and extraction of gold	Basis for trade	60% jewellery; 15% chemistry (catalyst)	Minor constituent of alloys	* Laboratory reagent only

N.B. The prices of metals fluctuate wildly. Current prices are given in the daily newspapers for Cu, Zn, Pb, Sn, Ag, and in the *Mining Journal* (weekly) for most of the others.

"noble" metals (Hg, Ag, Au, Pt) by roasting the ore alone to decompose it, or extracting the native metal by physical processes.

Some of the more important domestic uses of the metals are shown in fig. 148, below.

FIG. 148.   Metals in the kitchen.

POTASSIUM

Although potassium is an abundant element (p. 50) it occurs mostly in the form of highly complicated silicates, e.g. felspar (p. 434). The most useful compound in salt deposits is carnallite, $KCl.MgCl_2.6H_2O$, at Stassfurt in Germany, and the chloride is obtained from salt lakes, e.g. the Dead Sea. About 90% of the world's use of potassium compounds is for fertilizers.

Potassium hydroxide and *potassium metal* are made by electrolytic methods similar to those for sodium hydroxide and sodium metal (see below), and have similar properties, but are far less important.

Important compounds of potassium are the chloride (p. 401), chlorate (p. 412), carbonate (p. 281), and nitrate (p. 333).

All common potassium compounds are soluble in water, and many are important as laboratory reagents because they have steep solubility curves (p. 108).

Test for Potassium Compounds

Expt. 171. The best test for potassium compounds is the *flame test*. A clean platinum* wire is dipped into concentrated hydrochloric acid, then into a potassium salt, and then held in a bunsen flame. A vivid lilac colour (p. 83) is obtained which should be viewed through blue glass, as this cuts out the yellow colour due to any sodium compounds present.

SODIUM

Occurrence. By far the most important source of sodium and its compounds is *sodium chloride*, NaCl. This has been described on pp. 395, 401, and the diagram (fig. 134) on p. 396 shows its main chemical uses. The nitrate (p. 333), carbonate (p. 162), and borate (p. 436) also occur naturally, and complex silicates (p. 433) are common in rocks.

Sodium Carbonate, Na_2CO_3

This is the second most important compound of sodium, and has been described in detail on p. 281.

* NOTE.—A *new* piece of Nichrome wire is equally good.

Sodium Hydroxide, NaOH

This is called "caustic soda" because it is corrosive to flesh, in contrast with the carbonate ("washing soda") above, which is only mildly alkaline. It is manufactured by one of two methods: (*a*) from sodium carbonate solution by treatment with calcium hydroxide (p. 283); (*b*) from sodium chloride solution by electrolysis (p. 405).

In both cases, the solution is evaporated to form dry sodium hydroxide, which is melted and cast into sticks or pellets, and is immediately sealed up out of contact with the air because it is so very hygroscopic.

Uses of Sodium Hydroxide

Sodium hydroxide is used on a large scale for treating wood-pulp, leaving the cellulose which is required for making rayon (p. 367); sodium hydroxide is also used in the latter process. Soap-making (p. 306 and PLATE 27—Na), and the textile industry (for "mercerizing" cotton) also use large quantities, and much is converted into sodium metal (see p. 450).

Properties of Sodium Hydroxide

It is a white deliquescent solid. On exposure to air it rapidly becomes a solution; the latter gradually absorbs carbon dioxide from the air, and as it dries it solidifies as sodium carbonate. For this reason the bottles in which its solution is kept are usually fitted with rubber stoppers and so can easily be recognized; glass stoppers would soon get stuck to the bottle. It dissolves in water, evolving much heat, to form a strong alkali. The solution feels "soapy" (because soap solutions are alkaline also).

The solid or its solution drives off ammonia from ammonium salts (p. 318) on heating.

Its solution reacts with solutions of the salts of all metals except potassium and sodium (and barium) to precipitate the insoluble hydroxide:

$$CaCl_2 + 2NaOH = Ca(OH)_2 \downarrow + 2NaCl$$

Many of these hydroxides are coloured (e.g. ferrous, green; ferric, brown; cupric, blue; mercurous, black; mercuric, yellow).

[Photo by courtesy of Lever and Unilever Bros., Ltd.

PLATE 27—Na. SODIUM HYDROXIDE FOR SOAP-MAKING

There are 50 soap pans in the room shown here, each pan being 14 feet square and holding 60 tons of material. One pan has just begun to be filled with palm oil from the near pipe and with caustic soda solution from the far pipe. Then steam will be injected from coils at the bottom and the resulting reaction will produce soap and glycerine.

Other hydroxides are "amphoteric," i.e. acidic as well as basic, and will dissolve in excess of alkali (the hydroxides of Al, Zn, Sn, Pb). This reaction is therefore important in helping to identify the metallic radical of an unknown substance (p. 480).

Sodium hydroxide solution also attacks the metals aluminium, zinc, and tin (p. 92), giving hydrogen, but even the molten alkali is without action on iron, nickel, or copper (see below—preparation of sodium).

Unlike all other hydroxides, potassium and sodium hydroxides are not decomposed to the oxide at red heat (see p. 64).

Sodium Metal

The metal is extracted on a large scale by electrolysis of either (a) fused sodium chloride (see p. 216) mixed with calcium chloride to lower the m.p., or (b) fused sodium hydroxide.

(a) *Fused salt* is electrolysed in iron tanks with a heat-resistant lining. A graphite anode is surrounded by a circular iron cathode. The electrodes are separated by a wire mesh to prevent the sodium from coming into contact with the chlorine. Sodium, which at the temperature of the cell (600° C.), is formed in the molten state, floats to the surface and is drawn off.

(b) *Fused caustic soda* is electrolysed in iron tanks with a copper cathode and nickel anodes (fig. 149).

Molten sodium (m.p. 97° C.) collects above the cathode, and hydrogen is also set free there. Oxygen is liberated at the anode.

The reactions occurring in the cell may be represented:

$$NaOH = Na^+ + OH^-$$

At cathode: $\quad 4Na^+ = 4Na$

At anode: $\quad 4OH^- = 2H_2O + O_2$

Later $2Na + 2H_2O = 2NaOH + H_2$, so that half the sodium originally formed is wasted.

This last reaction occurs as the water formed at the anode diffuses into the region of the cathode. The atmosphere of hydrogen so produced helps to protect the sodium from further oxidation.

Although this method is evidently less economical than the electrolysis of sodium chloride, the temperature required (320° C.) is much lower and therefore the process is easier.

Properties and Uses of Sodium Metal

It is too reactive for use in constructional work like ordinary metals (see expt. 37, p. 83 for a detailed description), but its reactivity makes it useful as a laboratory reducing agent (as the amalgam). Industrially it is prepared very cheaply on a large scale for making sodium peroxide and sodium cyanide,

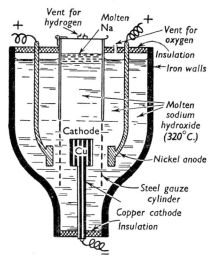

FIG. 149. Preparation of sodium metal.

and especially (alloyed with lead) to make lead tetra-ethyl for anti-knock petrol.: $Na_4Pb+4C_2H_5Cl=Pb(C_2H_5)_4+4NaCl$.

Sodium peroxide, Na_2O_2, is formed by burning sodium in a plentiful supply of air. This is a true peroxide which gives hydrogen peroxide with dilute acid (p. 388), but with water it forms sodium hydroxide and oxygen:

$$Na_2O_2+2HCl=2NaCl+H_2O_2$$
$$2Na_2O_2+2H_2O=4NaOH+O_2$$

Owing to the latter reaction sodium peroxide is used as a cleansing agent and also to restore the "freshness" of the air in a confined space, e.g. submarines. The sodium hydroxide produced by the reaction with water absorbs carbon dioxide from the air breathed out, and the oxygen produced replaces that used up in breathing.

Sodium cyanide, NaCN, prepared by reacting sodium with ammonia gas and carbon at red heat, is used for extracting gold from its ores, for making pest-killers, and for making solutions for electroplating (p. 220).

Test for Sodium Compounds

As all common compounds of sodium are soluble, the best test is the *flame test* (see expt. 171, p. 447), which gives the same yellow colour as sodium vapour lamps (often used for street lighting).

Other important compounds of sodium are the bicarbonate (p. 285), the sulphate (p. 375), nitrate (p. 333), and hypochlorite (pp. 411, 424).

CALCIUM

Large numbers of calcium compounds are useful because of their abundance and because they are cheap to prepare (see fig. 94, p. 271). The oxide and hydroxide (pp. 267–8) are important bases, the hydroxide being only slightly soluble in water (unlike sodium hydroxide). Other important compounds include the carbonate (p. 270); carbide (p. 294), sulphide (p. 353), sulphate (p. 375), bisulphite (p. 345), phosphate (p. 429), fluoride (p. 425), bleaching powder (p. 412), cement (p. 269), and glass (p. 435). The chloride (p. 402) is a drying agent.

Calcium Metal

Calcium is also too reactive to find much use as a metal, though small amounts are made commercially by a method similar to that for magnesium (see below). Magnesium factories can be used for the manufacture of calcium, but owing to the higher melting-point of calcium, it is deposited as a solid on the electrode; this is gradually withdrawn, forming a solid stick of calcium. The addition of 0·04% of calcium to lead makes the latter three times as hard.

The action of oxygen was described on p. 47, and of cold water on p. 82, and of heated nitrogen on p. 33.

Test for Calcium Compounds. Calcium compounds give an orange-red colour in the *flame test* (expt. 171, p. 447). Compounds of the related elements **strontium** and **barium** give crimson and pale green colours respectively. Magnesium compounds give no colour.

MAGNESIUM

Magnesium is a metal of very rapidly increasing importance, as can be seen from the table on p. 444. Its chief advantage is that it is the lightest metal (density 1·7 gm. per c.c.) which is not too active for general use. Although it will burn brilliantly when finely divided and heated strongly, under ordinary atmospheric conditions it is actually less corroded (i.e. chemically attacked) than iron or steel.

Occurrence

Magnesium compounds are very common in nature. Chlorophyll, the green pigment of leaves which acts as catalyst in photosynthesis (p. 36), is one. *Ores* of magnesium, i.e. metallic compounds from which the metal can be profitably extracted, include carnallite ($KCl.MgCl_2.6H_2O$, p. 447), the carbonate ($MgCO_3$, p. 284), dolomite ($CaCO_3.MgCO_3$, of which the Houses of Parliament are built), and especially the chloride, $MgCl_2$, in sea-water (p. 77).

Extraction of Magnesium Metal

In Great Britain the extraction of magnesium from sea-water began in 1939. The addition of slaked lime (the cheapest alkali) precipitates magnesium hydroxide, which is much less soluble than calcium hydroxide:

$$MgCl_2 + Ca(OH)_2 = CaCl_2 + Mg(OH)_2 \downarrow$$

The fused hydroxide cannot be electrolysed directly, unlike sodium hydroxide, because it decomposes to give magnesium oxide, which has a very high melting-point (i.e. is "refractory"). It must therefore be converted to the *anhydrous* chloride by heating with hydrogen chloride (p. 400), or with coke and chlorine (p. 402). The molten ("fused") chloride is then electrolysed at a temperature of 700° C. (N.B.—A *solution* of the chloride would give hydrogen on electrolysis, not magnesium, see pp. 216–22.) The anode is of graphite, and the cathode of iron.   Molten magnesium is removed in ladles (fig. 150 and PLATE 27—Mg).

Properties and Uses of Magnesium

Magnesium is used "alloyed," (mixed with other metals), e.g. up to 10% of aluminium, and zinc and manganese. Some of these alloys are *weight for weight* as strong as steel, because their densities are only one-quarter of that of steel. They are therefore especially important in aircraft, and are useful for moving parts such as fans.

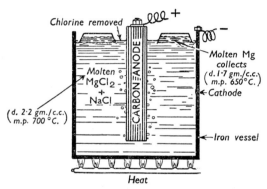

FIG. 150.   Preparation of magnesium metal.

Magnesium has a great affinity for oxygen (p. 223), so that its bright metallic, silvery colour is normally obscured by a dull film of oxide.   To prevent corrosion, it is dipped into a bath of potassium chromate solution, which deposits a protective film of chromium oxide (p. 329); this can then be painted.   Magnesium is used for *sacrificial protection* (p. 461).

The affinity for oxygen is shown also by the use of magnesium for photographic flashlight powder and for the casings of incendiary bombs.

In the laboratory magnesium reacts readily with oxygen (pp. 15, 47), nitrogen (p. 33), acids (p. 134); and with the oxygen of steam (p. 82), carbon dioxide (p. 249), nitrogen dioxide

(p. 336), and sulphur dioxide (p. 360). The ability of magnesium to react with oxygen and nitrogen is used to remove the last traces of air from radio valves.

Magnesium Oxide, MgO, like calcium oxide (quicklime p. 267), is prepared by heating the carbonate. It is very refractory (p. 453), m.p. 2500° C., and so is used in the lining

[*Photo by courtesy of F. A. Hughes and Co., Ltd.*

PLATE 27—Mg. MAGNESIUM PRODUCED BY ELECTROLYSIS

The interior of the electrolytic cell room, showing the large number of individual cells used in any electrolytic process. Chlorine is led away from the back of the cells, to produce more magnesium chloride. The magnesium is ladled out through the small inclined trap-door shown in the foreground ($MgCl_2 = Mg + Cl_2 \nearrow$).

of furnaces for making steel (p. 468); being basic, it combines with acidic oxides (e.g. P_2O_5) to make "basic slag," which is a valuable fertilizer (p. 301). Unlike quicklime, it gives out no heat when mixed with water.

Magnesium Hydroxide, $Mg(OH)_2$, is only very slightly soluble in water, but it is a strong base and so the solution turns red litmus blue (p. 47). A suspension of it in water, known as "Milk of Magnesia," is used to neutralize excess acid in the stomach.

Magnesium Sulphate, which occurs in solution in springs, e.g. at Epsom, has already been mentioned (p. 375). It and the *bicarbonate* are partly responsible for the hardness of water (p. 272)

ALUMINIUM

Like magnesium, aluminium is a metal of rapidly increasing importance, though it has been in commercial use now for sixty years. It has many advantages over iron, including especially its lightness and resistance to corrosion.

Its greatest drawback is its high heat of combustion (p. 223) which means that its oxide cannot be reduced by carbon, as iron oxide is. One ton of aluminium needs 20,000 "units" (kilowatt-hours) of electricity to split up the oxide, which at $\frac{1}{2}d$. per unit (the average cost of generation in this country) works out at £40 worth. This means that it is only economic to produce aluminium where electricity is especially cheap, e.g. from water-power in the Highlands of Scotland (PLATE 27—Al).

Although aluminium is ten times as expensive as iron, it is as cheap as any other "non-ferrous" metal (see pp. 444–45).

Occurrence

Aluminium is an extremely abundant element (p. 44), but its commonest compound is the silicate, "clay" (p. 434), from which the metal cannot yet be profitably extracted. Under tropical conditions the clay has been almost completely weathered to leave deposits of the impure hydrated oxide bauxite, $Al_2O_3.2H_2O$, e.g. in British Guiana or the Gold Coast.

Deposits at Les Baux in France and in other temperate countries were produced in earlier geological times, when the climate there was tropical.

Extraction of Aluminium

Chemically, aluminium is on the border-line between metals and non-metals (fig. 14, p. 49), and two consequences of this are important in its extraction. (*a*) Its chloride is volatile, and in any case is a non-conductor of electricity when liquefied (compare PCl_5, $SnCl_4$); unlike magnesium chloride, therefore,

[*Photo by courtesy of British Aluminium Co.*

PLATE 27—Al. WATER-POWER FOR ALUMINIUM MANUFACTURE

Hydro-electric aluminium works at Lochaber, Scotland, seen from the pipe-line.

it is useless for electrolysis. (*b*) Its oxide will dissolve in alkalis (like those of non-metals), and so it can be purified from ferric oxide, Fe_2O_3, which is the main impurity in the ore.

Pure anhydrous aluminium oxide is dissolved in molten cryolite, Na_3AlF_6, and the solution is then electrolysed as shown in fig. 151. Cryolite is a mineral found in Greenland

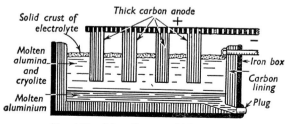

FIG. 151. Manufacture of Aluminium.

and can be made artificially; its melting-point (1000° C.) is 1000° lower than that of aluminium oxide. Molten aluminium (m.p. 660° C.), is run off from the floor of the cell (cathode), whilst the oxygen given off unavoidably burns up the carbon anode within a few days:

$$2Al_2O_3 = 4Al + 3O_2 \nearrow \; ; \; C + O_2 = CO_2 \nearrow$$

Physical Properties and Uses of Aluminium

1. The *lightness* of aluminium (density 2·7 gm. per c.c.) is of course especially useful for aircraft, of which it forms about 60% of the weight, and for the moving parts of machinery, such as pistons. Other important uses are for transport generally, such as railway trains, trams, and cars; the first aluminium cargo ship was built in 1949.

The other physical properties of aluminium are all typically metallic (see p. 44), and use is made of them all.

2. The *metallic lustre* is useful for reflecting the sun's rays from petrol storage tanks, milk tank-wagons, etc., which must not be overheated, and for the mirrors of telescopes.

3. The *conductivity for heat* is useful for cooking vessels (fig. 148), but owing to the action of alkalis these should not be cleaned with strong soda (expt. 173, below).

4. The *conductivity for electricity* (and *ductility*) results in aluminium wires (with a core of steel) being used throughout the "Grid" system.

5. The *malleability* is useful in making "silver paper" for milk-bottle caps, etc. (fig. 148, p. 446).

6. The *tensile strength* is very greatly increased by alloying, as is the case with all other metals (especially iron). Alloys such as "Duralumin" (Al+Cu, etc.) can therefore be generally used for construction, whether of aircraft, houses, or furniture.

Chemical Properties of Aluminium

The thin film of oxide on the surface of aluminium protects it from any further attack. This makes aluminium vessels useful in the manufacture of nitric acid and in many food and fermentation industries, such as the manufacture of penicillin (PLATE 1B, p. 7).

Expt. 172. When aluminium is treated with mercuric chloride solution, it will displace mercury because it is higher up the electro-chemical series (p. 223):

$$2Al + 3HgCl_2 = 2AlCl_3 + 3Hg \downarrow$$

Some unchanged aluminium then forms aluminium amalgam, which is no longer protected by a solid film of oxide, so that it decomposes the cold water and gives off hydrogen.

Thermit Process

The affinity of aluminium for oxygen is so great (see p. 223) that at high temperatures aluminium will reduce metallic oxides, e.g. those of Fe, Mn, Cr:

$$Fe_2O_3 + 2Al = Al_2O_3 + 2Fe + heat$$

This is useful in welding because the heat evolved is so great that the iron is liquefied and can be run into otherwise inaccessible places, such as cracks in tramlines.

Aluminium Hydroxide

This is obtained as a colourless, gelatinous ("jelly-like") precipitate when a little sodium hydroxide is added to a solution of an aluminium salt:

$$6NaOH + Al_2(SO_4)_3 = 3Na_2SO_4 + 2Al(OH)_3 \downarrow$$

It is amphoteric (p. 391) and dissolves in excess of sodium hydroxide; as an acid it behaves as H_3AlO_3 minus a molecule of water, i.e. as $HAlO_2$, giving sodium *meta*luminate in solution:

$$Al(OH)_3 + NaOH = NaAlO_2 + 2H_2O$$

Aluminium metal (pp. 458, 340, 92) and aluminium oxide (p. 457) similarly dissolve in alkalis:

Expt. 173. Warm a jam-jar by rinsing with hot water. Put in a handful of washing-soda crystals, one or two aluminium milk-bottle caps, and pour on boiling water. The hydrogen set free by the aluminium will (*a*) "pop" on lighting a bubble with a match, (*b*) reduce the black silver sulphide on an egg-tarnished silver spoon touching the cap. This is a rapid and safe method of cleaning silver.

$$2Na_2CO_3 + 2Al + 4H_2O = 2NaHCO_3 + 2NaAlO_2 + 3H_2 \nearrow$$
$$Ag_2S + H_2 = H_2S \nearrow + 2Ag$$

Aluminium hydroxide and oxide (like other bases) will, of course, also dissolve in acids:

$$2Al(OH)_3 + 3H_2SO_4 = Al_2(SO_4)_3 + 6H_2O$$

This reaction is used in preparing *aluminium sulphate* (p. 375). *Aluminium oxide* occurs naturally (coloured by impurities) as *Rubies, Sapphires* and *Emery. Aluminium chloride* (p. 402) is also important.

ZINC

Occurrence

Zinc is found mainly as its insoluble sulphide, ZnS, "zinc blende," usually with the sulphides of lead and silver. The carbonate, $ZnCO_3$, "calamine," also occurs naturally. In the early nineteenth century, Britain produced one-third of the world's supply of zinc, largely from Derbyshire and Wales

Extraction of Zinc

The ores, after purification, are first roasted in air to produce the oxide. Sulphur dioxide is evolved and helps to increase the supply required for making sulphuric acid (p 356)

$$2ZnS + 3O_2 = 2ZnO + 2SO_2 \nearrow \; ; \quad ZnCO_3 = ZnO + CO_2 \nearrow$$

The prepared oxide is then mixed with coke and heated, by producer gas, in fireclay retorts:

$$ZnO + C = Zn \nearrow + CO \nearrow$$

These, as shown in fig. 152, are fitted with "condensers" which cool the vapour and form molten zinc. The carbon monoxide produced burns at the mouth of an extension to the condenser called a "prolong." The volatility of zinc (b.p. 900°C) accounts for its late discovery (1720), although *brass* coins are known dating from A.D. 40.

The extraction of zinc electrolytically (p. 220) is being developed where electricity is cheap; for this purpose the prepared oxide is dissolved in dilute sulphuric acid (p. 367)

Properties and Uses of Zinc

1 Zinc is a bright, greyish-white metal, with a surface usually tarnished by a protective film of oxide. This prevents any further attack on the metal by air and water, and accounts

for the most important use of zinc, i.e. making "*galvanized*" iron for roofs of outhouses, gutters, cisterns buckets (fig. 148),

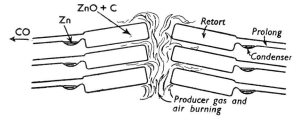

FIG. 152. Manufacture of zinc.

bath-tubs, wire-fences, wire-netting, screws, etc. The protective coating of zinc may be applied:

(*a*) by dipping clean sheets of iron in molten zinc;

(*b*) by electrolysis of zinc sulphate solution, using sheet iron cathodes;

(*c*) by "sherardizing," i.e. the sheet iron is stirred with hot zinc dust in rotating drums.

When galvanized iron is scratched, the two metals are exposed to air and water. The latter is often slightly acidic, because of the presence of carbon dioxide or sulphur dioxide. A small electrolytic cell is thus set up, the iron being the positive and the zinc the negative electrode. because zinc is

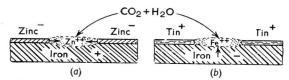

FIG. 153. Zinc is better than tin as protection for iron.

above iron in the electrochemical series (p. 223). The result is that the zinc goes into solution (not the iron), and so the rusting does not spread. Similarly magnesium rods embedded in the ground near oil pipe-lines (of steel) are used to provide "sacrificial protection." Tin, on the other hand, becomes the positive electrode so that rusting spreads rapidly (fig. 153).

In a similar way, zinc is used as the negative electrode in Leclanché cells (*i.e. the outer casing of ordinary dry batteries*),

$$Zn + 2NH_4Cl + 2MnO_2 =$$
$$Zn(NH_3)_2Cl_2 + Mn_2O_3 + H_2O + energy,$$

and in light-weight accumulators (with KOH electrolyte)

$$Zn + H_2O + AgO \rightleftharpoons Zn(OH)_2 + Ag + energy.$$

Impure zinc is more readily attacked than the pure metal by the acid in a hydrogen Kipp (p. 90), because in the presence of metals such as lead an electrolytic cell is set up.

2. Zinc has a very low boiling-point (900° C.), which is useful in the extraction of the metal, and also for purifying it. Its low melting-point (420° C.) is useful in making *die-castings* such as the handles of cars and the curved reflectors of electric radiators, which are then often chromium plated.

3. The most important alloy of zinc is *brass* (with copper): see p. 476, and fig. 148, p 446, used in threepenny pieces.

Zinc oxide is a white solid, used as a white paint and in zinc ointment, obtained by burning zinc vapour in air (PLATE 27—Zn). In the laboratory it is formed by heating the nitrate, carbonate, or hydroxide, and is easily recognizable by being yellow when hot. If a drop of cobalt nitrate solution is added and the mixture reheated, *green* cobalt zincate, $CoZnO_2$, is formed. The *aluminate*, $CoAl_2O_4$, is "Cobalt Blue."

Zinc hydroxide is a colourless, gelatinous precipitate formed by adding a little alkali to a solution of a zinc salt. Like aluminium hydroxide (p 459) it is amphoteric, dissolving in acids to form zinc salts and in alkalis to form zincates.

$$ZnSO_4 + 2NaOH = Zn(OH)_2 \downarrow + Na_2SO_4$$
$$\begin{cases} Zn(OH)_2 + H_2SO_4 = ZnSO_4 + 2H_2O \\ H_2ZnO_2 + 2NaOH = Na_2ZnO_2 + 2H_2O \end{cases}$$

Test for Zinc

A zincate (i.e. a zinc salt in alkaline solution), unlike an aluminate, will give a precipitate of the white sulphide when treated with hydrogen sulphide:

$$Na_2ZnO_2 + H_2S = ZnS \downarrow + 2NaOH$$

Zinc sulphide, mixed with barium sulphate, is very widely

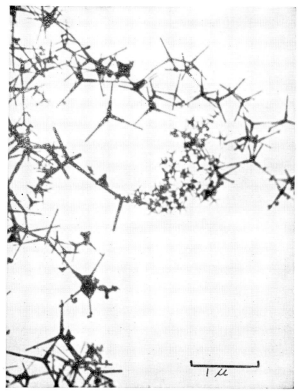

PLATE 27—Zn. ZINC OXIDE SMOKE

Produced by burning metallic zinc. The electron microscope shows that the smoke consists of long crystals. Magnification about 7000 diameters. The unit of scale is the *micron* $(\mu) = \frac{1}{1000}$ of a millimetre (mm.)

used as a non-poisonous white paint ("*Lithopone*"), which does not blacken on exposure to hydrogen sulphide, as "white lead" does. It is formed by mixing solutions of zinc sulphate (made from dilute sulphuric acid and the oxide or metal residues from galvanizing) and barium sulphide:

$$ZnSO_4 + BaS = ZnS \downarrow + BaSO_4 \downarrow$$

Zinc sulphate, used above, is "white vitriol" (p. 69); a 4 gm. dose is used as an emetic; 40 gm. is fatal.

Zinc chloride (p. 402) is also important.

IRON

Iron is by far the most important of all the metals. Ten times as much of it is produced as of all the other metals put together. The main reason for this is that the cost of iron is only one-tenth of that of any other metal, and this is due to four factors:

(*a*) Raw materials for its manufacture are abundant (p. 50).

(*b*) They usually contain a high percentage of iron (p. 444).

(*c*) It is fairly easy to extract metallic iron from them by heating with coke (pp. 224 and 522).

(*d*) This method of extraction is suitable for working on a very large scale (see below).

One particular type of iron alloy, steel, can have its properties varied in so many ways that it is the basis of modern industrial civilization. As iron and its alloys are the only common magnetic materials, some idea of their importance can be gained by testing to see how many everyday objects are attracted by a magnet.

Occurrence of Iron

Iron occurs free in meteorites, and it is possible that the inner core of the earth (4000 miles in diameter) consists of molten iron. One very common compound of iron, iron pyrites, FeS_2, has already been mentioned (p. 355), but the *ores* (see p. 453) of iron are mostly oxides. Magnetite, Fe_3O_4, and haematite, Fe_2O_3, are the most important, but the commonest

British iron ore is an impure clay ironstone from Northamptonshire, which contains only 25% of iron, as the carbonate mixed with clay.

Extraction of Iron

This is carried out in a *"blast furnace"* (fig. 154 and PLATE 27—Fe), which is a huge structure, capable of producing up to 1000 tons of iron every 24 hours. To make this, the following amounts of raw materials are added continuously through a hopper at the top:

Iron ore   (2000 tons or more according to purity)
Coke   (800   ,,   ,,   ,,   ,,   ,,   ,,   )
Limestone (500   ,,   ,,   ,,   ,,   ,,   ,,   )

"Red-hot" dry air (4000 tons per day) is blown in through tuyères (pronounced "tweers") near the base of the furnace. This reacts with the coke to form first carbon dioxide and then with more coke to form carbon monoxide, together with very much heat, producing a temperature of about 1800° C.:

$$C + O_2 = CO_2 \nearrow$$
$$CO_2 + C = 2CO \nearrow$$

The carbon monoxide and the coke reduce the iron oxide to iron, which is molten at this temperature, and trickles through to the bottom:

$$Fe_2O_3 + 3CO = 2Fe + 3CO_2 \nearrow$$

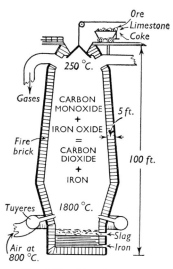

FIG. 154.   Blast furnace.

(If the coke was burnt without a "blast" of hot air, the temperature reached would not be hot enough to melt the iron.) The impurities, silica, etc., are removed by combination with

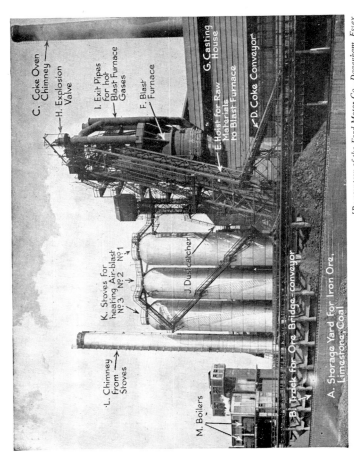

[By courtesy of the Ford Motor Co., Dagenham, Essex

PLATE 27—Fe. BLAST FURNACE FOR MAKING IRON

the limestone, which acts as a "flux," forming calcium silicate, " slag " which is molten at these temperatures:

$$CaCO_3 = CO_2 \nearrow + CaO; \quad CaO + SiO_2 = CaSiO_3$$

(In the preparation of other metals, the proportion of impurities is so high that the ore must first be purified.)

The waste gases which emerge from the chimney are mostly nitrogen and carbon dioxide, but contain enough carbon monoxide to be burnt in suitable stoves ("Cowper stoves") which are used to heat the air blast and for other purposes.

The molten iron dissolves some of the carbon, etc., and forms a liquid layer (density 8 gm. per c.c.) below the molten slag (density less than 3 gm. per c.c.). These are tapped off separately at intervals. The molten iron is either run into grooves in a sand bed, where it sets as "pigs" of *cast iron* ("pig iron"); more often it is used directly for making steel.

Cast Iron. This contains about 4% of carbon with another 2% or so of other impurities, such as Si, P, S, in the form of the carbide, silicide, phosphide, sulphide, etc. These lower the melting-point of the iron to 1200° C., which makes it useful for castings, especially because it expands on solidification. The impurities, however, make it brittle, so that it cannot be shaped except by melting it. It is therefore used for such purposes as lamp-posts, water-pipes, domestic cookers (fig. 148), closed coal stoves, hot-water radiators, etc.

Wrought Iron is a much purer form of iron obtained by heating cast iron with iron oxide. The carbon and sulphur are removed as gaseous oxides, and the product contains about 99% of iron with 1% of slag (iron silicate):

$$3C + Fe_2O_3 = 2Fe + 3CO \nearrow$$

Unlike cast iron, it can be worked ("wrought") by a blacksmith into chains, horseshoes, or ornamental iron gates (PLATE 4, p. 46). It has now been replaced for many purposes by "mild" steel (0·2% C), which is much cheaper to produce.

Steel is a form of iron containing between 0·15% and 1·5% of carbon. Its hardness and other properties can be altered in three ways:

(*a*) by altering the percentage of carbon;

(b) by various heat-treatments ("tempering," see below);

(c) by adding other metals such as nickel, cobalt, manganese, chromium, molybdenum, wolfram, vanadium, titanium, etc., which are near to it in the Periodic Table (p. 49).

(Almost all steel contains at least 0.5% Mn, see table, p. 444, and fig. 148, p. 446.)

This accounts for the extraordinary versatility of steel, which is limited only by two main disadvantages—its high density, and its liability to corrosion. Huge amounts of it are in use as railways, ships, bridges, cars, steel-frame buildings, etc.

Steel is mostly made in a so-called "*basic open-hearth*" furnace (actually totally enclosed), in which cast iron, scrap steel, and iron oxide are heated by burning producer gas (p. 257) mixed with air. (Very often more scrap is used than cast iron.) The chemical reaction is the same as that for making wrought iron (p. 467), but the furnace is lined with magnesium carbonate (p. 455), or dolomite ($MgCO_3.CaCO_3$), which combines with the acidic oxide of phosphorus to make "basic slag," a valuable fertilizer. As a result of the chemical changes involved, the temperature rises to 1700° C.; the metal is then liquid, and manganese (in the form of an alloy with iron and carbon) and other metals are then added.

The acidic open-hearth and the *Bessemer* converter are other processes for making steel. In the Bessemer converter, air is blown through molten cast iron, and the carbon is burnt out in a great flame; this was the first large-scale process for making steel (p. 524).

The Tempering of Steel

Expt. 174. (See "Metals in the Service of Man," by Alexander and Street—Penguin Books.) Four steel knitting-needles are taken. No. 1 is bent slightly to and fro to show that it is tough and springy. No. 2 is held by tongs and heated red hot in a gas-ring or bunsen flame, and then suddenly "*quenched*" in a basin of cold water; it is found to be exceedingly hard, but if pliers are used in an attempt to bend it the tip is so brittle that it will break off. No. 3 after heating red hot is *annealed* by allowing it to cool slowly; it is soft and easily bent like wire. No. 4 is heated red hot and quenched like No. 2; after cleaning with sand-paper it is then heated very gently for a short time until a blue tint of the oxide appears on the surface; after being allowed to cool. this is found to be "tempered," i.e. tough and springy like No. 1.

On the commercial scale tempering is of course very carefully controlled, a temperature of 230° C. being suitable for hard, brittle razor blades, whilst 300° C. is suitable for large saws, which must be springier.

Alloy Steels

Nickel steels are used for armour plating, and an alloy with 36% of nickel is known as "Invar," with an extremely small coefficient of expansion. Cobalt steels are used for magnets, manganese steels for railway points and for rock-crushing, and molybdenum and wolfram steels for tools. Stainless steel (fig. 148) contains up to 20% of chromium, and is about ten times as expensive as "mild" steel, costing about £150 per ton. A well-known type of stainless steel used in chemical apparatus contains 18% Cr, 8% Ni, 1% W, 1% Ti.

The Rusting of Iron and Steel

This has been discussed on p. 24. Chemically the changes may be represented thus:

$$Fe \ + \ 2H_2O \ = \ Fe(OH)_2 \ + \ H_2$$
$$\text{Ferrous Hydroxide}$$

the change being accelerated by the presence of acidic oxides of carbon and sulphur in the air; then:

$$4Fe(OH)_2 + O_2 + 2H_2O = 4Fe(OH)_3$$
$$\text{Ferric Hydroxide}$$

This shows that the reason why iron is so much more badly attacked than the more active metals magnesium and aluminium (p. 223) is because it has two valencies (2 and 3), and so the first product does not form a stable film on the surface.

Iron may be protected from rusting by coating with a layer of paint (especially red lead, p. 475), plastics, zinc (p. 461), tin (p. 472), or by electroplating with chromium, etc. (p. 220), or by the use of stainless steel (above).

General Reactions of Iron

We have already discussed the action of oxygen (p. 47) and steam (p. 81), which form Fe_3O_4; of acids (pp. 69, 134, 140), and of sulphur (p. 51). Iron is not attacked by alkalis (p. 451), unlike Al, Zn, Sn.

Ferrous and Ferric Salts

Iron is divalent in ferrous salts, and trivalent in ferric salts, derived from the basic oxides FeO and Fe_2O_3 respectively (p. 381).

Fe_3O_4 is a "mixed basic oxide" which gives a mixture of ferrous and ferric salts when treated with acids (p. 381).

Ferrous salts are easily *converted to ferric* salts by oxidizing agents (p. 382), even including atmospheric oxygen.

Expt. 175A. An extremely sensitive test for ferric salts is the blood-red colour which they give with potassium thiocyanate (KCNS) solution; absolutely pure ferrous salts will give no colour. To show this, try this test on the bench reagent bottles of ferric chloride and ferrous sulphate solution; both will give the colour, showing that the ferrous sulphate has been oxidized to some extent. Now prepare a *fresh* solution of ferrous sulphate by washing crystals of it several times with distilled water and then dissolving them in *cold* distilled water; this solution should not give more than a very slight colour with potassium thiocyanate solution.

Expt. 175B. The fresh solution of ferrous sulphate, prepared above, is treated with sodium hydroxide solution. Ferrous hydroxide, very pale blue-green in colour, is precipitated:

$$FeSO_4 + 2NaOH = Fe(OH)_2 \downarrow + Na_2SO_4$$

It rapidly darkens, and on filtering it off it goes unmistakably rusty, owing to oxidation by the air to ferric hydroxide (p. 469).

Ferric salts are easily *converted to ferrous* salts by reducing agents (p. 382). The most sensitive test for traces of ferrous salts is the "prussian blue" precipitate which they give with potassium ferricyanide solution; ferric salts only give a brown colour. Ferrous sulphate was described on pp. 69 and 376, the "brown-ring" test on p. 332, ferrous chloride on p. 400, ferrous nitrate on p. 71, and ferrous sulphide on pp. 51, 353.

Ferric oxide was described on p. 376, ferric chloride on p. 400, and the ferric alums on p. 376.

TIN

Occurrence

Tin is a very valuable industrial metal, though the world's output is considerably less than that of metals such as copper, aluminium, lead, and zinc (p. 445).

It is found as tin dioxide, SnO_2, "tinstone" or "cassiterite," in Malaya and in Indonesia. The Cornish tin industry, though of ancient date, is on a small scale.

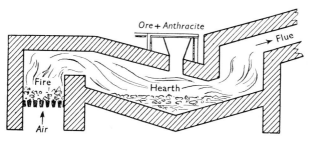

FIG. 155. Reverberatory furnace (manufacture of tin).

Extraction of Tin

After preliminary roasting, the prepared ore is heated, with anthracite as a reducing agent and limestone as a flux, in a reverberatory furnace (see fig. 155), the heat being reflected ("reverberated") from the roof.

$$SnO_2 + C = Sn + CO_2 \nearrow$$

It should be noticed that the product here is carbon *di*oxide, because carbon monoxide can reduce tin oxide. In the case of iron, the reduction is reversible and the exit gases contain much carbon monoxide (p. 467). Zinc oxide can only be reduced by carbon, not by carbon monoxide (p. 460). Aluminium oxide cannot be reduced even by carbon (p. 456).

Properties and Uses of Tin

Tin is not attacked by air or water (p. 81) or dilute acids (p. 134), and so is used in large quantities for making *tinplate* as containers for food (fig. 148), paint, petrol, etc. Mild steel (p. 467) is "pickled" in acid (p. 367) and then passed through a bath of molten tin (m.p. 232° C.). The final "tin can" contains only about 1% of tin by weight; (see p. 461 for its rusting). *Pure tin* is used for toothpaste tubes, etc.

The low melting-point of tin is also useful for making *solder* and (thick) *fuse-wire*, being alloyed with lead in both cases.

Owing to the scarcity and high price of tin, many alloys now contain much less tin, e.g. British *bronze* coinage contains 0·5% of tin with 2·5% Zn, 97% Cu, instead of 4% tin (pre-1939). *Type-metal* (p. v) contains up to 10% of tin, whilst the metal for *bells* and *organ-pipes* contains rather more.

Tin will dissolve in concentrated acids (pp. 399, 369, 140, 149) or in concentrated alkali (p. 92). It forms stannous compounds (valency 2) and stannic compounds (valency 4); the chlorides have been considered on p. 402, and the sulphides on p. 353. The hydroxides are amphoteric (p. 481).

LEAD

Occurrence

Lead sulphide, "galena," PbS, occurs in almost every country in the world, but rich ores of lead are being rapidly worked out (p. 48) and lead is no longer a cheap metal (p. 444). Britain (Derbyshire, Somerset) was the main source of the lead needed for the plumbing systems of the Roman Empire.

Extraction of Lead

The ore is roasted in a reverberatory furnace (see p. 471). The supply of air is regulated so that the sulphide is converted partly into oxide and partly into sulphate:

$$2PbS + 3O_2 = 2PbO + 2SO_2 \nearrow$$
$$PbS + 2O_2 = PbSO_4$$

In the second stage of the process the air is shut off and the temperature is raised so that the oxide and sulphate react with more sulphide thus:

$$PbS + 2PbO = 3Pb + SO_2 \nearrow$$
$$PbS + PbSO_4 = 2Pb + 2SO_2 \nearrow$$

The product is impure and often contains silver, which it is profitable to extract; nearly all the world's production of silver is obtained as a by-product from the refining of lead, zinc, or copper.

A good deal of lead is now made by the reduction of the oxide with coke in a blast furnace, using limestone as a flux.

Properties and Uses of Lead

The *malleability* and *resistance to corrosion* of lead make it useful for plumbing (fig. 148), roofing, and for covering telephone or electricity cables. Lead sheet for roofing is sufficiently soft to be rolled up into coils (PLATE 27—Pb, p. 474).

Lead rapidly tarnishes to a grey-blue colour in air, and soft water in the presence of air will attack lead, so that it should not be used for conveying drinking water (pp. 81, 276).

The *low melting-point* (327° C.) is useful for casting the type-metal (alloyed with antimony and tin, p. v) used for printing this book, for bullets, for making solder and fuse-wire, and for joining pipes by simply melting them together.

Because of its *high density* lead is used for making the bobs of "plumb-lines" and other weights.

The two valencies of lead and the *insolubility of lead sulphate* account for its use in accumulators (p. 367), and the insolubility of lead sulphate is also important in the Lead-Chamber process for making sulphuric acid (p. 365).

Lead is sufficiently soft to mark paper—hence the term "lead" pencils (see p. 242).

Lead Monoxide, "*Litharge*," PbO

This is a yellow or orange crystalline powder made by heating lead in air or oxygen. It is slightly soluble in water, turning litmus blue, and is largely used in making glass and glazing pottery, because it acts as a basic oxide. Strictly speaking it is an amphoteric oxide, because it will dissolve in alkalis forming plumbites, as well as giving lead salts with acids:

$$PbO + 2HNO_3 = Pb(NO_3)_2 + H_2O \quad \text{(expt. 29, p. 70)}.$$

Photo by courtesy of the Lead Industries Development Council

PLATE 27—Pb. ROLLING UP A SHEET OF CAST LEAD

Molten lead is poured on to a bed of sand, where it solidifies in a thin sheet. (In the more modern method, solid lead is passed through rollers which squeeze it to the required shape). Lead sheet is soft enough to be rolled up (p. 473).

Red Lead, Pb_3O_4

This red powder is made by heating litharge in air at 400° C.

$$6PbO + O_2 = 2Pb_3O_4$$

With dilute nitric acid it gives lead nitrate solution (a salt of PbO) and lead dioxide, PbO_2, as a chocolate-coloured powder. In this respect it behaves as a mixed oxide, $PbO_2.2PbO$, and differs from Fe_3O_4, which behaves as $FeO.Fe_2O_3$, giving a mixture of ferrous and ferric salts with acids:

$$Pb_3O_4 + 4HNO_3 = 2Pb(NO_3)_2 + PbO_2 \downarrow + 2H_2O$$

Red lead is used in plumbing to give watertight joints, and also as a red paint, especially used for ships and for protecting ironwork generally.

Lead Dioxide, PbO_2

This is obtained from red lead as above, or by the oxidizing action of chlorine water on litharge:

$$PbO + Cl_2 + H_2O = PbO_2 \downarrow + 2HCl \quad (p. 410)$$

With hot, concentrated hydrochloric acid and lead dioxide this equation is reversed (compare manganese dioxide, p. 404), because $PbCl_4$ is easily decomposed:

$$PbO_2 + 4HCl = PbCl_2 + Cl_2 \nearrow + 2H_2O$$

It is sometimes called "lead peroxide," but is not a true peroxide (p. 392), because it does not give hydrogen peroxide when treated with acids. Its most important use is in accumulators (p. 367).

Salts of Lead (N.B. Poisonous; 10 gm. may be fatal).

The nitrate (p. 335) can be formed by dissolving lead in hot dilute nitric acid :

$$3Pb + 8HNO_3 = 3Pb(NO_3)_2 + 4H_2O + 2NO \nearrow$$

The acetate (pp. 284, 349), the chloride (pp. 71, 403), iodide (p. 71), sulphate (p. 70), sulphide (p. 353), and carbonate (pp. 73, 284) are also important; the chromate is "chrome yellow."

For lead tetra-ethyl, see p. 421.

COPPER

Copper was the first metal to be used by man, having been known since the so-called "Bronze Age," over 6000 years ago. Being low in the electrochemical series, it sometimes occurs "native" (i.e. as the uncombined element), and its ores can be smelted by charcoal at the temperature of an ordinary fire without needing a blast furnace.

Occurrence

Its chief source is cuprous sulphide, Cu_2S, which is often combined with iron sulphide as "copper pyrites," $CuFeS_2$.

Extraction of Copper

This is complicated because the ores contain very little copper (often only 1%) and because large numbers of other metals are also present. The principle of the method is similar to that used for lead, the sulphide being partly converted to oxide by roasting in air; oxide and sulphide then react to give the crude metal:

$$Cu_2S + 2Cu_2O = 6Cu + SO_2 \nearrow$$

The crude metal must then be carefully refined by electrolysis (see p. 215, example 4 and PLATE 14, p. 219) to give copper 99·95% pure. This purity is essential for electrical conduction (fig. 148 and PLATE 27—Cu), which accounts for 60% of the total output of copper.

Properties and Uses of Copper

Copper has the highest *electrical conductivity* per unit volume and the highest *conductivity for heat* of any metal except silver. Apart from its all-important electrical uses (see above), it is therefore important in locomotive fireboxes, car radiators, ships' condensers, preserving pans (fig. 148), etc., often alloyed with up to 30% zinc (as brass), or nickel (80% Cu + 20% Ni for "silver" coinage in Britain from 1947), or tin (as bronze, p. 472).

Its red colour is attractive for decorative and architectural work. Among its many *alloys* is "nickel silver" (p. 446) (copper, zinc, nickel), which is often electroplated with silver for tableware. Brass (fig. 148) is specially useful because it is more malleable and stronger than pure copper. Present-day bronze pennies are twice as strong as the pre-1860 ones of pure copper, and are therefore made with only half the weight. In general, alloys (mixtures of metals) are stronger than pure metals (see pp. 454, 469), *pure* iron being a remarkably soft metal.

Copper out of doors—i.e. exposed to sulphur dioxide, carbon dioxide, or sodium chloride from sea-spray, etc.— slowly becomes covered with a bright green basic sulphate or carbonate or chloride (e.g. on roofs, lightning conductors or bronze statues), though the attack is very slight.

Copper is only attacked by acids under oxidizing conditions, i.e. in the presence of air (p. 377), or by nitric acid (p. 337) or

[Photo by courtesy of the British Electricity Authority

PLATE 27—Cu. COPPER TRANSMISSION WIRES

High-voltage copper wires, 3060 feet long, crossing the River Thames at Dagenham. The pylons are 487 feet high.

by *hot* concentrated sulphuric acid (p. 355) or by ferric chloride solution as in the etching of a half-tone plate (p. v).

$$Cu + 2FeCl_3 = CuCl_2 + 2FeCl_2$$

With sulphur, copper readily forms *cuprous* sulphide (pp. 151, 475); as vulcanised rubber insulation contains sulphur (p. 345),

16*

household copper electric wires are usually tinned and so appear white instead of red.

Compounds of Copper

Cupric Oxide, CuO, appears on the surface of copper when the metal is heated strongly in air. It is a basic oxide which is *prepared* as a black powder by the usual methods (p. 64), i.e. heating the hydroxide, carbonate, or nitrate. It is easily reduced to the metal (pp. 84, 140, 246, 256, 384, 475).

Cupric Hydroxide, $Cu(OH)_2$. When sodium or potassium hydroxide is added to a solution of a cupric salt, a blue-green precipitate of cupric hydroxide is formed:

$$CuSO_4 + 2NaOH = Cu(OH)_2 \downarrow + Na_2SO_4$$

When heated even below 100° C. in suspension in the liquid, this precipitate turns black as $4CuO.H_2O$ is formed. If this is filtered off and heated more strongly, the black oxide CuO is obtained.

Copper hydroxide dissolves in excess of ammonium hydroxide, forming a clear, dark-blue solution due to the formation of the complex ion $Cu(NH_3)_4{}^{++}$. This is a very sensitive **test for copper compounds**; an old penny placed in ammonium hydroxide solution will give a noticeable blue colour and emerge much cleaner.

Another test is that copper and its compounds, if moistened with hydrochloric acid, give a *green flame test*. This is often seen when a bunsen burner "strikes back" and burns at the brass jet inside.

Cupric salts are all blue in dilute solution, though the chloride (p. 403) is brown when anhydrous and green in concentrated solution. The sulphate (pp. 69, 376), carbonate (expt. 100, pp. 73, 283), nitrate (p. 334), and sulphide (pp. 151, 353) are important. They are fairly poisonous (10 gm. fatal).

Cuprous salts do not exist in solution in water (see below).

Cuprous oxide, Cu_2O (p. 150) is obtained as a red precipitate when a solution of copper sulphate, with just sufficient ammonium hydroxide added to redissolve the copper hydroxide at first formed, is reduced by boiling with glucose (grape sugar).

Fehling's solution (copper sulphate, sodium hydroxide with sodium potassium tartrate to keep copper hydroxide in solution) also gives cuprous oxide when heated with a reducing agent, e.g. glucose (p. 305):

$$2Cu(OH)_2 = Cu_2O \downarrow + 2H_2O + O \text{ (oxidizes the reducing agent).}$$

Cuprous oxide with dilute acids does not give cuprous salts, but cupric salts and a deposit of copper:

$$Cu_2O + H_2SO_4 = CuSO_4 + Cu \downarrow + H_2O$$

Cuprous iodide, CuI, is a white precipitate obtained together with free iodine by mixing solutions of potassium iodide and a copper salt. The cupric iodide which might have been expected decomposes immediately; the iodine dissolves in the potassium iodide solution to give a deep red colour and affords a convenient means for estimating (p. 424) the amount of copper, e.g. in a coin.

$$CuSO_4 + 2KI = K_2SO_4 + CuI_2 \qquad 2CuI_2 = 2CuI \downarrow + I_2$$

Cuprous chloride, CuCl, is also a white insoluble solid (pp. 256, 403); it is formed when *cupric* chloride is heated strongly.

MERCURY

Occurrence and Extraction

Mercury is a rare, and therefore costly, metal, which occurs almost entirely as the sulphide, "cinnabar," HgS, especially at Almaden in Spain, where the mine has been worked since 415 B.C.

Its extraction is simple. The ore is roasted to red heat in air, and the mercury vapour, b.p. 360° C., is condensed:

$$HgS + O_2 = Hg \nearrow + SO_2 \nearrow$$

Any mercuric oxide formed would be decomposed by heat (p. 20):

$$2HgO = 2Hg \nearrow + O_2 \nearrow$$

Properties and Uses of Mercury

It is the only metal which is liquid at room temperature (m.p. −39° C.) and so is used in thermometers (fig. 148), barometers, and other scientific instruments.

Its high density means that every 1 c.c. (13·6 gm.) cost about 7d. at the 1947 price (though it varies greatly).

It dissolves many other metals, forming liquid "amalgams,"

and so is used in the extraction of silver and gold which occur "native" (i.e. uncombined). Dental alloy, Ag_3Sn, forms an amalgam which gradually sets solid and so is used in the filling of teeth. Sodium amalgam (pp. 188, 407) and zinc amalgam are useful reducing agents. Zinc rods in Leclanché cells are amalgamated with mercury to prevent "local action" of the acid on the zinc. Aluminium amalgam is *more* active than aluminium itself (see p. 459). The low boiling-point of mercury (360° C.) is responsible for the use of the increasingly popular fluorescent lamps which are filled with mercury vapour under low pressure; they give two and a half times as much light as tungsten-filament lamps for the same amount of power (see p. 353).

It does not dissolve in dilute acids except nitric acid, which slowly forms mercurous nitrate. Stronger acid forms the mercuric salt. Mercurous nitrate solution is useful in cleaning mercury because all metals above it in the electrochemical series (p. 223) liberate mercury from it and pass into solution.

Compounds of Mercury

The chlorides (p. 403), iodides (pp. 423–24), and sulphide (p. 353) are the commonest. Mercury fulminate, $Hg(CNO)_2$, is an extremely important detonator; it is so sensitive to shock that the violence of *its* explosion is used to set off a less sensitive explosive such as T.N.T.

The Identification of Metallic Salts in Solution

The salt should be dissolved in water if possible (there are no common insoluble salts of ammonium, potassium, or sodium); if impossible, treat with dilute hydrochloric acid or dilute nitric acid and heat till no more gas is given off. A clear solution, *not* a suspension, is necessary.

Treat the solution with sodium hydroxide solution (not too weak).

A. Ammonia gas given off on heating:
   Ammonium salt.
B. No precipitate or gas:
   K or Na (distinguish by flame test, pp. 447, 452).

C. White precipitate, insoluble in excess:

Ca or Mg: ($(NH_4)_2CO_3$ solution gives a white precipitate of $CaCO_3$ from the original solution even in the presence of NH_4Cl; $MgCO_3$ is not so precipitated).

D. White precipitate, soluble in excess:

Al, Zn, Sn or Pb.

To distinguish, treat original solution with:

(a) HCl: white ppt.=Pb; if no ppt., then

(b) HCl+H_2S: brown ppt.=Sn (ous)
                    yellow ppt.=Sn (ic); if no ppt., then

(c) NH_4Cl+NH_4OH: white ppt.=Al; if no ppt., then

(d) NH_4Cl+NH_4OH+H_2S: white ppt.=Zn.

E. Coloured precipitate, insoluble in excess:

Fe, Cu, Hg or Ag.

Blue-green:	Fe (ous)
Red-brown:	Fe (ic)
Blue:	Cu
Black:	Hg (ous)
Yellow:	Hg (ic)
Brown:	Ag

The standard method of analysis, including tests for other metals or mixtures of metals, is based on the solubility of the sulphides (see p. 353), and separates them into groups: the first four groups are (a), (b), (c), and (d) of D above; Group 5 is Ca, Sr, Ba (precipitated by $(NH_4)_2CO_3$+ NH_4Cl); Group 6 is the remainder, i.e. Mg, Na, K, NH_4.

Suggestions for Practical Work on the Metals and their Salts

1. Action of acids and alkalis on the metals Mg, Al, Zn, Fe, Sn, Pb, Cu. (Use dilute H_2SO_4, concentrated HCl, concentrated HNO_3, NaOH solution, and heat if necessary.)

2. Preparation of crystalline specimens of the sulphates from the oxides of Mg, Zn, Cu; also expts. 142, 143 (p. 376).

3. Action of heat on the oxides of Zn, Hg.

4. Action of dilute HNO_3 and of concentrated HCl on CuO and on the three oxides of lead.

Treatment of solutions of metallic salts with:

5. $NaHCO_3$ solution; filter off the products and examine the action of heat and of dilute acids (see p. 284).

6. Gradually increasing amounts of sodium hydroxide solution (see The Identification of Metallic Salts in Solution, p. 480).

7. Dilute hydrochloric acid and hydrogen sulphide (see also pp. 351 and 481).

8. Metallic zinc (see pp. 222 and 100).

9. Potassium iodide solution (p. 424).

Also

10. The oxidation of ferrous salts by air, nitric acid, and acidified potassium permanganate (see pp. 384 and 470).

11. The reducing action of stannous chloride solution on ferric chloride and mercuric chloride solutions (p. 402).

12. The preparation of cuprous oxide and chloride (pp. 478, 403).

The general methods for the preparation of salts (pp. 67–73) should be carefully revised.

QUESTIONS ON CHAPTER XXVII

1. What physical and chemical properties do you regard as belonging to a typical metal?

Choosing any metal you please, indicate how far its properties agree with or differ from those you have mentioned. (O.)

2. Tabulate the chief characteristic physical and chemical differences between metals and non-metals.

Indicate two laboratory methods, with an example in each case, of converting metals into (*a*) oxides, (*b*) chlorides, and (*c*) carbonates. (C.)

3. What *chemical* properties distinguish metals as a class?

Give *three separate and distinct* methods by which metals may be converted into their oxides, taking as your examples the metals copper, magnesium, and zinc respectively. (L.)

4. Compare and contrast the properties of iron and sulphur, showing how they illustrate the differences between metals and non-metals.

5. Why is potassium nitrate preferred to sodium nitrate for use in gunpowder, and sodium nitrate generally used rather than potassium nitrate in fertilizers?

How would you distinguish between pure specimens of these two salts?

6. In what way is sodium prepared commercially?

Describe the preparation, properties and uses of three compounds of this metal. (O.)

7. How may caustic soda be prepared from sodium carbonate? What is the action on a solution of caustic soda of (*a*) sulphur dioxide, (*b*) ammonium chloride?

Mention carefully the necessary conditions for each action you describe. (C.)

8. Outline the industrial preparation from sodium chloride of (*a*) sodium hydroxide, (*b*) sodium carbonate.

How does a solution of each of these substances react with a solution of lead nitrate? (C.)

9. Define an element. Give two chemical properties of each of the elements calcium and carbon that distinguish them as metal and non-metal respectively. Describe clearly the reactions of these elements with (*a*) oxygen, (*b*) water. (L.)

10. Describe how you would investigate what substances are produced when magnesium burns in air.

11. Point out the resemblances, physical and chemical, between the metals calcium and magnesium.

How would you prepare from magnesium specimens of its sulphate and carbonate?

12. Outline the preparation of magnesium on a commercial scale.

An alloy is reputed to contain only aluminium, magnesium, and copper. How would you proceed to test the truth of this statement? (Navy.)

13. Outline the preparation of aluminium on a commercial scale. What are the chief applications of the metal? Mention two experiments which show the great affinity of aluminium for oxygen. (Navy.)

14. What reactions occur between aluminium and (*a*) hydrochloric acid, (*b*) chlorine, (*c*) sodium hydroxide, (*d*) iron oxide?

15. How would you prepare, starting from the metal aluminium, a crystalline specimen of any alum. What is the action on a solution of aluminium sulphate of (*a*) sodium hydroxide, (*b*) sodium carbonate?

16. Outline the extraction of metallic zinc from one of its named naturally occurring compounds.

State *two* common uses of zinc.

Describe concisely, giving essential practical details, how you would prepare dry crystals of zinc sulphate from zinc. (O. Gen. Sc.)

17. State the chief physical properties of metallic zinc. Explain how zinc reacts with the three mineral acids (hydrochloric, nitric, sulphuric), stating carefully the conditions of temperature and concentration of the acids.

Give two methods of preparing zinc oxide, and give the reactions which occur between zinc oxide and (*a*) dilute nitric acid, (*b*) caustic soda solution. (W.)

18. Compare and contrast the physical and chemical properties of magnesium and zinc. For what purposes are these metals used ?

19. Describe briefly how, starting with zinc blende (zinc sulphide), it is possible to obtain (*a*) metallic zinc, (*b*) crystals of zinc sulphate.

What is the action of zinc on (i) dilute sulphuric acid, (ii) a solution of copper sulphate, (iii) an acidified solution of ferric chloride? (L.)

20. Metals are obtained from their compounds either by chemical means or by electrolysis. Illustrate these two methods by outlining the extraction of (*a*) zinc, (*b*) sodium. (In describing electrolysis a labelled sketch should show the electrolyte, the container material, the names, polarities, and materials of the electrodes, and where the metal is obtained.)

Describe what happens and state the chemical reactions which take place when (i) ammonium sulphide is added to a solution of zinc chloride, (ii) sodium hydroxide solution is added to a solution of zinc sulphate until no further change takes place.

State the chemical reasons why, when used for certain purposes, iron is galvanized. (N.)

21. What are the chief ores of iron, and how is cast iron obtained from any one of them? (O. Gen. Sc.)

22. Write a short account of the properties of the three chief varieties of iron.

Explain the peculiar smell noticed when iron filings are dissolved in hydrochloric acid. State two methods of converting a ferrous salt into a ferric salt. (W.)

23. How is iron converted into steel? What is meant by the tempering of steel, and what is the object of this process? (O.)

24. Describe how you would obtain from iron pure crystalline specimens of (*a*) ferrous sulphate, (*b*) ferrous ammonium sulphate. What changes occur when aqueous solutions of these substances are boiled with nitric acid? (O. and C.)

25. Starting with metallic iron, describe how to obtain specimens of (a) the red oxide of iron, (b) the black oxide of iron, (c) ferric chloride solution, (d) ferrous sulphide.

What is the effect of passing hydrogen over heated samples of these two oxides of iron? State two tests which will enable you to distinguish between solutions of a ferrous and a ferric salt. (W.)

26. Given metallic iron, describe how you would prepare a sample of each of its chlorides. (O.)

27. Describe, giving full practical details, how you would prepare crystalline ferrous sulphate from metallic iron.

What happens when (a) the crystals are heated gradually to a high temperature, (b) a solution of the salt is mixed with a solution of sodium hydroxide? (C.)

28. Describe experiments you have performed in order to discover the conditions for iron to rust. What is the main constituent in rust? How would you show that it contained iron? (L.)

29. Explain how iron forms two series of salts.

What properties of the two kinds of salts would you use to distinguish between them?

How would you prepare a specimen of ferric sulphate from iron? (O.)

30. Write an essay on the importance of steel, pointing out the scientific reasons for this.

31. Give a summary of the physical properties and uses of tin.

How does this metal react with (a) hydrochloric acid, (b) concentrated nitric acid?

32. Describe briefly the preparation of two chlorides of tin.

Give examples to illustrate the statement that stannous chloride is a reducing agent.

33. (a) Briefly describe how metallic lead can be obtained from galena.

(b) Starting from lead, how would you prepare and isolate specimens of (i) crystals of lead nitrate, (ii) lead carbonate?

(c) What happens when a stick of zinc is allowed to stand in a solution of lead nitrate? (L.)

34. State three important purposes for which lead is used.

What is the action of (a) concentrated hydrochloric acid on lead peroxide, (b) dilute nitric acid on red lead, (c) dilute sulphuric acid on litharge? (N.)

35. If you were given some solid lead nitrate and the ordinary laboratory reagents and apparatus, what would you do to obtain specimens of (a) lead monoxide, (b) nitric acid, (c) oxygen, (d) lead sulphide? Give details of your operations. (D.)

36. Name *three* everyday uses for metallic copper.

Explain how you would produce a specimen of copper from copper oxide. Point out any precautions to be observed.

How and under what conditions does copper react with sulphuric acid? (L.)

37. Name the chief ores of copper and outline *one* method for the extraction of this metal.

Discuss the practical importance of copper.

Starting with black copper oxide, how would you prepare samples of (i) crystalline copper sulphate and (ii) cupric sulphide? (Navy.)

38. Describe and explain, giving equations, the actions of copper on (a) dilute nitric acid, (b) concentrated sulphuric acid.

Starting from a cupric salt, how may cuprous chloride be prepared? (O. and C.)

39. Describe how you would prepare *two* different oxides of copper, starting with copper sulphate.

Describe briefly *two* simple tests by which you could distinguish these two oxides from each other. (O.)

40. Compare the properties of copper and zinc.

What are the products of the reactions (if any) of these metals with (a) hydrochloric acid; (b) sulphuric acid; (c) moist air? In each case state the conditions under which the action takes place. (D.)

41. Describe how you would obtain pure specimens of black oxide of copper from (a) copper sulphate, (b) a penny (an alloy of copper and tin).

Copper sheet is occasionally used for roofing purposes and in course of years becomes coated with a green material which is stated to be copper carbonate or a form of copper sulphate (basic). What tests would you apply to decide which compound is responsible for the green covering? (A.)

42. What is the principal natural source of mercury?

Explain how the uses of mercury are determined by its unique properties.

43. What solutions of mercury salts do you find in an ordinary laboratory? Describe how you would obtain any two insoluble mercury compounds from them.

44. Name some metal other than iron of importance in everyday life. Describe the properties of the metal you name and of any of its compounds, pointing out how the applications of the metal and its compounds depend on the properties you describe. (A.)

45. Describe the effect of long exposure to moist air on the metals iron, lead, copper, zinc, and sodium.

What devices are used to protect iron from the action of moist air, and to what extent are these devices successful? (D.)

46. Make a list of eight metals, other than the four given below in this question, which you have seen, and discuss the properties which they all have in common. (Alloys may be included, but if you include any in your list, you should state which they are.) How would you quickly distinguish between aluminium, silver, iron, platinum? (C. Gen. Sc.)

47. In each of the following cases name *one* metal which (*a*) burns readily when heated in air, (*b*) forms an insoluble sulphate, (*c*) displaces hydrogen from cold water, (*d*) displaces hydrogen from cold dilute hydrochloric acid but not from cold water, (*e*) ignites spontaneously in chlorine. (L.)

48. Give an account of the chemistry underlying three common methods by which metals may be converted into their oxides. Illustrate by reference to the production of the oxides of the metals sodium, iron, lead, or copper. (N.)

49. Starting with the appropriate metal, describe how you would prepare:

(*a*) crystalline copper sulphate;

(*b*) crystalline lead nitrate;

(*c*) ferrous sulphide. (C.)

50. A given solution may contain a salt of one of the metals, iron, copper, lead, sodium, or calcium.

What tests would you do to find out which metal is present? (D.)

51. Potassium cyanide, KCN, in solution reacts with ferrous sulphate solution to precipitate ferrous cyanide, and then dissolves the precipitate forming potassium ferrocyanide solution, $K_4Fe(CN)_6$. This reacts with ferrous sulphate solution to precipitate pale blue ferrous ferrocyanide, and with ferric sulphate to precipitate dark "Prussian Blue" ferric ferrocyanide. Write equations for these reactions.

CHAPTER XXVIII

REVISION NOTES ON GASES, AND ANALYSIS

The identification of gases

The following tests should be applied to identify any of the common gases, whether in a gas-jar or being set free in a reaction: observe the colour and smell, and the effects on wet litmus-paper, on lime-water, on a glowing splint, and on a burning splint.

(*a*) *Observe the colour:*

1. Cl_2 is yellowish-green (p. 407).
2. NO_2 is brown (p. 336), and gives a colourless solution in water.
3. Br_2 vapour is also brown (p. 418), but gives a red solution in water.
4. I_2 vapour is violet (p. 423).
5. NO is colourless, but immediately goes brown in air (p. 337).
6. H_2O vapour (colourless) condenses on a cool surface as a colourless liquid, and turns anhydrous copper sulphate blue (p. 80).

(*b*) *Hold wet litmus-paper* in the gas (or over the end of a test-tube):

turning *blue* indicates NH_3 (p. 315);
bleaching indicates Cl_2 (p. 410);
turning *red* indicates HCl, SO_2, H_2S or CO_2 (only slightly red):

HCl (p. 398) goes cloudy when blown upon;
SO_2 (p. 360) turns potassium dichromate paper from orange to green;
H_2S (p. 349) blackens lead acetate paper;
CO_2 (p. 249) turns *lime-water* cloudy when passed in

through a delivery tube or when a tube dipped in lime-water is held in the gas.

(c) The *smells* of all the above gases (except H_2O and CO_2) are easily recognizable with practice.

(d) The *lime-water* test (above) for CO_2 should be repeated.

(e) A feebly *glowing splint* is ignited by O_2 (p. 31); a strongly glowing splint by N_2O (p. 339).

(f) A *lighted splint* will cause CO (p. 256) to burn quietly; H_2, if enough is present and mixed with air, will explode with a "pop" (p. 51).

(g) "No result" probably means N_2 (p. 34).

The Preparation, Drying, and Collection of Gases

A. *Solid+liquid in the cold*

A Kipp (fig. 25, p. 90), or flask with dropping-funnel (fig. 26, p. 91) is suitable.

1.	CO_2	from	$CaCO_3$	+ HCl	(p. 247)
2 (a).	H_2	from	Zn	+ HCl	(p. 90)
3.	H_2S	from	FeS	+ HCl	(p. 350)
4 (a).	Cl_2	from	$CaOCl_2$	+ HCl	(p. 404)

B. *Solid+liquid on heating*

A flask, with dropping-funnel, on a gauze, is suitable (fig. 137, p. 403).

4 (b).	Cl_2	from	MnO_2	+ conc. HCl	(p. 403)
5 (a).	SO_2	from	Na_2SO_3	+ conc. HCl	(p. 357)
5 (b).	SO_2	from	Cu	+ conc. H_2SO_4	(p. 357)
6.	HCl	from	NaCl	+ conc. H_2SO_4	(p. 397)
7 (a).	CO	from	HCOONa (Sodium Formate)	+ conc. H_2SO_4	(p. 254)
8	NO	from	Cu	+ mod. HNO_3	(p. 337)

C. *Heating a solid or a mixture of solids*

A hard-glass test-tube or round-bottom flask is suitable (fig. 6, p. 19, or fig. 106, p. 315).

9.	O_2	from	$KClO_3 (+ MnO_2)$		(p. 29)
10.	NH_3	from	$NH_4Cl + Ca(OH)_2$		(p. 314)
11 (*a*).	N_2	from	$NH_4Cl + NaNO_2$		(p. 33)
12.	N_2O	from	$NH_4Cl + NaNO_3$		(p. 338)
13.	NO_2	from	$Pb(NO_3)_2$		(p. 335)

D. *Passing a gas over a heated solid*

An iron tube (fig. 12, p. 32) is most suitable.

2 (*b*).	H_2	from	H_2O	+ Fe	(p. 81)
11 (*b*).	N_2	from	air	+ Fe	(p. 32)
7 (*b*).	CO	from	CO_2	+ C	(p. 253)

Drying agents suitable for the various gases are listed on p. 38. Concentrated sulphuric acid is the commonest and is used in a wash-bottle (p. 95). The solids may be contained in U-tubes (p. 40).

It should be noted that many gases require purification (e.g. from HCl or CO_2) *before* drying (pp. 93, 404, 253).

Collection of gases is done in one of three ways:

(*a*) If *pure and dry*, a gas must be collected over mercury (fig. 28, p. 92) (unless of course it is to be used at once);

(*b*) If *dry* (and the presence of air does not matter), light gases (H_2 or NH_3) are collected by displacing air downward (fig. 106, p. 315); similarly heavy gases (the others except O_2, N_2, NO, CO) are collected by displacing air upward (fig. 83, p. 247);

(*c*) If required *free from air* (but not dry), very slightly soluble gases (H_2, O_2, N_2, CH_4, CO, NO) may be collected over water (fig. 6, p. 19); fairly soluble gases (CO_2, N_2O, H_2S) require *hot* water (fig. 120, p. 338; fig. 126, p. 350), whilst extremely soluble gases (SO_2, NH_3, HCl) cannot be collected in this way.

Identification of Acid Radicals

(N.B.—The tests for identifying gases (above, p. 488), must be thoroughly known already.)

(a) In the solid state

1. *Heat*

H_2O is given off from hydrated salts (p. 86)

H_2O+CO_2 from bicarbonates (p. 285)

NO_2 from nitrates (except those of NH_4, K, Na—see p. 332).

2. *Treat with dilute HCl, and heat if necessary*

CO_2 is given off at once from carbonates and bicarbonates (p. 279)

SO_2 from sulphites (p. 358)

H_2S from most sulphides (expt. 135, p. 350)

Cl_2 from hypochlorites and other oxidizing agents (p. 383)

H_2 from many free metals (p. 97)

NO_2 from nitrites (p. 340).

3. *Heat with concentrated H_2SO_4*

SO_2 is given off with all free metals and many other reducing agents (p. 369)

HNO_3 (turns brown on heating strongly) from nitrates (p. 332)

HCl (test by breathing on it. MnO_2 gives Cl_2) from chlorides (p. 401)

$HBr+Br_2$ from bromides (p. 421)

I_2 from iodides (p. 424).

4. If no result, it is probably a sulphate (see below "Tests in solution").

(b) Tests in solution

Sulphates give a white precipitate when treated with barium chloride solution *and* dilute hydrochloric acid (p. 374).

Chlorides give a white precipitate (soluble in ammonium hydroxide) when treated with silver nitrate solution *and* dilute nitric acid (p. 401).

Nitrates give the brown-ring test (p. 332) when treated with ferrous sulphate solution and then concentrated sulphuric acid (added down the side of the tube).

Carbonates, etc., react with dilute HCl as described in (*a*) 2 above.

Identification of Metallic Radicals (see p. 480)

Suggestions for Practical Work

Identify unknown gases and acid radicals as above.

QUESTIONS ON CHAPTER XXVIII

1. How would you distinguish between jars of oxygen, nitrogen, hydrogen, water gas? Describe the manufacture of one of these gases on a large scale, and state the purposes for which it is used. (C. Gen. Sc.)

2. Give *one* simple experiment in each case which could enable you to distinguish (*a*) nitrous oxide from oxygen, (*b*) carbon dioxide from nitrogen, (*c*) carbon monoxide from hydrogen, (*d*) sulphur dioxide from hydrogen chloride, (*e*) pure sulphuretted hydrogen from a mixture of sulphuretted hydrogen and hydrogen. (W.)

3. Describe two tests in each case by which you could distinguish (*a*) nitric oxide from carbon monoxide, (*b*) red lead from mercuric oxide, and (*c*) zinc oxide from calcium carbonate. (N.)

4. For each of the following pairs give one *chemical* test to distinguish between the two substances, briefly describing what happens to each substance: (*a*) solutions of sodium chloride and sodium sulphate, (*b*) potassium hydroxide and potassium carbonate, (*c*) water and a solution of hydrogen peroxide, (*d*) chlorine and gaseous hydrogen chloride. (L).

5. You are given five white powders which you are told are quicklime, slaked lime, chalk, common salt, washing soda (sodium carbonate).

State and explain the tests by which you would identify them. (C. Gen. Sc.)

6. Name the chemical substances you have used in the laboratory for drying gases, and explain the reasons for the absorption of water by the drying agents.

Give diagrams to show two different ways in which gases may be brought into contact with the drying material; name the gases and the drying materials. (Navy.)

7. The following six pairs of substances are given:

(*a*)   Black copper oxide and manganese dioxide.

(*b*)   Anhydrous sodium carbonate and sodium bicarbonate.

(*c*)   Red mercuric oxide and red lead.

(*d*)   Ammonium chloride and potassium chloride.

(*e*)   Sodium sulphate and sodium sulphite.

(*f*)   Potassium nitrate and potassium nitrite.

For each of the pairs (*a*) to (*f*) describe *one* test only, which, when applied to each of the two substances in a pair, will enable you to distinguish between them.

Give such explanations of the tests as you are able to do.   (W.)

8. Four different substances are provided.   For each substance two tests are described below, together with the results of each test. *Name* each substance.

Substance A.   Test 1: the liquid turns blue litmus red and effervesces with sodium carbonate solution.   Test 2: addition of barium chloride solution in the presence of hydrochloric acid gives a white precipitate.

Substance B.   Test 1: heated on a clean platinum wire in the bunsen flame colours the flame lilac.   Test 2: addition of concentrated sulphuric acid, followed by warming, gives a gas which turns dichromate paper green.

Substance C.   Test 1: addition of ammonia to the solution gives a blue precipitate which is soluble in excess of ammonia to give a deep-blue solution.   Test 2: addition of nitric acid, followed by a solution of silver nitrate, gives a white precipitate.

Substance D.   Test 1: the solid heated on a clean platinum wire in the bunsen flame colours the flame brick-red.   Test 2: a solution of the substance when mixed with a solution of ferrous sulphate followed by concentrated sulphuric acid forms a "brown ring." (**N.**)

CHAPTER XXIX

VOLUMETRIC ANALYSIS

It is much quicker to measure the volume of a liquid with reasonable accuracy than to do a weighing. For this reason much analytical work is *volumetric* (PLATE 29), and in this chapter we shall consider such methods for finding the strengths of acids and alkalis.

A definite volume of one solution is measured out by sucking up in a *pipette* (fig. 156); the other solution is then run out of a *burette* (fig. 158, p. 496) until an *indicator* dissolved in the solution changes colour; the volume delivered by the burette is then read off. The whole operation is called a *titration*. If the strength of one solution is known, that of the other may then be calculated.

Use of Pipettes

Pipettes are of various sizes, the commonest being 10 ml., 20 ml., or 25 ml. 1 ml. is now exactly the same as 1 c.c. Until 1950, the definition of a millilitre (ml.) had been the volume of 1 gm. of water at 4° C. and 760 mm. pressure, which is equal to 1·0000027 cubic centimetres (c.c.).

1. The pipette should be washed out before use. Some of the liquid to be used is sucked up, keeping the jet end well below the level of the liquid (to avoid getting a mouthful!), and is then allowed to drain into the sink.

2. The liquid is then sucked up again, until it is about a centimetre or so above the graduation scratch, and is held there by placing a moistened forefinger over the open end of the pipette.

3. The level of liquid is then adjusted by slightly releasing the forefinger and allowing liquid to drip out drop by drop (this technique should be practised until it becomes automatic). The lower edge of the liquid "meniscus" must be

[Photo by courtesy of Boots Pure Drug Co.

PLATE 29. AN INDUSTRIAL ANALYTICAL LABORATORY

On the right of the nearest bench are standard flasks and a rack of pipettes. (Titrations are usually done with a plain white wall as background.) Careful analysis is necessary at every stage of a manufacturing process; for checking the nature of the raw material, the course of the reaction, and the quality of the product.

level with the scratch (fig. 156, (a)) when the scratch is at eye-level (b). The pipette should be held vertically (c), no longer dipping into the liquid (d), and with all drips carefully removed by touching the pipette on to the beaker (e).

4. The contents of the pipette are now transferred to a clean conical flask (fig. 157 (a)) and the jet held against the side in

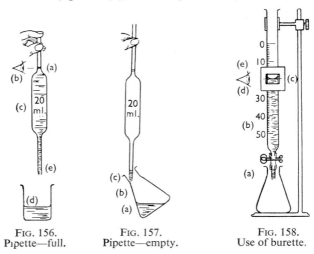

FIG. 156.
Pipette—full.

FIG. 157.
Pipette—empty.

FIG. 158.
Use of burette.

order to drain out (b), but the remaining drops are not blown out (c), because they have been allowed for in the graduating of the pipette.

Use of Burettes

Ordinary laboratory burettes usually contain 50 ml. of a liquid, and are graduated to read 0·1 ml. One drop is about 0·05 ml.

1. As with pipettes, burettes should be washed out with the liquid to be used.

2. In filling the burette (fig. 158), care should be taken to see that (a) there are no air-bubbles in the space between the jet and the clip or tap, and (b) no drips are left on the outside.

Any drips would probably run down, and the air bubbles may well be displaced by liquid during the titration, thus giving rise to serious errors.

3. There is no need to adjust the liquid level to 0·0 ml., because this is a waste of time. Any other graduation (*c*) may be used as the starting-point, provided that a note is made of it. The reading should be taken at eye-level (*d*) as with a pipette, and this is usually easier if a piece of white paper (*e*) is fixed behind the burette.

Titration

1. Much time is saved by first obtaining an approximate result. 10 ml. of one liquid (e.g. potassium hydroxide solution) is taken by means of a pipette, a *few* drops of litmus solution added as an indicator, and the other liquid (e.g. nitric acid solution) run in from the burette about 1 ml. at a time, until the litmus has changed from blue to red. In this way it will be found that (say) 8 ml. is too little and 9·5 ml. is too much.

This result must be written down, at once, in ink, in a note-book. No good scientist trusts unnecessarily to memory, nor does he run the risk of losing an odd scrap of paper, nor does he give himself the extra trouble of copying out his results. E.g.:

10 ml. KOH soln. needed $>10·0-2·0$, i.e. $>8·0$ ml. HNO_3 soln.

2. For more accurate readings, a 20-ml. pipette must be used, so as to halve the error due to one drop more or less. 16 ml. may now be run in from the burette; the exact *end-point*, at which the colour of the indicator changes, is then found by adding the liquid drop by drop. Three of these accurate readings are usually taken and noted down; their average gives the correct result to be used in the calculation. (Of course, if one of these readings is very different—by 0·2 ml.— from any other, it must *not* be included in the average, but another reading obtained instead).

3. The results may now be calculated as shown in the following example:

A solution of potassium hydroxide containing 5·6 gm. KOH

per litre when titrated against a solution of nitric acid, gave the following results:

20 ml. KOH soln. needed $27 \cdot 9 - 11 \cdot 5 = 16 \cdot 4$ ml. HNO_3 soln.
20 ml.   ,,   ,, $44 \cdot 3 - 28 \cdot 0 = 16 \cdot 3$ ml.   ,,
20 ml.   ,,   ,, $16 \cdot 9 - 0 \cdot 6 = 16 \cdot 3$ ml.   ,,
                            average = $16 \cdot 3$ ml.

Now 1000 ml. of KOH soln. contained $5 \cdot 6$ gm. of KOH

$\therefore$ 20 ml. ,,   ,,   ,, $\dfrac{5 \cdot 6 \times 20}{1000} = 0 \cdot 112$ gm.

The equation for the reaction is:

$$\underbrace{KOH}_{39+16+1} \quad + \quad \underbrace{HNO_3}_{1+14+48} \quad = \quad KNO_3 \ + \ H_2O$$

56 gm. neutralize 63 gm.

$\therefore 0 \cdot 112$ gm. KOH neutralize $63 \times \dfrac{0 \cdot 112}{56}$ gm. $= 0 \cdot 126$ gm. HNO_3

This weight of HNO_3 must have been present in that volume ($16 \cdot 3$ ml.) of its solution which neutralized the 20 ml. of KOH solution.

$\therefore 16 \cdot 3$ ml. HNO_3 soln. contain $0 \cdot 126$ gm. HNO_3

$\therefore 1000$ ml.   ,,   ,, $0 \cdot 126 \times \dfrac{1000}{16 \cdot 3} = 7 \cdot 73$ gm. HNO_3

The accuracy of this estimation is about $0 \cdot 1$ ml. in 16, i.e. about $0 \cdot 05$ gm. in $7 \cdot 7$ gm., so that this result should be quoted to two significant figures only:

$\therefore$ *The strength of the nitric acid solution is $7 \cdot 7$ gm. per litre.*

Such calculations are very much simpler if the idea of "Normal Solutions" is used.

Normal Solutions

A NORMAL SOLUTION of a substance is defined as one which contains the gram equivalent of that substance in one litre (1000 ml.) of solution.

This is not necessarily the same as one which contains 1000 ml. of water.

It is therefore necessary to know the definition of the gram equivalent of a compound. It is similar to that for an element, which, it will be remembered, was "that weight in grams which will combine with or replace 1 gm. of hydrogen" (p. 133).

The GRAM EQUIVALENT of an ACID is defined as that weight of it in grams which contains 1 gm. of replaceable hydrogen.*

For example, the gram equivalent of nitric acid is 63 gm., because this contains 1 gm. of hydrogen replaceable by a metal:

$$HNO_3 + KOH = KNO_3 + HOH$$
$$\underbrace{1+14+48}_{63 \text{ gm. } HNO_3} \qquad 1 \text{ gm. H replaced}$$

A normal solution of nitric acid will therefore contain **63 gm.** of HNO_3 in 1000 ml. of solution.

Now acids and bases react in equivalent proportions (see p. 149), and so:

The GRAM EQUIVALENT of a BASE is defined as that weight of it in grams which will neutralize the gram equivalent of an acid.†

In the above equation, 56 gm. of KOH $(39+16+1)$ will neutralize one gram equivalent (63 gm.) of HNO_3. The gram equivalent of *potassium hydroxide* is therefore 56 gm.

The gram equivalent of an oxidizing agent or reducing agent is defined on p. 507.

The importance of Normal Solutions is that:

1000 ml. of normal acid (i.e. containing 1 gram equivalent) will neutralize 1000 ml. of normal alkali (i.e. containing 1 gram equivalent); and so any volume of one solution will neutralize an equal volume of another of the same normality.

* More strictly, the gram equivalent of an acid gives 1 gm. of hydrogen ion (H^+) in solution.

† More strictly, the gram equivalent of a base will neutralize 1 gm. of hydrogen ion (H^+).

Use of Normal Solutions in Calculations

In the titration example above (p. 498), the potassium hydroxide solution contained 5·6 gm. KOH per litre. Now the gram equivalent of potassium hydroxide is 56 gm., and so a normal solution would contain 56 gm. KOH per litre. The strength of the solution used was therefore one-tenth normal, or "deci-normal," and is often written as N./10 or 0·1 N.

Now

> 1 gram equivalent of acid neutralizes 1 gram equivalent of alkali

∴ 1000 ml. of a normal solution of an acid neutralizes
    1000 ml. of a normal solution of an alkali

∴ 20 ml. of a deci-normal solution of an acid neutralizes
    20 ml. of a deci-normal solution of an alkali.

But

> 16·3 ml. of HNO_3 soln. neutralized 20 ml. of N./10 KOH soln.

∴ this solution of HNO_3 was *stronger* than deci-normal, i.e.
$$\frac{20\cdot0}{16\cdot3} \times \text{N./10}$$

But a normal (N.) solution of nitric acid contains 63 gm. per litre (p. 499).

∴ this $\frac{20\cdot0}{16\cdot3} \times$ N./10 solution contains $\frac{20\cdot0}{16\cdot3} \times \frac{63}{10}$ gm. per litre

= 7·73 gm. HNO_3 per litre.

Gram Equivalents of other Common Acids and Bases

Any "monobasic" acid, which only forms one sodium salt (p. 72), contains one replaceable hydrogen atom per molecule, e.g. *hydrochloric acid*, and therefore has its gram equivalent equal to the molecular weight, i.e. HCl = 1 + 35·5 = 36·5.

This gram equivalent will neutralize 40 gm. of *sodium hydroxide* (NaOH = 23 + 16 + 1) *or* 37 gm. of $Ca(OH)_2$ i.e. $\left(\frac{40 + 2 \times 17}{2}\right)$; 1 molecule of calcium hydroxide will neutralize 2 molecules (2 equivalents) of HCl, and must therefore contain 2 equivalents:

$$Ca(OH)_2 + 2HCl = CaCl_2 + 2H_2O$$

2 equivs.   2 equivs.

Calcium Hydroxide is therefore said to be a "di-acidic" base, or to have an "acidity" of 2; and its equivalent (i.e. 37) is half the molecular weight.

Sodium Carbonate, although a salt, behaves as a diacidic base when methyl orange is used as an indicator. (Carbonic acid does not affect methyl orange.)

$$Na_2CO_3 + 2HCl = 2NaCl + H_2CO_3$$

One gram-molecule ($= 46 + 12 + 48 = 106$ gm.) neutralizes 2 gram equivalents of acid, and so the gram equivalent is $\frac{106}{2} = 53$ gm.

In the case of *sodium carbonate crystals*, 286 gm. of Na_2CO_3. $10H_2O$ are required to neutralize 2 gram equivalents of acid, and so the gram equivalent is 143 gm., i.e. different from that of the anhydrous salt.

Sulphuric acid, which is "dibasic," contains 2 gm. of replaceable hydrogen per 98 gm. of H_2SO_4 ($2 + 32 + 64$), as is shown by the equation:

$$H_2SO_4 + 2NaOH = Na_2SO_4 + 2H_2O$$

98 gm.   2 gm. H replaced

Its gram equivalent is therefore $\frac{98}{2} = 49$ gm.

The gram equivalent of any substance must be worked out by writing down the equation for its neutralization and then applying the definitions. Mere guesswork is worse than useless.

The Preparation of Standard Solutions

A "standard solution" is one whose strength is accurately known; this is usually expressed in terms of "Normality," e.g. N. or N./10 or 1·2 N. or 0·8 N. It is not possible to make a standard solution of the common acids or alkalis directly, because they are hygroscopic substances (p. 87) and cannot therefore be weighed accurately. It is, however, possible to prepare a standard solution of sodium carbonate by direct weighing, and then to standardize an acid by titrating it against the carbonate solution (see below).

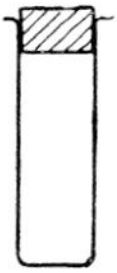

FIG. 159. Weighing-bottle.

Expt. 176. Preparing a standard solution of sodium carbonate.

Anhydrous sodium carbonate is purified by heating to red heat and then allowing to cool in a desiccator; alternatively it may be obtained by heating pure sodium bicarbonate to constant weight.

A clean, dry "weighing-bottle" (fig. 159) is partly filled with the prepared sodium carbonate and carefully weighed. Rather more than 5 gm. of this is then shaken out into a beaker containing about 50 ml. of hot distilled water. The weighing-bottle is then reweighed, so as to obtain the exact weight of solid used.

The solution is stirred with a glass rod until all solid has dissolved, and is then transferred to a 100-ml. standard flask (fig. 160), by pouring it down the glass rod through a funnel. The beaker must be washed several times with distilled water, the washings being added to the flask.

The contents of the flask should now be shaken thoroughly, and then made up to the mark with distilled water, the last few drops being added from a pipette.

It is now necessary to shake *really thoroughly*, far more so than is realized by beginners, in order to get a homogeneous solution. Failure to do this is the commonest cause of "queer" titration results.

The strength is now expressed in terms of normality: N.Na_2CO_3 contains 53 gm. per litre (see p. 501),

∴ a solution containing (say) 5·51 gm. per 100 ml. is

$$\frac{5 \cdot 51}{53} \times \frac{1000}{100} = 1 \cdot 04 \text{ N.}$$

FIG. 160. Making a standard solution.

Dilution of Standard Solutions

For most practical purposes a solution which is accurately 1·04 N. is as useful as one which is 1·00 N. For examination purposes it might be necessary to know how to dilute it to the required strength:

A 1·00 N. solution contains 1·00 equivalents in 1000 ml.
∴　　,,　　　,,　　　　,,　　1·04　,,　　　　,, 1040 ml.
This 1·04 N. solution contains 1·04 equivalents in 1000 ml.

Therefore 40 ml. of distilled water must be added (from a burette) to every 1000 ml. of this solution in order to dilute it to 1·00 N. (i.e. 4 ml. to the 100 ml. made up in expt. 176) and the solution then shaken well.

More often it may be necessary to dilute a solution to (say) one-tenth of its former strength in order to give a titration reading of convenient size (e.g. expt. 167, p. 424). This is done by pipetting 20 ml. of the solution into a 200-ml. standard flask, diluting up to the mark with distilled water, and shaking well.

Expt. 177. Preparing and standardizing a sulphuric acid solution.

An approximately normal solution of sulphuric acid is prepared as follows: about 30 ml. (from a measuring cylinder) of concentrated sulphuric acid (density 1·84 gm. per ml.) are added very gradually, with good shaking after each addition, to about 200 ml. of distilled water contained in a large flask.

After more shaking, the flask is cooled under the tap and the contents transferred to a litre standard flask. It is then made up to the mark with distilled water and shaken thoroughly.

Standardization is done by titrating (p. 497) against the standard sodium carbonate solution, using methyl orange as indicator.

Expt. 178. Preparing and standardizing a sodium hydroxide solution.

Weigh out approximately rather more than 40 gm. of sodium hydroxide pellets into a beaker. (They are very hygroscopic and so some of the weight is water.) Slowly add distilled water which has been freshly boiled to expel carbon dioxide and then allowed to cool somewhat. (Much heat is given out when sodium hydroxide dissolves.) Stir to dissolve, allow to cool, transfer to a litre flask, and make up to the mark. Transfer to a bottle fitted with a good rubber stopper and shake thoroughly. This solution is approximately "normal."

17*

Standardize by titrating against the standardized sulphuric acid, with litmus as indicator.

Specimen Calculation

If 17·5 ml. of the acid neutralized 20 ml. of the 1·04 N. Na_2CO_3, and 16 ml. of the acid neutralized 20 ml. of sodium hydroxide, then the acid is $\frac{20}{17·5} \times 1·04$ N.,

and the sodium hydroxide is $\frac{16}{20} \times$ the acid $= \frac{16}{20} \times \frac{20}{17·5} \times 1·04$ N.

i.e. $0·95$ N. $= 0·95 \times 40$ gm. NaOH per litre $=$ **38 gm. NaOH per litre.**

Alternatively, if a standard acid solution has been made by dissolving oxalic acid crystals in water (as in expt. 176), phenolphthalein must be used as indicator. Oxalic acid crystals are $H_2C_2O_4.2H_2O$ and the acid is dibasic, so that the equivalent is $\frac{126}{2} = 63$:

$$2NaOH + H_2C_2O_4.2H_2O = Na_2C_2O_4 + 4H_2O$$

Use of Indicators

The accuracy of titrations depends partly on using the correct indicator. This should show when the relative quantities of substances indicated by the chemical equation have reacted together. To take just one example, if litmus is used instead of methyl orange for the titration of sodium carbonate with a strong acid, the "end-point" will be shown when only about half has been used up; this is because sodium *bi*carbonate is almost neutral to litmus:

$$Na_2CO_3 + HCl = NaCl + NaHCO_3$$
1 equiv. only

Rules for the correct use of indicators are:

Ordinary "strong" acids and alkalis: litmus (or, indeed, almost any indicator).

Weak bases, e.g. ammonium hydroxide and also sodium carbonate: methyl orange.

Weak acids, e.g. oxalic or acetic: phenolphthalein.

No indicator will show the very vague end-point in the reaction of a weak base with a weak acid.

Uses of Standard Solutions

(a) *Estimation of the percentage of calcium carbonate in a specimen of chalk or marble.* (N.B.—Blackboard "chalk" is calcium sulphate.)

Expt. 179. Take a known weight of chalk, dissolve it in excess of hydrochloric (or sulphuric) acid, and titrate the excess with sodium hydroxide solution. This method is suitable, as in the following two cases, for substances which cannot be titrated directly.

Specimen Calculation

A sample of marble weighing 1·44 *gm. was dissolved in* 40 *ml. of* N.*HCl, and the resulting solution was made up to* 100 *ml. When* 25 *ml. of this solution were titrated with caustic soda solution,* 19·0 *ml. of* 0·2 N.*NaOH were required to neutralize the excess acid. Calculate the percentage of* $CaCO_3$ *in the sample of marble.*

25 ml. of solution required 19·0 ml. of 0·2 N.NaOH

∴ 100 ml. of solution required $4 \times 19 \times 0·2 = 15·2$ ml. of N.NaOH.

Now 15·2 ml. of N.NaOH must have neutralized 15·2 ml. of N.HCl
∴ amount of HCl used to react with $CaCO_3 = 40 - 15·2 = 24·8$ ml. N.HCl.

This represents $\dfrac{24·8}{1000}$ gram equivalents HCl, and therefore $\dfrac{24·8}{1000}$ gram equivalents $CaCO_3$.

The equivalent of $CaCO_3$ is *half* the molecular weight, i.e. $\dfrac{100}{2} = 50$, because $CaCO_3 + 2HCl = CaCl_2 + H_2O + CO_2$

∴ $\dfrac{24·8}{1000}$ gram equivalents $= \dfrac{24·8 \times 50}{1000}$ gm. $= 1·24$ gm. $CaCO_3$

∴ Percentage of $CaCO_3$ in specimen of marble $= \dfrac{1·24}{1·44} \times 100 = \mathbf{86\%}$.

(b) *Finding the equivalent of a metal, e.g. magnesium.*

Expt. 180. 0·31 *gm. of metal was dissolved in* 100 *ml. of acid, and the resulting solution required* 31·2 *ml. of* N.*NaOH to neutralize the excess of acid present.* 10 *ml. of this NaOH solution were found to require for neutralization* 17·4 *ml. of the original acid. Calculate the equivalent of the metal.*

$\therefore$ 100 ml. of the acid solution were equivalent to $\dfrac{100 \times 10}{17\cdot4}$ ml. of N.NaOH = 57·5 ml. of N.NaOH.

$\therefore$ 57·5 − 31·2 = 26·3 ml. N.NaOH is equivalent to the acid used in dissolving the metal.

i.e. $\dfrac{26\cdot3}{1000}$ gram equivalents of acid dissolve 0·31 gm, of metal.

1 gram equivalent of acid dissolves $\dfrac{0\cdot31 \times 1000}{26\cdot3} = 11\cdot8$ gm. of metal.

Hence the equivalent of the metal = **11·8** (magnesium).

(c) *Estimation of the ammonia in a specimen of an ammonium salt.*

Expt. 181. About 1 gm. of an ammonium salt is accurately weighed out into a conical flask. 25 ml. of standard (approx. normal) sodium hydroxide solution and 50 ml. of distilled water are added. The contents are then boiled gently until no more ammonia is evolved, as tested by smell or wet red litmus-paper.

$$NH_4X + NaOH = NaX + NH_3 \nearrow + H_2O$$

Any splashes on the neck or sides of the flask are washed back with distilled water, and the unused sodium hydroxide is then titrated with standard acid.

N.B.—$\underset{14+3}{NH_3} + HCl = NH_4Cl,$

$\therefore$ the gram equivalent of ammonia gas is 17 gm.

Specimen Calculation

1·13 gm. of specimen taken. 25 ml. of N.NaOH used. 5·0 ml. of N.H$_2$SO$_4$ required for neutralization.

5 ml. N.H$_2$SO$_4$ neutralized 5 ml. N.NaOH.

$\therefore$ 25 − 5 = 20 ml. N.NaOH were used in expelling ammonia

$\therefore \dfrac{20}{1000}$ gram equivalents were used and expelled $\dfrac{20}{1000}$ gram equivalents of ammonia

$$= \dfrac{20 \times 17}{1000} \text{ gm. of ammonia}$$

$\therefore$ ammonia in the ammonium salt $= \dfrac{20 \times 17 \times 100}{1000 \times 1\cdot13} = \mathbf{30\cdot1\%}.$

Oxidizing and Reducing Agents

The *Gram Equivalent of an oxidizing agent* is that weight of it which will provide 8 gm. of oxygen (i.e. the gram equivalent of oxygen $= \frac{1}{2}$ atomic weight in grams) for oxidizing purposes.

EXAMPLE:

Potassium permanganate in acid solution (see p. 352)

$$2KMnO_4 + 3H_2SO_4 = K_2SO_4 + 2MnSO_4 + 3H_2O + 5O$$

∴ $2(39 + 55 + 64)$ gm.   give 5×16 gm. of oxygen.

∴ $\frac{316}{10}$ gm. of permanganate give $\frac{80}{10}$ gm. of oxygen.

∴ the gram equivalent of potassium permanganate (which gives 8 gm. of oxygen) is 31·6 gm.

The *Gram Equivalent of a reducing agent* will react with the gram equivalent of an oxidizing agent.

Thus 10 ml. of N./10 ferrous sulphate solution are oxidized by 10 ml. of N./10 potassium permanganate solution, if dilute sulphuric acid is present.

The Equivalent Weight in grams of any substance

	provide	1 gm. of hydrogen
	or	or
will	react with	8 gm. of oxygen
	or	or
	displace	1 gm. equivalent weight of another substance

Suggestions for Practical Work

Expts. 176–181 inclusive.

QUESTIONS ON CHAPTER XXIX

1. Write down the gram equivalents of the following:

HNO_3, $NaOH$, H_2SO_4, Na_2CO_3, $Na_2CO_3.10H_2O$, $H_2C_2O_4.2H_2O$.

2. What weight of anhydrous sodium carbonate is required to make 250 ml. of N./2 solution?

3. Calculate the weight of oxalic acid crystals, $H_2C_2O_4.2H_2O$ required to give a litre of 2/5 N. solution.

4. What volume of $N.H_2SO_4$ is required to neutralize: (a) 10 ml. of N.NaOH, (b) 15 ml. of 3/5 N.KOH, (c) 20 ml. of 1·25 $N.Na_2CO_3$?

5. How many ml. of 2/5 N.NaOH are required to neutralize

(a) 15 ml. of $N.H_2SO_4$, (b) 20 ml. $N./2$ HNO_3, (c) 25 ml. 0.16 N. $H_2C_2O_4$?

6. What is the strength of an acid solution of which 18.4 ml. are required to neutralize 20 ml. of 1.12 N. alkali?

7. 7.5 ml. of a solution of HNO_3 neutralize 10 ml. of a solution containing 15.9 gm. of Na_2CO_3 per litre. What is the strength of the acid (a) in terms of normal, (b) in grams per litre?

8. If 24 ml. of a tenth-normal solution of an alkali have been added to 10 ml. of normal sulphuric acid, what volume of fifth-normal sodium carbonate will be required to neutralize exactly the remaining acidity? (L.)

9. Describe how you would prepare an accurately normal solution of sulphuric acid.

If 25 ml. of normal sulphuric acid neutralized 21 ml. of a solution of sodium carbonate and 22 ml. of a solution of sodium bicarbonate, calculate the strengths of each of these two solutions in grams per litre. (O.)

10. Define (a) "equivalent weight of a metal," (b) "equivalent weight of an acid," (c) "equivalent weight of an alkali." 0.48 gm. of a metal is dissolved in 50 ml. of normal sulphuric acid. This solution now requires 10 ml. of normal caustic soda for neutralization. Find the equivalent weight of the metal. (N.)

11. What is a normal solution? Illustrate your answer by reference to (a) an acid, (b) a base, and (c) a salt.

0.87 gm. of a metal was dissolved in 50 ml. of normal sulphuric acid. It was found that to neutralize the sulphuric acid left over, 23 ml. of normal sodium hydroxide were required. What is the equivalent of the metal? Describe briefly how you would carry out the above experiment. (B.)

12. Explain why 53 gm. of anhydrous sodium carbonate (Na_2CO_3) are used in making a litre of a normal solution of this substance. It was found by titration that 34 ml. of the above solution neutralized 50 ml. of a hydrochloric acid solution of unknown strength. Calculate the normality of the acid solution. What is the percentage of anhydrous sodium carbonate in a specimen, of which 2.0 gm. (in solution) were neutralized by 31.4 ml. of 0.96 N. sulphuric acid? (N.)

13. If you were provided with pure anhydrous sodium bicarbonate, describe carefully, giving all *essential* precautions and *reasons* for them, how you would prepare 250 ml. of an exactly normal solution of sodium carbonate. (L.)

14. Define the equivalent weight of an acid.

A certain carbonate reacts with an acid according to the equation:

$$XCO_3 + 2HCl = XCl_2 + H_2O + CO_2$$

If 1 gm. of this carbonate is dissolved in 50 ml. of normal hydrochloric acid, the remaining acid requires 30 ml. of normal sodium hydroxide for neutralization. Find the equivalent weight of the carbonate and from it deduce the atomic weight of X. (C.)

15. A solution of an acid is found to be $1 \cdot 12$ N.

How many ml. of distilled water must be added to a litre of this solution to give an exactly normal solution?

What volumes of the acid solution and water will be required to give exactly a litre of N. solution? Explain carefully your calculation. (Assume that the volume of a mixture is the sum of the volumes of its constituents.)

16. Anhydrous sodium carbonate weighing $0 \cdot 477$ gm. is dissolved in distilled water and made up to 100 ml. Separate portions, each of 20 ml. are found to require $16 \cdot 3$ ml., $16 \cdot 1$ ml., and $16 \cdot 2$ ml. respectively of a sulphuric acid solution for neutralization. Determine the strength of the latter (a) in terms of normal, (b) in grams of sulphuric acid per litre.

To what extent must this solution be diluted to give an accurately tenth-normal solution?

17. 25 ml. of a solution of caustic soda, containing 2 gm. of NaOH in a litre, were neutralized by 10 ml. of a solution of sulphuric acid.

Calculate (a) the weight of H_2SO_4 in 1 litre of the sulphuric acid solution, and (b) the volume of water it is necessary to add to a litre of the sulphuric acid solution to make its strength $4 \cdot 9$ gm. of H_2SO_4 per litre. (D.)

18. Give an equation for the reaction which occurs when sulphuric acid is completely neutralized with sodium hydroxide.

A quantity of commercial sulphuric acid weighing 40 gm. was diluted with water and the volume made up to 1 litre. Of the resulting solution 25 ml. was titrated with a solution of sodium hydroxide containing 40 gm. per litre, and required $19 \cdot 7$ ml. for complete neutralization. Calculate the percentage weight of H_2SO_4 in the commercial acid. (L.)

19. (*a*) On titration, 20 ml. of an alkaline solution (K) are found to neutralize 30 ml. of deci-normal hydrochloric acid. What volume of water should be added to 50 ml. of K in order to obtain a deci-normal alkaline solution?

(*b*) If 50 ml. of half-normal sulphuric acid are shaken with 100 ml. of a normal solution of caustic soda, what will be the normality of the resulting alkaline solution? (L.)

20. 12·5 ml. of sulphuric acid solution neutralize 10 ml. of a solution of N./2 sodium carbonate. 17·5 ml. of the acid solution are required to neutralize 20 ml. of a solution of potassium hydroxide.

Find the strength of the latter.

21. A solution of oxalic acid is made up to be accurately 2/5 N. 9·3 ml. of this solution are required to neutralize 10 ml. of a solution of sodium hydroxide, of which 20 ml. are neutralized by 15·5 ml. of a solution of nitric acid. What is the strength of the latter?

22. An excess of metallic zinc was added to 100 ml. of dilute sulphuric acid, and the volume of hydrogen produced found to be 1000 ml. at N.T.P. What was the concentration of the sulphuric acid? (O. and C.)

23. A piece of marble weighing 1·05 gm. was placed in 25 ml. of a given solution of hydrochloric acid. After the action had ceased, it was found that 0·55 gm. of the marble remained unattacked. Calculate the weight of hydrogen chloride (HCl) present in a litre of the acid. Find also the volume of the carbon dioxide produced, assuming it to be measured at 17° C. and 750 mm. pressure. (L.)

24. A piece of calcspar ($CaCO_3$) was placed in 200 ml. of dilute hydrochloric acid and warmed, until no more dissolved. The original weight of the calcspar was 4·5 gm.; after the reaction it weighed 2·0 gm. Calculate the concentration of the acid in grams of hydrochloric acid per litre.

What volume of gas at N.T.P. will be evolved during the reaction? (O. and C.)

25. A sample of marble weighing 0·72 gm. was dissolved in 25 ml. of N.HCl and the resulting solution was made up to 100 ml. When 25 ml. of this solution were titrated with caustic soda solution, 15·75 ml. of N./5 NaOH were required for neutralization. Calculate the percentage of calcium carbonate in the sample of marble. (N.)

26. Calculate the volume of normal sodium hydroxide solution required to precipitate the copper as hydroxide from a solution prepared by dissolving 3 gm. of crystallized copper sulphate, $CuSO_4.5H_2O$, in water.   (C.)

27. 40 ml. of a solution of lead nitrate were precipitated as lead sulphate by the addition of 30 ml. of 1·5 N. sulphuric acid.   The excess acid neutralized 15 ml. of N. sodium hydroxide.   What was the strength of the lead nitrate solution?

28. To 2·26 gm. of an ammonium salt were added 50 ml. of normal sodium hydroxide solution, and the liquid was boiled until the escaping steam was neutral.   Normal sulphuric acid was then added to the liquid until it was neutral.   The volume of acid required was 10 ml.   Find the percentage of ammonia in the given salt.

Describe in detail and explain the method by which you would carry out the experiment.   (S.)

29. 2·1 gm. of a specimen of sal-ammoniac were boiled with 70 ml. of a caustic soda solution until all the ammonia had been expelled. The remaining solution was made up to 100 ml. with distilled water and the average of several titrations showed that 10 ml. required 8·4 ml. of N./2 sulphuric acid to neutralize the excess caustic soda. 10 ml. of the original caustic soda required 21 ml. of the sulphuric acid.   Determine the percentage of ammonia in the sal-ammoniac.

30. Some lawn sand was known to contain sulphate of ammonia and sand only.   1·10 gm. of this mixture after boiling with 25 ml. of sodium hydroxide solution required 11·2 ml. of sulphuric acid to neutralize the excess of sodium hydroxide.   The acid was 1·15 N. and 16·0 ml. of it neutralized 20 ml. of the original sodium hydroxide. Calculate the percentage of sand in the mixture.

31. 20 ml. of a solution A containing nitric and hydrochloric acids required for complete neutralization 10·5 ml. of normal sodium hydroxide.   On precipitation with excess of silver nitrate, 20 ml. of A yielded 0·98 gm. silver chloride.   From these data calculate the weights of nitric and hydrochloric acids respectively contained in 1 litre of A.   (C.)

32. 1·44 gm. of a mixture of washing soda ($Na_2CO_3.10H_2O$) and baking soda ($NaHCO_3$) required 18·5 ml. of 0·7 N hydrochloric acid for complete neutralization.   Determine the percentage amount of each substance present in the mixture.

MISCELLANEOUS QUESTIONS

1. Explain, with examples, what is meant by the Law of Definite proportions.

What do you understand by the words: element, atom, molecule? How do these conceptions help us to understand the law?

(C. Gen. Sc.)

2. Describe the effects of water (or steam) upon the following: (*a*) iron, (*b*) potassium, (*c*) chlorine, (*d*) phosphorus pentoxide, mentioning the conditions under which the reactions described occur. (O. and C.)

3. Mention one example of the use of coke for each of the following purposes, giving an outline of the chemical changes: (i) the manufacture of a gaseous fuel; (ii) the manufacture of hydrogen; (iii) the smelting of the ore of a metal; (iv) the reduction of an acid or an acidic oxide. (Navy.)

4. Describe carefully experiments which show that chemical changes may be brought about by (*a*) heat, (*b*) light, (*c*) an electric current. In each case state clearly the reasons for believing that a chemical change has occurred. (L.)

5. Give as many differences in physical and chemical properties as you can between distilled water and a solution of common salt in water.

Tabulate your answer, carefully distinguishing between the physical and chemical properties you mention. (W.)

6. Describe, giving essential practical details, how you would obtain in the laboratory fairly pure specimens of (*a*) common salt from a mixture of common salt and gypsum (calcium sulphate); (*b*) sal-ammoniac (ammonium chloride) from a mixture of sal-ammoniac and common salt; and (*c*) nitrogen from a mixture of nitrogen and carbon dioxide. (O. Gen. Sc.)

7. A. Define or explain the meaning of: gas, solution, filtrate, crystallization, anhydrous salt.

B. State:

(*a*) The Law of Definite Proportions (or Constant Composition)
(*b*) Gay-Lussac's Law of Gaseous Combination.

(c) The relation between molecular weight and relative density for a gas or vapour.

(d) The relation between atomic weight, equivalent weight, and valency for an element.

C. (i) How many grams of oxygen combine with 10 gm. of sulphur to make sulphur dioxide?

(ii) How many litres of sulphur dioxide can be made from 10 litres of oxygen?

(iii) How many more litres of oxygen will be required to make the sulphur dioxide into sulphur trioxide? (O = 16, S = 32.) (O. and C.)

8. A. X is a trivalent element; write down the formula of (i) its sulphate, (ii) its oxide.

If its atomic weight is 27, what is its equivalent weight?

B. Which of the following gases can and which cannot be collected over water: (i) hydrogen chloride, (ii) nitric oxide, (iii) oxygen, (iv) sulphur dioxide?

C. Which of the following compounds can be used and which cannot be used to dry hydrogen chloride: (i) concentrated sulphuric acid, (ii) calcium oxide, (iii) calcium carbonate?

D. In each of the following reactions state whether (i) a gas is evolved, or (ii) a precipitate produced, or (iii) no visible change takes place:

(i) The action of dilute hydrochloric acid on sodium sulphite.

(ii) The action of potassium hydroxide solution on ferrous sulphate solution.

(iii) The action of sodium sulphate solution on potassium nitrate solution.

(iv) The action of sodium sulphate solution on lead nitrate solution.

E. Lead nitrate decomposes, when heated, according to the equation:

$$2Pb(NO_3)_2 = 2PbO + 4NO_2 + O_2$$

(i) Write this equation in words.

(ii) Calculate the weight of lead oxide obtained from 33·12 gm. of lead nitrate.

(iii) Calculate the volume of oxygen at N.T.P. obtained from 33·12 gm. of lead nitrate. (O. and C.)

9. Describe briefly how you would obtain specimens of (a) charcoal and washing soda from a mixture of the two substances,

(b) sand from a mixture of sand and chalk, (c) oxygen from a mixture of oxygen and ammonia, (d) pure water from sea-water. (L. Gen. Sc.)

10. Suggest methods—*one* in each case—for separating the ingredients of the following mixtures:

(i) carbon dioxide and carbon monoxide;

(ii) sulphur, black copper oxide, and copper sulphate;

(iii) sodium chloride and potassium nitrate;

(iv) sodium chloride and ammonium chloride. (Navy.)

11. State briefly one method of preparing each of the following substances: magnesium oxide; iodine; sodium chloride; sulphur trioxide; sodium hydroxide.

In what class would you place each of these substances? Give reasons. (S.)

12. Answer any *two* of the following:

(a) Describe the manufacture of quicklime. How is it converted into slaked lime? Mention, giving reasons, two purposes for which slaked lime is used.

(b) Give a brief outline of the chemical processes taking place in the extraction of either iron or aluminium from the ore. (Details of the commercial apparatus are not required.)

(c) Describe two experiments you would make to demonstrate that gases diffuse. (C. Gen. Sc.)

13. State briefly how you would prepare specimens of the following:

(a) ferric oxide from ferrous sulphate;

(b) anhydrous calcium chloride from calcium carbonate;

(c) copper from copper sulphate.

State *one* common use for each of the following: (i) ferric oxide, (ii) calcium chloride, (iii) copper sulphate. (L.)

14. The elements mercury and bromine are liquid at ordinary temperatures. Give reasons for the classification of the one as a metal and the other as a non-metal. Describe the methods you would employ to isolate each of these elements from a compound in which it occurs in nature. (S.)

15. Explain the meaning of each of the following terms, giving illustrative examples: (a) allotropy, (b) dialysis, (c) exothermic compound, (d) hydrolysis, (e) thermal dissociation. (S.)

16. How could you prove that nitric acid contains both hydrogen and nitrogen?

What is the action of nitric acid on sodium carbonate, lime, copper, red lead?

17. Describe briefly how you would obtain samples of:
(a) Chlorine from potassium chlorate.
(b) Iron from ferric oxide.
(c) Hydrogen from hydrogen chloride. (O.)

18. State briefly but clearly how you would obtain:
(a) chlorine from common salt;
(b) oxygen from bleaching powder;
(c) nitrogen from ammonia;
(d) lead from lead nitrate. (L.)

19. What is a reversible reaction? Describe experiments by which you could show conclusively that the following reactions are reversible:

$$Ca(HCO_3)_2 = CaCO_3 + CO_2 + H_2O,$$
$$3Fe + 4H_2O = 4H_2 + Fe_3O_4$$

(C.)

20. How, and under what conditions, do the following pairs of substances react with one another: (a) hydrogen and chlorine, (b) chlorine and water, (c) iron and water, (d) sulphuric acid and zinc, (e) carbon and water? (O.)

21. Define the term thermal dissociation and explain carefully the difference between thermal dissociation and thermal decomposition. Describe any experiment you have seen to demonstrate thermal dissociation.

State the action of heat on (a) potassium chlorate, (b) nitrogen dioxide, (c) ammonium chloride indicating in each case whether the action is dissociation or decomposition. (L.)

22. Explain and illustrate the terms: water of crystallization, anhydrous salt, deliquescence, efflorescence.

When barium chloride crystals ($BaCl_2$, xH_2O) are heated, steam is given off and a loss in weight of $14·81\%$ occurs. Calculate the value of x. (Navy.)

23. Describe experiments by which you would distinguish between (a) manganese dioxide and carbon; (b) hydrogen and nitrogen; (c) sulphuric acid and hydrochloric acid; (d) red phosphorus and mercuric oxide; (e) potassium nitrate and potassium sulphate. (S.)

24. Describe *one* chemical experiment in each case by which you could distinguish between (*a*) sulphur dioxide and hydrogen chloride, (*b*) lead dioxide and copper oxide, (*c*) a solution of zinc nitrate and a solution of calcium nitrate, (*d*) a dilute solution of chlorine and a solution of hydrogen peroxide.   (C.)

25. Write a short account of the manufacture of *one* of the following: sulphuric acid, washing soda, bleaching powder.   (S.)

26. Explain the following facts:

(i) When sodium hydroxide solution is added to zinc sulphate solution, a white precipitate is formed. When more sodium hydroxide solution is added, the precipitate dissolves.

(ii) When chlorine water is allowed to stand in sunlight, the greenish colour of the solution gradually disappears and bubbles of a colourless gas are given off.

(iii) Ammonia is dried by passing it through quicklime, not through sulphuric acid or calcium chloride.

(iv) Hydrogen sulphide ignites on coming into contact with sodium peroxide.   (Navy.)

27. State clearly what it meant by the equivalent weight of an element, and write short notes on four different ways of determining equivalents. Describe in detail the method you would adopt to find the equivalent of copper.

1·5 gm. of a metal whose valency is known to be three gave 1·8 gm. of oxide when completely oxidized.   Find (*a*) the equivalent weight of the metal, (*b*) its atomic weight, (*c*) its specific heat.   (S.)

28. What relative weights of potassium chlorate and nitrate would give off equal volumes of oxygen when heated?

How would you show that the residual solids differ from the original substances?   (O.)

29. Explain what is meant by "water of crystallization."

A hydrated salt was found to contain 19·17% of sodium, 13·33% of sulphur, and 67·50% of water.   Deduce its formula.   (O. and C.)

30. Describe in detail how you would find the equivalent weight of *either* aluminium *or* mercury.

When 0·277 gm. magnesium was strongly heated in a crucible, 0·464 gm. of magnesium oxide was formed.   A strip of clean bright magnesium weighing 0·161 gm. was found to displace 1·47 gm. of silver from a solution of silver nitrate.   Calculate the equivalent of silver from these results.   (Navy.)

DATES OF DISCOVERIES, ETC., MENTIONED
IN THIS BOOK

B.C.

3,000,000,000	Earth took shape.
750,000,000	Life appeared.
250,000,000	Coal being formed.
100,000,000	Chalk being deposited.
500,000	Early man evolved and used stone tools.
50,000	*Homo sapiens* evolved.
20,000	Ferric oxide used for paint (Lascaux Caves, France)
5000	Native metals used (gold, silver, copper).
3500	Metals obtained by smelting (copper, silver, lead).
2600	Iron known in Egypt.
2000	Bronze Age beginning in Britain.
1600	Glass vessels made in Egypt.
1300	Iron tools becoming fairly common in Egypt.
1000	Tin ores exported from Britain.
600	Soap made.
500	Iron Age beginning in Britain.
400	Mercury known (Spain).
300	White-lead paint used.

A.D.

100–1600	Chemistry overshadowed by alchemy.
300	Methods of separating mixtures described (solution, filtration, distillation, etc.).
1100	Alcohol distilled (Arabia).
1200	Arabic numerals being introduced into Europe.
1242	Gunpowder discovered (Roger Bacon).
1440	Printing from movable type began in Europe.
1500	Scientific method of observation and experiment in use (Leonardo da Vinci).
1540	Sulphuric acid described.
1550	Transparent glass available fairly cheaply (Italy).
1560	Coal increasingly used as fuel (England).
1590	Decimals used.
1600	Compound microscope (Galileo).
1604	Thermometer (Galileo).
1614	Logarithms published (Napier).
1620	Scientific method advocated and its nature explained (Francis Bacon).

A.D.
1643   Barometer (Torricelli).
1649   Eleven elements known (seven above+C, S, Sb, As).

1650   First university laboratory (Leyden).
1658   Glauber's salt discovered.
1660   Boyle's Law (and definition of a chemical element).
1662   Royal Society of London founded.
1665   Burning almost explained (Hooke).
1669–
  1776   False theories of burning.
1674   Air shown to consist of two gases (Mayow).
1675   Lead crystal glass (England).
1680   Corks first used (for champagne!).
1687   Theory of gravitation (Newton).
1742   Centigrade scale of temperature.
1746   Sulphuric acid manufactured in lead chambers (England).
1747   Lemon juice used to prevent scurvy (British ships).
1749   Fifteen elements known (eleven above+P, Pt, Co, Zn).
1750   Iron ore being smelted by coke, not charcoal (Darby).
1756   Carbon dioxide discovered (Black).
1769   Oxygen discovered (Scheele).
1774   Chlorine discovered (Scheele).
1774   Law of Conservation of Mass (Lavoisier).
1776   Steam engine used for power (James Watt and Boulton).
1777   Burning explained (Lavoisier).
1770–
  1785   Common gases discovered or systematically investigated by
          Priestley: C SO_2, SO_3, H_2S, HCl, N_2O, NO, NO_2, NH_3,
          CO. CH_4,   .
'779   Nature of p   nthesis shown (Ingen-Housz).
1781   Water prov   be a compound (Cavendish).
1782   Charles's Law.
1785   Breathing proved to be similar to burning (Lavoisier).
1791   Sodium carbonate manufactured on large scale (Leblanc).
1792   Coal gas used for lighting.
1792   Electrochemical Series (Volta).
1793   Law of Equivalent Proportions (Richter).
1799   Law of Constant Composition (Proust).
1799   Bleaching powder manufactured (Tennant).
1799   Twenty-seven elements known.
1800   Sugar manufactured from beet (Germany).

A.D.

1800 First electric battery (Volta).
1801 Law of Partial Pressures (Dalton).
1803 Atomic Theory (Dalton).
1803 Henry's Law of gaseous solubility.
1807 Sodium and potassium prepared (Davy).
1808 Gay-Lussac's Law of Volumes.
1811 Avogadro's Hypothesis.
1813 Iodine discovered (Courtois).
1815 Miner's safety lamp (Davy).
1818 Modern atomic symbols (Berzelius).
1819 Dulong and Petit's Law of Atomic Heats.
1820 Tinplate used for canning.
1823 Rubber solution used for waterproofing (Macintosh).
1824 Cement manufactured.
1825 Railways began (Stockton to Darlington).
1826 Matches used.
1826 Bromine prepared (Balard).
1827 Aluminium prepared.
1828 First synthesis of organic compounds (urea and alcohol).
1829 Analytical methods using hydrogen sulphide.
1831 British Association founded.
1831 Sulphur trioxide prepared by catalytic oxidation of sulphur dioxide.
1834 Laws of electrolysis (Faraday).
1835 Kipp's apparatus.
1836 Acetylene discovered.
1837 Galvanizing of iron.
1838 Creosoting of timber.
1839 Vulcanizing of rubber.
1839 First photographs published (Daguerre and Fox Talbot).
1840 Carbon and nitrogen cycles (Liebig).
1840 Superphosphate fertilizers (Lawes).
1841 Chemical Society of London founded.
1841 Phenol prepared from coal-tar.
1842 Ether used as anaesthetic for operations (U.S.A.)
1842 Dumas's experiment on water.
1846 Graham's Law of Diffusion.
1849 Fifty-seven elements known.

1850 Ammonia recovered from coal gas.
1853 Bunsen's burner.

A.D.

1854	First English school laboratory (Rugby).
1855	Bacteria discovered (Pasteur).
1856	First coal-tar dyestuff (Perkin's mauve).
1856	First large-scale process for steel (Bessemer).
1858	Cannizzaro's method for atomic weights.
1858	4-valency of carbon (Kekulé).
1859	Bunsen's flame tests.
1859	Lead accumulator.
1860	U.S. petroleum industry began.
1862	Haemoglobin crystallized.
1864	Law of Mass Action (Guldberg and Waage).
1860–	
1865	Stas's work on atomic weights.
1865	Phenol used as antiseptic (Lister).
1865	Solvay process for sodium carbonate.
1866	Nobel's dynamite (nitroglycerine).
1867	Paper from wood-pulp by sulphur dioxide method (U.S.A.).
1868	First plastic (celluloid).
1869	Periodic Table of the Elements (Mendeléev).
1870	Drinkable water supplied to London.
1877	Oxygen liquefied.
1879	Saccharin discovered.
1880	Refrigeration introduced (British ships).
1882	Manganese steel used (Hadfield).
1882	First electrical power plant (Edison; New York).
1884	Rayon prepared (Chardonnet).
1885	First coal-tar explosive (picric acid).
1886	Fluori isolated (Moissan).
1886	Alui um prepared on large scale (Hall, Héroult).
1887	Electrolytic preparation of chlorine i d alkali (Castner).
1888	Le Chatelier's Principle.
1889	Nitrocellulose film introduced (Eastman).
1890	Mond nickel process.
1892	Direct Fast Scarlet 4 BS Dyestuff prepared.
1893	Calcium carbide prepared (Moissan).
1894	Inert gases discovered in air (Ramsay and Rayleigh).
1895	X-Rays discovered (Röntgen).
1896	Radioactivity discovered (Becquerel).
1897	Electron discovered (Thomson).
1898	Radium discovered (Curie).
1899	Aspirin manufactured.

ANSWERS TO NUMERICAL QUESTIONS

CHAPTER II (p. 26)

1. 2·00 gm.

CHAPTER VII (p. 105)

8. 125 sec. **9.** (a) About 155,000,000,000 calories.

CHAPTER VIII (p. 116)

4. (a) 17 gm.; (b) 470 gm. **6.** 15·6 gm. **7.** (a) 41 gm., 185 gm.; (b) 65 gm. 35 gm.; (c) 50 gm. **8.** 35·6% O_2, 64·4% N_2.

CHAPTER IX (p. 130)

1. 161·5 c.c. **2.** 480 cu. ft. **3.** 34° C. **4.** 106⅔ cm., 53⅓ cm. **5.** 134·8 c.c.

CHAPTER X (p. 143)

1. 12·45 gm. **2.** 28·0. **3.** 0·54 gm. **4.** 52·65%. **5.** 51·4. **6.** 7·93. **7.** 31. **8.** 14·2. **9.** 79·7. **10.** 21·6%. **11.** 35·454. **12.** 48·76. **13.** 103·5. **14.** 31·74. **15.** 12, 9, 20.

CHAPTER XI (p. 160)

6. 515·4 parts. **8.** 103·9, 78·44, 51·7.

CHAPTER XII (p. 183)

1. 2; 66·7. **2.** 23·56. **3.** 40·3. **4.** 8·986, 26·96. **8.** CH_4, C_3H_8, CH, **9.** C_2NOH_5. **10.** $Na_2SO_4.10H_2O$. **11.** 10. **12.** 7·1. **13.** $2CuCO_3$. $Cu(OH)_2$. **14.** C_2H_6O. **15.** $C_6H_{10}O_5$. **16.** ⁻ 39 gm., 36·8 gm., 9·34 gm. **17.** (a) 2·01 gm.; (b) 1·43 gm. **18** (a) 36· ₀; (b) 47·1%. **19** (a) 22 gm.; (b) 17·7 gm.; (c) 11·5 gm. **23.** 39·1. **24.** 26·95.

CHAPTER XIII (p. 206)

... 10 c.c., 5 c.c. **4.** (a) 10 c.c. CO_2, 5 c.c. O_2; (b) 10 c.c. CO_2, 5 c.c. O_2, 20 c.c. H_2O. **6.** (a) CH_2Cl; (b) $C_2H_4Cl_2$. **8.** 64·5. **9.** 59. **10.** 163·6. **14.** N_2O. **17.** CH_4. **18.** C_2H_6. **19.** 21%. **20.** 8 : 13. **21.** (a) 10 c.c.; b) 50 c.c.; (c) 160 c.c. **22.** 1·4 litres N_2O, 1·6 litres NO. **23.** 7·2 c.c. CH_4, 1·6 c.c. C_2H_6. **24.** 32. **25.** 31. **26.** 4, 208. **27.** 307·5 c.c. **28.** 2·96 litres. **29.** (a) 9·33 litres; (b) 3·11 litres; (c) 6·22 litres. **30.** 8250 c.c.; 21·0 gm., 5·96 gm. **31.** 4·5, 9·0, 2. **32.** 56.

CHAPTER XIV (p. 225)

2. 31·8. **5.** 446 c.c.

CHAPTER XVI (p. 266)

8. 35 c.c.

CHAPTER XVII (p. 288)

17. 22 lb.

CHAPTER XVIII (p. 309)

10. 1·067 gm.

CHAPTER XXIV (p. 416)

13. 2·6 litres. **14.** 4·96 litres, 15·2 gm. **17.** 106·0 litres.

CHAPTER XXV (p. 427)

5. 39·14.

CHAPTER XXIX (p. 507)

2. 6·625 gm. **3.** 25·2 gm. **6.** 1·22 N. **7.** 0·4 N., 25·2 gm. per litre. **8.** 38 ml. **9.** 63·1 gm. per litre; 95·5 gm. per litre. **10.** 12·0. **11.** 32·2. **12.** 0·68 N.; 79·9%. **14.** 50; 40. **15.** 120, 893 ml., 107 ml. **16.** 0·111 N, 5·44; 11·1 ml. water; 100 ml. acid. **17.** 6·125 gm., 250 ml. **18.** 96·53%. **19.** (a) 25 ml.; (b) 0·5 N. **20.** 0·35 N. **21.** 0·48 N. **22.** 43·75 gm. H_2SO_4 per litre. **23.** 14·6 gm., 120·5 ml. **24.** 9·125, 560 ml. **25.** 86·1% **26.** 24 ml. **27.** 124 gm. per litre. **28.** 30·1%. **29.** 25·5%. **30.** 39·28% **31.** 11·56 gm., 12·46 gm. **32.** 59·2% $Na_2CO_3.10H_2O$, 40·8% $NaHCO_3$.

MISCELLANEOUS (p. 515)

22. 2. **27.** 40, 120, 0·0525. **29.** $Na_2S.9H_2O$. **30.** 108·2.

The rule that compounds ending in -ate always* contain oxygen will also prevent confusion between hydrocarbons, e.g. CH_4, methane, and carbohydrates, e.g. $C_6H_{12}O_6$, glucose.

Variable Valency

If an element has two valencies, -ous compounds are those of the lower valency (e.g. the smallest proportion of oxygen), and -ic compounds are those of the higher valency, e.g.:

Ferrous oxide, FeO   Ferric oxide, Fe_2O_3
Ferrous sulphate, $FeSO_4$ Ferric sulphate, $Fe_2(SO_4)_3$
Cuprous sulphide, Cu_2S Cupric sulphide, CuS
Nitrous oxide, N_2O Nitric oxide, NO
Sulphurous acid, H_2SO_3 Sulphuric acid, H_2SO_4.

Another way of distinguishing between valencies is to use the Greek numbers (p. 171), e.g.:

Carbon monoxide, CO   Carbon dioxide, CO_2
Tin dichloride, $SnCl_2$ Tin tetrachloride, $SnCl_4$
Phosphorus trioxide, P_2O_3 Phosphorus pentoxide, P_2O_5.

* Except potassium thiocyanate, KCNS, p. 470.

SUGGESTIONS FOR FURTHER READING

If the reader of this book has found chemistry interesting, he will want to know some books to read which give more details without being technical or difficult. All the following can be highly recommended:

Lancelot Hogben: "Science for the Citizen" (Allen and Unwin),
Williams Haynes: "This Chemical Age" (Secker and Warburg),
Sherwood Taylor: "The Century of Science" (Heinemann),
John Read: "Direct Entry to Organic Chemistry" (Methuen),
H. Stafford Hatfield: "What Things are Made Of" (Basic English Publishing Co.),
Philbrick: "Inorganic Chemistry" (Bell),
Weaver and Foster: "Chemistry for Our Times" (McGraw Hill),
George Gamow: "Mr Tompkins Explores the Atom" (Cambridge).

In addition, many books in the "Penguin" series, including those on Metals, Minerals, Geology, Plastics, Explosives, "Food the Deciding Factor," "Man, Microbe and Malady," "Microbes by the Million," "Why Smash Atoms?", "Science and Everyday Life," "Science and the Nation," "Atomic Energy," "British Scientists of the Nineteenth Century" (2 vols.), and the regular "Science News" (Indexes in Vols. 15, 23, 27, 31, 35, 39, etc.), and "New Biology" (Indexes in Vols. 10, 20).

All these have provided material and inspiration for this book, which the authors gratefully acknowledge.

The magazine "Discovery" (Empire Press, Norwich) is probably the most interesting of all popular science magazines (2/- per month) and is very well written.

INDEX

531

LOGARITHMS

	0	1	2	3	4	5	6	7	8	9	1	2	3	4	5	6	7	8	9
10	0000	0043	0086	0128	0170	0212	0253	0294	0334	0374	4	9	13	17	21	26	30	34	38
											4	8	12	16	20	24	28	32	37
11	0414	0453	0492	0531	0569	0607	0645	0682	0719	0755	4	8	12	15	19	23	27	31	35
											4	7	11	15	19	22	26	30	33
12	0792	0828	0864	0899	0934	0969	1004	1038	1072	1106	3	7	11	14	18	21	25	28	32
											3	7	10	14	17	20	24	27	31
13	1139	1173	1206	1239	1271	1303	1335	1367	1399	1430	3	7	10	13	16	20	23	26	30
											3	7	10	12	16	19	22	25	29
14	1461	1492	1523	1553	1584	1614	1644	1673	1703	1732	3	6	9	12	15	18	21	24	28
											3	6	9	12	15	17	20	23	26
15	1761	1790	1818	1847	1875	1903	1931	1959	1987	2014	3	6	9	11	14	17	20	23	26
											3	5	8	11	14	16	19	22	25
16	2041	2068	2095	2122	2148	2175	2201	2227	2253	2279	3	5	8	11	14	16	19	22	24
											3	5	8	10	13	15	18	21	23
17	2304	2330	2355	2380	2405	2430	2455	2480	2504	2529	3	5	8	10	13	15	18	20	23
											2	5	7	10	12	15	17	19	22
18	2553	2577	2601	2625	2648	2672	2695	2718	2742	2765	2	5	7	9	12	14	16	19	21
											2	5	7	9	11	14	16	18	21
19	2788	2810	2833	2856	2878	2900	2923	2945	2967	2989	2	4	7	9	11	13	16	18	20
											2	4	6	8	11	13	15	17	19
20	3010	3032	3054	3075	3096	3118	3139	3160	3181	3201	2	4	6	8	11	13	15	17	19
21	3222	3243	3263	3284	3304	3324	3345	3365	3385	3404	2	4	6	8	10	12	14	16	18
22	3424	3444	3464	3483	3502	3522	3541	3560	3579	3598	2	4	6	8	10	12	14	15	17
23	3617	3636	3655	3674	3692	3711	3729	3747	3766	3784	2	4	6	7	9	11	13	15	17
24	3802	3820	3838	3856	3874	3892	3909	3927	3945	3962	2	4	5	7	9	11	12	14	16
25	3979	3997	4014	4031	4048	4065	4082	4099	4116	4133	2	3	5	7	9	10	12	14	15
26	4150	4166	4183	4200	4216	4232	4249	4265	4281	4298	2	3	5	7	8	10	11	13	15
27	4314	4330	4346	4362	4378	4393	4409	4425	4440	4456	2	3	5	6	8	9	11	13	14
28	4472	4487	4502	4518	4533	4548	4564	4579	4594	4609	2	3	5	6	8	9	11	12	14
29	4624	4639	4654	4669	4683	4698	4713	4728	4742	4757	1	3	4	6	7	9	10	12	13
30	4771	4786	4800	4814	4829	4843	4857	4871	4886	4900	1	3	4	6	7	9	10	11	13
31	4914	4928	4942	4955	4969	4983	4997	5011	5024	5038	1	3	4	6	7	8	10	11	12
32	5051	5065	5079	5092	5105	5119	5132	5145	5159	5172	1	3	4	5	7	8	9	11	12
33	5185	5198	5211	5224	5237	5250	5263	5276	5289	5302	1	3	4	5	6	8	9	10	12
34	5315	5328	5340	5353	5366	5378	5391	5403	5416	5428	1	3	4	5	6	8	9	10	11
35	5441	5453	5465	5478	5490	5502	5514	5527	5539	5551	1	2	4	5	6	7	9	10	11
36	5563	5575	5587	5599	5611	5623	5635	5647	5658	5670	1	2	4	5	6	7	8	10	11
37	5682	5694	5705	5717	5729	5740	5752	5763	5775	5786	1	2	3	5	6	7	8	9	10
38	5798	5809	5821	5832	5843	5855	5866	5877	5888	5899	1	2	3	5	6	7	8	9	10
39	5911	5922	5933	5944	5955	5966	5977	5988	5999	6010	1	2	3	4	5	7	8	9	10
40	6021	6031	6042	6053	6064	6075	6085	6096	6107	6117	1	2	3	4	5	6	8	9	10
41	6128	6138	6149	6160	6170	6180	6191	6201	6212	6222	1	2	3	4	5	6	7	8	9
42	6232	6243	6253	6263	6274	6284	6294	6304	6314	6325	1	2	3	4	5	6	7	8	9
43	6335	6345	6355	6365	6375	6385	6395	6405	6415	6425	1	2	3	4	5	6	7	8	9
44	6435	6444	6454	6464	6474	6484	6493	6503	6513	6522	1	2	3	4	5	6	7	8	9
45	6532	6542	6551	6561	6571	6580	6590	6599	6609	6618	1	2	3	4	5	6	7	8	9
46	6628	6637	6646	6656	6665	6675	6684	6693	6702	6712	1	2	3	4	5	6	7	8	8
47	6721	6730	6739	6749	6758	6767	6776	6785	6794	6803	1	2	3	4	5	5	6	7	8
48	6812	6821	6830	6839	6848	6857	6866	6875	6884	6893	1	2	3	4	4	5	6	7	8
49	6902	6911	6920	6928	6937	6946	6955	6964	6972	6981	1	2	3	4	4	5	6	7	8
50	6990	6998	7007	7016	7024	7033	7042	7050	7059	7067	1	2	3	3	4	5	6	7	8